Statistical Modeling

A FRESH APPROACH

Second Edition

DANIEL T. KAPLAN

MACALESTER COLLEGE

Cover Photo: A bamboo grove in Brisbane, Australia. [Photo credit: the author.]

To my wife, Maya.

Contents

Preface   viii

1   Introduction   **13**
    1.1   Models and their Purposes 16
    1.2   Observation and Knowledge 17
    1.3   The Main Points of this Book 20
    1.4   Introduction to Computation with R 22

2   Data: Cases, Variables, Samples   **35**
    2.1   Kinds of Variables 37
    2.2   Data Frames and the Unit of Analysis 38
    2.3   Populations and Samples 39
    2.4   Longitudinal and Cross-Sectional Samples 42
    2.5   Computational Technique 43

3   Describing Variation   **49**
    3.1   Coverage Intervals 51
    3.2   The Variance and Standard Deviation 54
    3.3   Displaying Variation 58
    3.4   Categorical Variables 63
    3.5   Computational Technique 65

4   Group-wise Models   **73**
    4.1   "Grand" and Group-wise Models 73
    4.2   Accounting for Variation 75
    4.3   Group-wise Proportions 77
    4.4   What's the Precision? 78
    4.5   Misleading Group-wise Models 79
    4.6   Computational Technique 81

iv

5 Confidence Intervals   85
   5.1 The Sampling Distribution 85
   5.2 The Resampling Distribution & Bootstrapping 88
   5.3 The Confidence Level 93
   5.4 Interpreting Confidence Intervals 93
   5.5 Confidence Intervals from Census Data 94
   5.6 Computational Technique 95

6 The Language of Models   101
   6.1 Models as Functions 103
   6.2 Multiple Explanatory Variables 105
   6.3 Reading a Model 108
   6.4 Choices in Model Design 110
   6.5 Model Terms 111
   6.6 Standard Notation for Describing Model Design 118
   6.7 Computational Technique 120

7 Model Formulas and Coefficients   129
   7.1 The Linear Model Formula 130
   7.2 Linear Models with Multiple Terms 131
   7.3 Formulas with Categorical Variables 133
   7.4 Coefficients and Relationships 133
   7.5 Model Values and Residuals 135
   7.6 Coefficients of Basic Model Designs 135
   7.7 Coefficients have Units 139
   7.8 Untangling Explanatory Variables 140
   7.9 Why Linear Models? 144
   7.10 Computational Technique 147

8 Fitting Models to Data   152
   8.1 The Least Squares Criterion 153
   8.2 Partitioning Variation 156
   8.3 The Geometry of Least Squares Fitting 157
   8.4 Redundancy 158
   8.5 Computational Technique 161

9 Correlation and Partitioning of Variation   165
   9.1 Properties of R^2 166
   9.2 Simple Correlation 168
   9.3 The Geometry of Correlation 171
   9.4 Nested Models 172
   9.5 The Geometry of R^2 174
   9.6 Computational Technique 175

10 Total and Partial Relationships   **178**
   10.1 Total and Partial Relationships 179
   10.2 Explicitly Holding Covariates Constant 189
   10.3 Adjustment and Truth 191
   10.4 The Geometry of Covariates and Adjustment 193
   10.5 Computational Technique 194

11 Modeling Randomness   **198**
   11.1 Describing Pure Randomness 198
   11.2 Settings for Probability Models 201
   11.3 Models of Counts 202
   11.4 Common Probability Calculations 204
   11.5 Continuous Probability Models 205
   11.6 The Normal Distribution 209
   11.7 Computational Technique 211

12 Confidence in Models   **218**
   12.1 The Sampling Distribution & Model Coefficients 220
   12.2 Standard Errors and the Regression Report 223
   12.3 Confidence Intervals 223
   12.4 Confidence in Predictions 226
   12.5 Confidence and Collinearity 230
   12.6 Confidence and Bias 232
   12.7 Computational Technique 233

13 The Logic of Hypothesis Testing   **238**
   13.1 An Example of a Hypothesis Test 240
   13.2 Inductive and Deductive Reasoning 242
   13.3 The Null Hypothesis 246
   13.4 The p-value 247
   13.5 Rejecting by Mistake 248
   13.6 Failing to Reject 249
   13.7 A Glossary of Hypothesis Testing 251
   13.8 An Update on Stock Prices 253

14 Hypothesis Testing on Whole Models   **255**
   14.1 The Permutation Test 256
   14.2 R^2 and the F Statistic 259
   14.3 The ANOVA Report 263
   14.4 Interpreting the p-value 266
   14.5 Computational Technique 271

15 Hypothesis Testing on Parts of Models   **275**
   15.1 The Term-by-Term ANOVA Table 276
   15.2 Covariates Soak Up Variance 278
   15.3 Measuring the Sum of Squares 281
   15.4 ANOVA, Collinearity, and Multi-Collinearity 284

15.5 Hypothesis Tests on Single Coefficients 291
15.6 Non-Parametric Statistics 295
15.7 Sample Size and Power 296
15.8 Computational Technique 299

16 Models of Yes/No Variables   **303**
16.1 The 0-1 Encoding 304
16.2 Inference on Logistic Models 309
16.3 Model Probabilities 312
16.4 Computational Technique 315

17 Causation   **319**
17.1 Interpreting Models Causally 320
17.2 Causation and Correlation 322
17.3 Hypothetical Causal Networks 325
17.4 Networks and Covariates 328

18 Experiment   **342**
18.1 Experiments 342
18.2 When Experiments are Impossible 354
18.3 Conclusion 362

Further Readings & Bibliography   **364**

A Additional Resources   **373**

B Traditional Tests   **374**

Indices   **379**
R Operator Index 379
Concept Index 381

Preface

The purpose of this book is to provide an introduction to statistics that gives readers a sufficient mastery of statistical concepts, methods, and computations to apply them to authentic systems. By "authentic," I mean the sort of multivariable systems often encountered when working in the natural or social sciences, commerce, government, law, or any of the many contexts in which data are collected with an eye to understanding how things work or to making predictions about what will happen.

The world is uncertain and complex. We deal with the complexity and uncertainty with a variety of strategies including the scientific method and the discipline of statistics.

Statistics deals with uncertainty, quantifying it so that you can assess how reliable — how likely to be repeatable — your findings are. The scientific method deals with complexity: reduce systems to simpler components, define and measure quantities carefully, do experiments in which some conditions are held constant but others are varied systematically.

Beyond helping to quantify uncertainty and reliability, statistics provides another great insight of which most people are unaware. When dealing with systems involving multiple influences, it is possible and best to deal with those influences simultaneously. By appropriate data collection and analysis, the confusing tangle of influences can sometimes be straightened out. In other words, statistics goes hand-in-hand with the scientific method when it comes to dealing with complexity and understanding how systems work.

The statistical methods that can accomplish this are often considered advanced: multiple regression, analysis of covariance, logistic regression, among others. With appropriate software, any method is accessible in the sense of being able to produce a summary report on the computer. But a method is useful only when the user has a way to understand whether the method is appropriate for the situation, what the method is telling about the data, and what the method is not capable of revealing. Computer scientist Richard Hamming (1915-1998) said: "The purpose of computing is insight, not numbers." Without a solid understanding of the theory that underlies a method, the numbers generated by the computer may not give insight.

Advanced methods of statistics can give tremendous insight. For this reason, these methods need to be accessible both computationally and theoretically to the widest possible audience. Historically, access has been limited because few people have the algebraic skills needed to approach the methods in the way they are usually presented. But there are many paths to understanding and I have undertaken to find one — the "fresh approach" in the title — that takes the greatest advantage of the actual skills that most people already have in abundance.

In trying to meet that challenge, I have made many unconventional choices. Theory becomes simpler when there is a unified framework for treating many aspects of statistics, so I have chosen to present just about everything in the context of models: descriptive statistics as well as inference.

George Cobb [1] cogently describes the logic of statistical inference as the three-Rs: "Randomize, Repeat, Reject." In a decade of teaching statistics, I have found that students can understand this algorithmic logic much better than the derivations of algebraic formulas for means and standard deviations of sampling distributions.

Consequently, algebraic notation and formulas are strongly de-emphasized in this book. The traditional role that formulas have played in providing instructions for how to carry out a calculation is no longer essential for effective use of statistical methods. Software now implements the calculations. What's needed is not a formula-based description that allows people to reproduce what computers do, but a way to understand the methods at a high level so that the rapidity and reliability of computers in performing calculations can be used to provide insight into real-world problems.

And then there is software. Traditionalists think that statistics should be taught without computers in order to help develop conceptual understanding. Others think that it is silly to ignore a technology that is universally used in practice and greatly expands our capabilities. Both points of view have merit.

The main body of this book is presented in a way that makes little or no reference to software; the statistical concepts are paramount. However, most chapters have a section on computational technique that shows how to get things done and aims to give the reader concrete skills in the analysis of data.

The software used is R, a modern, powerful and freely available system for statistical computations and graphics. The book assumes that you know nothing at all about scientific software and, accordingly, introduces R from basics. If you have experience with statistics, you probably already have a preferred software package. So long as that software will fit linear models with multiple explanatory variables and produce a more-or-less standard regression report, it can be used to follow this book. That said, I strongly encourage you to consider learning and using R. You can learn it easily by following the examples and can be doing productive statistics very quickly. Not only will you easily be able to fit models and get reports, but you can use R to explore ideas such as resampling and randomization. If you now use "educational" software, learning R will give you a professional-level tool for use in the future.

For many instructors, this book can support a nice *second* course in statistics — a follow-up to a conventional first introductory course. Increasingly, such a course is needed as more and more young people encounter basic statistical ideas in grade school and many of the topics of the conventional university course are absorbed into the high-school curriculum. At Macalester College, where I developed this book, mainstream students of biology, economics, political science, and so on use this book for their *first* statistics course. Accordingly, the book is written to be self-contained, making no assumption that readers have had any previous formal study in statistics.

For the Second Edition ...

This second edition of *Statistical Modeling: A Fresh Approach* provides me the opportunity to implement many suggestions provided by readers and instructors who used the First Edition. An early chapter now introduces simple, group-wise models. This allows the problems of confounding to be demonstrated earlier and therefore motivates the more sophisticated modeling techniques that are the central theme of the book. Another early chapter introduces confidence intervals via re-sampling.

The second edition continues to feature R, but now makes use of the *mosaic* package distributed through the standard R channels.

One of the most distinctive aspects of the First Edition was the use of geometry to provide a theory for statistical models. Many people find that geometrical explanations strongly support their development of an understanding of the statistical methods. Many others found the geometrical material an undesired detour. To accomodate both groups, I have broken down the basics of the geometrical material into short sections in early chapters. More extensive introductory material about vectors, subspaces, etc., as well as interpretations of the advanced modeling techniques in geometrical terms, is being published on-line on the book's web site.

Thanks and acknowledgments ...

I have been fortunate to have the assistance and support of many people. Some of the colleagues who have played important roles are David Bressoud, George Cobb, Dan Flath, Tom Halverson, Gary Krueger, Weiwen Miao, Phil Poronnik, Victor Addona, Alicia Johnson, Karen Saxe, Michael Schneider, and Libby

Shoop. Critical institutional support was given by Brian Rosenberg, Jan Serie, Dan Hornbach, Helen Warren, and Diane Michelfelder at Macalester and Mercedes Talley at the Keck Foundation.

I received encouragement from many in the statistics education community, including George Cobb, Joan Garfield, Dick De Veaux, Bob delMas, Julie Legler, Milo Schield, Paul Alper, Dennis Pearl, Jean Scott, Ben Hansen, Tom Short, Andy Zieffler, Sharon Lane-Getaz, Katie Makar, Michael Bulmer, Frank Shaw, and the participants in our monthly "Stat Chat" sessions. Helpful suggestions came from from Simon Blomberg, Dominic Hyde, Michael Lavine, Erik Larson, Julie Dolan, and Kendrick Brown. Michael Edwards helped with proofreading. Nick Trefethen and Dave Saville provided important insights about the geometry of fitting linear models.

It's important to recognize the role played by the developers of the R software — the "core" R team as well as the group of volunteers who have provided numerous packages that extend R's capabilities. Hadley Wickham, in particular, developed the `ggplot2` package used to create many of the graphics in this Second Edition, as well as a remarkable array of other utilities for treating data in a unified way. The design of R (and its progenitor S) are not just a matter of good software design, but of a brilliant understanding and systematization of statistics that makes the underlying logic of statistics accessible to students as well as experts. Further extending the reach of R, J.J. Allaire, Joe Chang, and Joshua Paulson have created the RStudio interface to R, which makes it much easier to teach and learn with R.

Special thanks are due to Randall Pruim and Nicholas Horton who, as *mosaic* activists, have improved the extensions to R used in this book and provided a wide range of suggestions that have found their way into the Second Edition.

Thanks also go to the hundred or so students at Macalester College who enrolled in the early, experimental sessions of Math 155 where many of the ideas in this book were first tested. Among those students, I want to acknowledge particular help from Alan Eisinger, Caroline Ettinger, Bernd Verst, Wes Hart, Sami Saqer, and Michael Snavely. Approximately 500 Macalester students have used the First Edition of this book, many of whom have helped identify errors and suggested clarifications and other improvements.

Crucial early support for this project was provided by a grant from the Howard Hughes Medical Institute. An important Keck Foundation grant was crucial to the continuing refinement of the approach and the writing of this book. Google provided summer-of-code funding for my student Andrew Rich to develop interactive applets that can be used along with this book.

Finally, my thanks and love to my wife, Maya, and daughters, Tamar, Liat, and Netta, who endured the many, many hours during which I was preoccupied by some or another statistics-related enthusiasm, challenge, or difficulty.

1

Introduction

All models are wrong. Some models are useful. — George Box

Art is a lie that tells the truth. — Pablo Picasso

This book is about **statistical modeling**, two words that themselves require some definition.

"Modeling" is a process of asking questions. "Statistical" refers in part to data — the statistical models you will construct will be rooted in data. But it refers also to a distinctively modern idea: that you can measure what you *don't* know and that doing so contributes to your understanding.

There is a saying, "A person with a watch knows the time. A person with two watches is never sure." The statistical point of view is that it's better not to be sure. With two watches you can see how they disagree with each other. This provides an idea of how precise the watches are. You don't know the time exactly, but knowing the precision tells you something about what you don't know. The non-statistical certainty of the person with a single watch is merely an uninformed self-confidence: the single watch provides no indication of what the person doesn't know.

The physicist Ernest Rutherford (1871-1937) famously said, "If your experiment needs statistics, you ought to have done a better experiment." In other words, if you can make a good enough watch, you need only one: no statistics. This is bad advice. Statistics never hurts. A person with two watches that agree perfectly not only knows the time, but has evidence that the watches are working at high precision. Sensibly, the official world time is based on an average of many atomic clocks. The individual clocks are fantastically precise; the point of averaging is to know when one or more of the clocks is drifting out of precision.

Why "statistical modeling" and not simply "statistics" or "data analysis?" Many people imagine that data speak for themselves and that the purpose of statistics is to extract the information that the data carry. Such people see data analysis as an objective process in which the researcher should, ideally, have no influence. This can be true when very simple issues are involved; for instance, how precise is the average of the atomic clocks used to set official time or what is the difference in time between two events? But many questions are much more complicated; they involve many variables and you don't necessarily know what is doing what to what.[2]

The conclusions you reach from data depend on the specific questions you ask. Like it or not, the researcher plays an active and creative role in constructing and interrogating data. This means that the process involves some subjectivity. But this is not the same as saying anything goes. Statistical methods allow you to make objective statements about how the data answer your questions. In particular, the methods help you to know if the data show anything at all.

The word "modeling" highlights that your goals, your beliefs, and your current state of knowledge all influence your analysis of data. The core of the scientific method is the formation of hypotheses that can be tested and perhaps refuted by experiment or observation. Similarly, in statistical modeling, you examine your data to see whether they are consistent with the hypotheses that frame your understanding of the system under study.

Example 1.1: Grades   A student is applying to law school. The schools she applies to ask for her class rank, which is based on the average of her college course grades.

A simple statistical issue concerns the precision of the grade-point average. This isn't a question of whether the average was correctly computed or whether the grades were accurately recorded. Instead, imagine that you could send two essentially identical students to essentially identical schools. Their grade-point averages might well differ, reflecting perhaps the grading practices of their different instructors or slightly different choices of subjects or random events such as illness or mishaps or the scheduling of classes. One way to think about this is that the students' grades are to some extent random, contingent on factors that are unknown or perhaps irrelevant to the students' capabilities.

How do you measure the extent to which the grades are random? There is no practical way to create "identical" students and observe how their grades differ. But you can look at the variation in a single student's grades — from class to class — and use this as an indication of the size of the random influence in each grade. From this, you can calculate the likely range of the random influences on the overall grade-point average.

Statistical models let you go further in interpreting grades. It's a common belief that there are easy- and hard-grading teachers and that a grade reflects not just the student's work but the teacher's attitude and practices. Statistical modeling provides a way to use data on grades to see whether teachers grade differently and to correct for these differences between teachers. Doing this involves some subtlety, for example taking into account the possibility that strong students take different courses than weaker students.

Example 1.2: Nitrogen Fixing Plants   All plants need nitrogen to grow. Since nitrogen is the primary component of air, there is plenty around. But it's hard for plants to get nitrogen from the air; they get it instead from the soil. Some plants, like alder and soybean, support nitrogen-fixing bacteria in nodules on the plant roots. The plant creates a hospitable environment for the bacteria; the bacteria, by fixing nitrogen in the soil, create a good environment for the plant. In a word, symbiosis.

Biologist Michael Anderson is interested in how genetic variation in the bacteria influences the success with which they fix nitrogen. One can imagine using this information to breed plants and bacteria that are more effective at fixing nitrogen and thereby reducing the need for agricultural fertilizer.

Anderson has an promising early result. His extensive field studies indicate that different genotypes of bacteria fix nitrogen at different rates. Unfortunately, the situation is confusing since the different genotypes tend to populate different areas with different amounts of soil moisture, different soil temperatures, and so on. How can he untangle the relative influences of the genotype and the other environmental factors in order to decide whether the variation in genotype is genuinely important and worth further study?

Example 1.3: Sex Discrimination   A large trucking firm is being audited by the government to see if the firm pays wages in a discriminatory way. The audit finds wage discrepancies between men and women for "office and clerical workers" but not for other job classifications such as technicians, supervisors, sales personnel, or "skilled craftworkers." It finds no discrepancies based on race.

A simple statistical question is whether the observed difference in average wages for men and women office and clerical workers is based on enough data to be reliable. In answering this question, it actually makes a difference what other groups the government auditors looked at when deciding to focus on sex discrimination in office and clerical workers.

Further complicating matters are the other factors that contribute to people's wages: the kind of job they have, their skill level, their experience. Statistical models can be used to quantify how these contributions and how they connect to one another. For instance, it turns out that men on average tend to have more job experience than women, and some or all of the men's higher average wages might be due to this.

Models can help you decide whether this potential explanation is plausible. For instance, if you see that both men's and women's wages increase with experience in the same way, you might be more inclined to believe that job experience is a legitimate factor rather than just a mask for discrimination.

1.1   Models and their Purposes

Many of the toys you played with as a child are models: dolls, balsa-wood airplanes with wind-up propellers, wooden blocks, model trains. But so are many serious objects of the adult world: architectural plans, bank statements, train schedules, the results of medical diagnostic tests, the signals transmitted by a telephone, the equations of physics, the genetic sequences used by biologists. There are too many to list.

What all models have in common is this:

> *A model is a representation for a particular purpose.*

A model might be a physical object or it might be an idea, but it always stands for something else: it's a representation. Dolls stand for babies and animals, architectural plans stand for buildings and bridges, a white blood-cell count stands for the function of the immune system.

When you create a model, you have (or ought to have) a purpose in mind. Toys are created for the entertainment and (sometimes) edification of children. The various kinds of toys — dolls, blocks, model airplanes and trains — have a form that serves this purpose. Unlike the things they represent, the toy versions are small, safe, and inexpensive.

Models always leave things out and get some things — many things — wrong. Architectural plans are not houses; you can't live in them. But they are easy to transport, copy, and modify. That's the point. Telephone signals — unlike the physical sound waves that they represent — can be transported over long distances and even stored. A train schedule tells you something important but it obviously doesn't reproduce every aspect of the trains it describes; it doesn't carry passengers.

Statistical models revolve around data. But even so, they are first and foremost models. They are created for a purpose. The intended use of a model should shape the appropriate form of the model and determines the sorts of data that can properly be used to build the model.

There are three main uses for statistical models. They are closely related, but distinct enough to be worth enumerating.

Description. Sometimes you want to describe the range or typical values of a quantity. For example, what's a "normal" white blood cell count? Sometimes you want to describe the relationship between things. Example: What's the relationship between the price of gasoline and consumption by automobiles?

Classification or prediction. You often have information about some observable traits, qualities, or attributes of a system you observe and want to draw conclusions about other things that you can't directly observe. For instance, you know a patient's white blood-cell count and other laboratory measurements and want to diagnose the patient's illness.

Anticipating the consequences of interventions. Here, you intend to do something: you are not merely an observer but an active participant in the system. For example, people involved in setting or debating public policy have to deal with questions like these: To what extent will increasing the tax on gasoline reduce consumption? To what extent will paying teachers more increase student performance?

The appropriate form of a model depends on the purpose. For example, a model that diagnoses a patient as ill based on an observation of a high number of white blood cells can be sensible and useful. But that same model could give absurd predictions about intervention: Do you really think that lowering the white blood cell count by bleeding a patient will make the patient better?

To anticipate correctly the effects of an intervention you need to get the direction of cause and effect correct in your models. But for a model used for classification or prediction, it may be unnecessary to represent causation correctly. Instead, other issues, e.g., the reliability of data, can be the most important. One of the thorniest issues in statistical modeling — with tremendous consequences for science, medicine, government, and commerce — is how you can legitimately draw conclusions about interventions from models based on data collected without performing these interventions.

1.2   Observation and Knowledge

How do you know what you know? How did you find it out? How can you find out what you don't yet know? These are questions that philosophers have addressed for thousands of years. The views that they have expressed are complicated and contradictory.

From the earliest times in philosophy, there has been a difficult relationship between knowledge and observation. Sometimes philosophers see your knowledge as emerging from your observations of the world, sometimes they emphasize that the way you see the world is rooted in your innate knowledge: the things that are obvious to you.

This tension plays out on the pages of newspapers as they report the controversies of the day. Does the death penalty deter crime? Does increased screening for cancer reduce mortality?

Consider the simple, obvious argument for why severe punishment deters crime. Punishments are things that people don't like. People avoid what they don't like. If crime leads to punishment, then people will avoid committing crime.

Each statement in this argument seems perfectly reasonable, but none of them is particularly rooted in observations of actual and potential criminals. It's artificial — a learned skill — to base knowledge such as "people avoid punishment" on observation. It might be that this knowledge was formed by our own experiences, but usually the only explanation you can give is something like, "that's been my experience" or give one or two anecdotes.

When observations contradict opinions — opinions are what you think you know — people often stick with their opinions. Put yourself in the place of someone who believes that the death penalty really does deter crime. You are presented with accurate data showing that when a neighboring state eliminated the death penalty, crime did not increase. So do you change your views on the matter? A skeptic can argue that it's not just punishment but also other factors that influence the crime rate, for instance the availability of jobs. Perhaps a generally improving economic condition in the other state kept the crime rate steady even at a time when society is imposing lighter punishments.

It's difficult to use observation to inform knowledge because relationships are complicated and involve multiple factors. It isn't at all obvious how people can discover or demonstrate causal relationships through observation. Suppose one school district pays teachers well and another pays them poorly. You observe that the first district has better student outcomes than the second. Can you legitimately conclude that teacher pay accounts for the difference? Perhaps something else is at work: greater overall family wealth in the first district (which is what enabled them to pay teachers more), better facilities, smaller classes, and so on.

Historian Robert Hughes concisely summarized the difficulty of trying to use observation to discover causal relationships. In describing the extensive use of hanging in 18th and 19th century England, he wrote, "One cannot say whether public hanging did terrify people away from crime. Nor can anyone do so, until we can count crimes that were never committed." [3, p.35] To know whether hanging did deter crime, you would need to observe a **counterfactual**, something that didn't actually happen: the crimes in a world without hanging. You can't observe counterfactuals. So you need somehow to generate observations that give you data on what happens for different levels of the causal variable.

A modern idea is the **controlled experiment**. In its simplest ideal form, a controlled experiment involves changing one thing — teacher pay, for example — while *holding everything else constant*: family wealth, facilities, etc.

The experimental approach to gaining knowledge has great success in medicine and science. For many people, experiment is the essence of all science. But experiments are hard to perform and sometimes not possible at all. How do you hold everything else constant? Partly for this reason, you rarely see reports of experiments when you read the newspaper, unless the article happens to be about a scientific discovery.

Scientists pride themselves on recording their observations carefully and systematically. Laboratories are filled with high-precision instrumentation. The quest for precision culminates perhaps in the physicist's fundamental quantities. For instance, the mass of the electron is reported as $9.10938215 \pm 0.00000045 \times 10^{-31}$ kg. The precision is about 1 part in twenty million.

Contrast this extreme precision with the humble speed measurements from a policeman's radar gun (perhaps a couple of miles or kilometers per hour — one part in 50) or the weight indicated on a bathroom scale (give or take a kilogram or a couple of pounds — about one part in 100 for an adult).

All such observations and measures are the stuff of **data**, the records of observations. Observations do not become data by virtue of high precision or expensive instrumentation or the use of metric rather than traditional units. For many purposes, data of low precision is used. An ecologist's count of the number of mating pairs of birds in a territory is limited by the ability to find nests. A national census of a country's population, conducted by the government can be precise to only a couple of percent. The physicists counting neutrinos in huge observatories buried under mountains to shield them from extraneous events waits for months for their results and in the end the results are precise to only one part in two.

The precision that is needed in data depends on the purpose for which the data will be used. The important question for the person using the data is whether the precision, whatever it be, is adequate for the purpose at hand. To answer this question, you need to know how to measure precision and how to compare this to a standard reflecting the needs of your task. The scientist with expensive instrumentation and the framer of social policy both need to deal with data in similar ways to understand and interpret the precision of their results.

It's common for people to believe that conclusions drawn from data apply to certain areas — science, economics, medicine — but aren't terribly useful in other areas. In teaching, for example, almost all decisions are based on "experience" rather than observation. Indeed, there is often strong resistance to making formal observations of student progress as interfering with the teaching process.

This book is based on the idea that techniques for drawing valid conclusions from observations — data — are valuable for two groups of people. The first group is scientists and others who routinely need to use statistical methods to analyze experimental and other data.

The second group is everybody else. All of us need to draw conclusions from our experiences, even if we're not in a laboratory. It's better to learn how to do this in valid ways, and to understand the limitations of these ways, than to rely on an informal, unstated process of opinion formation. It may turn out that in any particular area of interest there are no useful data. In such situations, you won't be able to use the techniques. But at least you will know what you're missing. You may be inspired to figure out how to supply it or to recognize it when it does come along, and you'll be aware of when others are misusing data.

As you will see, the manner in which the data are collected plays a central role in what sorts of conclusions can be legitimately made; data do not always speak for themselves. You will also see that strongly supported statements about causation are difficult to make. Often, all you can do is point to an "association" or a "correlation," a weaker form of statement.

Statistics is sometimes loosely described as the "science of data." This description is apt, particularly when it covers both the collection and analysis of data, but it does not mean much until you understand what data are. That's the subject of the next chapter.

1.3   The Main Points of this Book

- Statistics is about variation. Describing and interpreting variation is a major goal of statistics.

- You can create empirical, mathematical descriptions not only of a single trait or variable but also of the relationships between two or more traits. Empirical means based on measurements, data, observations.

- Models let you split variation into components: "explained" versus "unexplained." How to measure the size of these components and how to compare them to one another is a central aspect of statistical methodology. Indeed, this provides a definition of statistics:

    Statistics is the explanation of variation in the context of what remains unexplained.

- By collecting data in ways that require care but are quite feasible, you can estimate how reliable your descriptions are, e.g., whether it's plausible that you should see similar relationships if you collected new data. This notion of reliability is very narrow and there are some issues that depend critically on the context in which the data were collected and the correctness of assumptions that you make about how the world works.

- Relationships between pairs of traits can be studied in isolation only in special circumstances. In general, to get valid results it is necessary to study entire systems of traits simultaneously. Failure to do so can easily lead to conclusions that are grossly misleading.

- Descriptions of relationships are often **subjective** — they depend on choices that you, the modeler, make. These choices are generally rooted in your own beliefs about how the world works, or the theories accepted as plausible within some community of inquiry.

- If data are collected properly, you can get an indication of whether the data are consistent or inconsistent with your subjective beliefs or — and this is important — whether you don't have enough data to tell either way.

- Models can be used to check out the sensitivity of your conclusions to different beliefs. People who disagree in their views of how the world works often may not be able to reconcile their differences based on data, but they will be able to decide objectively whether their own or the other party's beliefs are reasonable given the data.

- Notwithstanding everything said above about the strong link between your prior, subjective beliefs and the conclusions you draw from data, by collecting data in a certain context — experiments — you can dramatically simplify the interpretation of the results. It's actually possible to remove the dependence on identified subjective beliefs by intervening in the system under study experimentally.

This book takes a different approach than most statistics texts. Many people want statistics to be presented as a kind of automatic, algorithmic way to process data. People look for mathematical certainty in their conclusions. After all, there are right-or-wrong answers to the mathematical calculations that people (or computers) perform in statistics. Why shouldn't there be right-or-wrong answers to the conclusions that people draw about the world?

The answer is that there can be, but only when you are dealing with narrow circumstances that may not apply to the situations you want to study. An insistence on certainty and provable correctness often results in irrelevancy.

The point of view taken in this book is that it is better to be useful than to be provably certain. The objective is to introduce methods and ideas that can help you deal with drawing conclusions about the real world from data. The methods and ideas are meant to guide your reasoning; even if the conclusions you draw are not guaranteed by proof to be correct, they can still be more useful than the alternative, which is the conclusions that you draw without data, or the conclusions you draw from simplistic methods that don't honor the complexity of the real system.

1.4   Introduction to Computation with R

Modern statistics is done on the computer. There was a time, 60 years ago and before, when computation could only be done by hand or using balky mechanical calculators. The methods of applied statistics developed during this time reflected what could be done using such calculators, not necessarily what was best for illuminating the system under study. These methods took on a life of their own — they became the operational definition of statistics. They continue to be taught today, using electronic calculators or personal computers or even just using paper and pencil. For the old statistical methods, computers are merely a labor saving device.

But not for modern statistics. The statistical methods at the core of this book cannot be applied in a authentic and realistic way without powerful computers. Thirty years ago, many of the methods could not be done at all unless you had access to the resources of a government agency or a large university. But with the revolutionary advances in computer hardware and numerical algorithms over the last half-century, modern statistical calculations can be performed on an ordinary home computer or laptop. (Even a cell phone has phenomenal computational power, often besting the mainframes of thirty years ago.) Hardware and software today pose no limitation; they are readily available.

Each chapter of this book includes a section on computational technique. Many readers will be completely new to the use of computers for scientific and statistial work, so the first chapters cover the foundations, techniques that are useful for many different aspects of computation. Working through the early chapters is essential for developing the skills that will be used later in actual statistical work. It will take a few hours, but this investment will pay off handsomely.

Chances are, you use a computer almost every day: for email, word-processing, managing your music or your photograph collection, perhaps even using a spreadsheet program for accounting. The software you use for such activities makes it easy to get started. Possibly you have never even looked at an instruction manual or used the "help" features on your computer.

When you use a word processor or email, the bulk of what you enter into the computer — the content of your documents and email — is without meaning to the computer. This is not at all to say that it is meaningless. Your documents and letters are intended for human readers; most of the work you do is directed so that the recipients can understand them. But the computer doesn't need to understand what you write in order to format it, print it, or transmit it over the Internet.

When doing scientific and statistical computing, things are different. What you enter into the computer is instructions to the computer to perform calculations and re-arrangements of data. Those instructions have to be comprehensible to the computer. If they make no sense or if they are inconsistent or ill formed, the computer won't be able to carry out your instructions. Worse, if the instructions make sense in some formal way but don't convey your actual intentions, the computer will perform some operation but the result will mislead you.

The difficulty with using software for mathematics and statistics is in making sure that your instructions make sense and do what you want them to do. This difficulty is not a matter of bad software design; it's intrinsic to the problem of communicating your intentions to the computer. The same difficulty would arise in word processing if the computer had to make sense of your writing, rejecting it when a claim is unconvincing or when a sentence is ambiguous. Statistical computing pioneer John Chambers refers to the "Prime Directive" of software[4]: "to program in such a way that computations can be understood and trusted."

Much of the design of software for scientific and statistical work is oriented around the difficulty of communicating intentions. A popular approach is based on the computer mouse: the program provides a list of possible operations — like the keys on a calculator — and lets the user choose which operation to apply to some selected data. This style of user interface is employed, for example, in spreadsheet software, letting users add up columns of numbers, make graphs, etc. The reason this style is popular is that it can make things extremely easy ... so long as the operation that you want has been included in the software. But things get very hard if you need to construct your own operation and it can be difficult to understand or trust the operations performed by others.

Another style of scientific computation — the one used in this book — is based on language. Rather than selecting an option with a mouse, you construct a **command** that conveys both the operation that you want and the data to which you want to apply that operation. There are dramatic advantages to this language-based style of computation:

- It lets you **connect** computations to one another, so that the output of one operation can become the input to another.

- It lets you **repeat** the operation on new or modified data, allowing you to automate tedious tasks and, importantly, to verify the correctness of your computations on data where you already know the answer.

- It lets you **accumulate** the results of previous operations, treating those results as new data.

- It lets you **document** concisely what was done so that you can demonstrate that what you said you did is what you actually did. In this way, you or others can repeat the analysis later if necessary to confirm your results.

- It lets you **modify** the computation in a controlled way to correct it or to vary some aspect of it while holding other aspects exactly the same as in the original.

In order to use the language-based approach, you will need to learn a few principles of the language itself: some vocabulary, some syntax, some grammar. This is much, much easier for the computer language than for a natural language like English or Chinese; it will take you only a couple of hours before you are fluent enough to do useful computations. In addition to letting you perform scientific computations in ways that use the computer and your own time and effort effectively, the principles that you will learn are broadly applicable to many computer systems and can provide significant insight even to how to use mouse-based interfaces.

1.4.1   The Choice of Software

The software package used in this book is called R. The R package provides an environment for doing statistical and scientific computation at a professional level. It was designed for statistics work, but suitable for other forms of scientific calculations and the creation of high-quality scientific graphics.[5]

There are several other major software packages widely used in statistics. Among the leaders are SPSS, SAS, and Stata. Each of them provides the computational power needed for statistical modeling. Each has its own advantages and its own devoted group of users.

One reason for the choice of R is that it offers a command-based computing environment. That makes it much easier to write about computing and also reveals better the structure of the computing process.[6] R is available for free and works on the major types of computers, e.g., Windows, Macintosh, and Unix/Linux. The RStudio software lets you work with a complete R system using an ordinary web browser or on your own computer.

In making your own choice, the most important thing is this: *choose something*! Readers who are familiar with SPSS, SAS, or STATA can use the information in each chapter's computational technique section to help them identify the facilities to look for in those packages.

Another form of software that's often used with data is the spreadsheet. Examples are Excel and Google Spreadsheets. Spreadsheets are effective for entering data and have nice facilities for formatting tables. The visual layout of the data seems to be intuitive to many people. Many businesses use spreadsheets and they are widely taught in high schools. Unfortunately, they are very difficult to use for statistical analyses of any sophistication. Indeed, even some very elementary statistical tasks such as making a histogram are difficult with spreadsheets and the results are usually unsatisfactory from a graphical point of view. Worse,

Figure 1.1: The R command console.

spreadsheets can be very hard to use reliably. There are lots of opportunities to make mistakes that will go undetected. As a result, despite the popularity of spreadsheets, I encourage you to reserve them for data entry and consider other software for the analysis of your data.

1.4.2 The R Command Console

Depending on your circumstances, you may prefer to install R as software on your own computer, or use a web-based ("cloud computing") service such as RStudio that runs through a web browser. If you are using this book with a course, your instructor may have set up a system for you. If you are on your own, follow the set-up instructions available on-line at www.r-project.org.

Depending on whether you run R on your own computer or in the cloud, you will start R either by clicking on an icon in the familiar way or by logging in to the web service. In either case, you will see a **console panel** in which you will be typing your commands to R. It will look something like Figure 1.1.

The R console gives you great power to carry out statistical and other mathematical and scientific operations. To use this power, you need to learn a little bit about the syntax and meaning of R commands. Once you have learned this, operations become simple to perform.

1.4.3 Invoking an Operation

People often think of computers as *doing* things: sending email, playing music, storing files. Your job in using a computer is to tell the computer *what* to do. There are many different words used to refer to the "what": a procedure, a task, a function, a routine, and so on. I'll use the word **computation**. Admittedly, this is a bit circular, but it is easy to remember: computers perform computations.

Complex computations are built up from simpler computations. This may seem obvious, but it is a powerful idea. An **algorithm** is just a description of a computation in terms of other computations that you already know how to perform. To help distinguish between the computation as a whole and the simpler parts, it is helpful to introduce a new word: an **operator** performs a computation.

It's helpful to think of the computation carried out by an operator as involving four parts:

1. The name of the operator

2. The input arguments

3. The output value

4. Side effects

A typical operation takes one or more **input arguments** and uses the information in these to produce an **output value**. Along the way, the computer might take some action: display a graph, store a file, make a sound, etc. These actions are called **side effects**.

To tell the computer to perform a computation — call this **invoking an operation** or giving a **command** — you need to provide the name and the input arguments in a specific format. The computer then returns the output value. For example, the command `sqrt(25)` invokes the square root operator (named `sqrt`) on the argument 25. The output from the computation will, of course, be 5.

The syntax or invoking an operation consists of the operator's name, followed by round parentheses. The input arguments go inside the parentheses.

The software program that you use to invoke operators is called an **interpreter**. (The interpreter is the program you are running when you start R.) You enter your commands as a dialog between you and the interpreter. To start, the interpreter prints a prompt, after which you type your command:

PROMPT ———————▶ > `sqrt(25)` ◀——— COMMAND

When you press "Enter," the interpreter reads your command and performs the computation. For commands such as this one, the interpreter will print the output value from the computation:

> `sqrt(25)`

OUTPUT MARKER ———▶ [1]   5 ◀——— OUTPUT VALUE

NEXT PROMPT ———▶ >

The dialog continues as the interpreter prints another prompt and waits for your further command.

To save space, I'll usually show just the give-and-take from one round of the dialog:

```
> sqrt(25)
[1] 5
```

(Go ahead! Type `sqrt(25)` after the prompt in the R interpreter, press "enter," and see what happens.)

Often, operations involve more than one argument. The various arguments are separated by commas. For example, here is an operation named `seq` that produces a sequence of numbers:

```
> seq(3, 10)
[1]  3  4  5  6  7  8  9 10
```

The first argument tells where to start the sequence, the second tells where to end it.

The order of the arguments is important. Here is the sequence produced when 10 is the first argument and 3 the second:

```
> seq(10, 3)
[1] 10  9  8  7  6  5  4  3
```

For some operators, particularly those that have many input arguments, some of the arguments can be referred to by name rather than position. This is particularly useful when the named argument has a sensible default value. For example, the `seq` operator can be instructed how big a jump to take between successive items in the sequence. This is accomplished using an argument named `by`:

```
> seq(3, 10, by = 2)
[1] 3 5 7 9
```

Depending on the circumstances, all four parts of a operation need not be present. For example, the `date` operation returns the current time and date; no input arguments are needed.

```
> date()
[1] "Tue Aug 23 16:52:29 2011"
```

Note that even though there are no arguments, the parentheses are still used. Think of the pair of parentheses as meaning, "Do this."

Naming and Storing Values

Often the value returned by an operation will be used later on. Values can be stored for later use with the **assignment operator**. This has a different syntax that reminds the user that a value is being stored. Here's an example of a simple assignment:

```
> x = 16
```

This command has stored the value 16 under the name x. The syntax is always the same: an equal sign (=) with a name on the left and a value on the right.

Such stored values are called **objects**. Making an assignment to an object defines the object. Once an object has been defined, it can be referred to and used in later computations.

Notice that an assignment operation does not return a value or display a value. Its sole purpose is to have the side effects of defining the object and thereby storing a value under the object's name.

To refer to the value stored in the object, just use the object's name itself. For instance:

```
> x
[1] 16
```

Doing a computation on the value stored in an object is much the same:

```
> sqrt(x)
[1] 4
```

You can create as many objects as you like and give them names that remind you of their purpose. Some examples: wilma, ages, temp, dog.houses, foo3. There are some rules for object names:

- Use only letters and numbers and the two punctuation marks "dot" (.) and "underscore" (_).

- Do NOT use spaces anywhere in the name.

- A number or underscore cannot be the first character in the name.

- Capital letters are treated as distinct from lower-case letters. The objects named wilma and Wilma are different.

For the sake of readability, keep object names short. But if you really must have an object named something like agesOfChildrenFromTheClinicalTrial, feel free.

Objects can store all sorts of things, for example a sequence of numbers:

```
> x = seq(1, 7)
```

When you assign a new value to an existing object, as just done to x, the former value of that object is erased from the computer memory. The former value of x was 16, but after the above assignment command it is

```
> x
```

```
[1] 1 2 3 4 5 6 7
```

The value of an object is changed only *via* the assignment operator. Using an object in a computation does not change the value. For example, suppose you invoke the square-root operator on **x**:

```
> sqrt(x)
```

```
[1] 1.00 1.41 1.73 2.00 2.24 2.45 2.65
```

The square roots have been returned as a value, but this doesn't change the value of **x**:

```
> x
```

```
[1] 1 2 3 4 5 6 7
```

If you want to change the value of **x**, you need to use the assignment operator:

```
> x = sqrt(x)
> x
```

```
[1] 1.00 1.41 1.73 2.00 2.24 2.45 2.65
```

Aside. 1.1 Assignment vs Algebra

An assignment command like **x=sqrt(x)** can be confusing to people who are used to algebraic notation. In algebra, the equal sign describes a relationship between the left and right sides. So, $x = \sqrt{x}$ tells us about how the quantity x and the quantity $\sqrt{x}$ are related. Students are usually trained to "solve" such relationships, going through a series of algebraic steps to find values for x that are consistent with the mathematical statement. (For $x = \sqrt{x}$, the solutions are $x = 0$ and $x = 1$.) In contrast, the assignment command **x=sqrt(x)** is a way of replacing the previous values stored in **x** with new values that are the square root of the old ones.

Connecting Computations

The brilliant thing about organizing operators in terms of input arguments and output values is that the output of one operator can be used as an input to another. This lets complicated computations be built out of simpler ones.

For example, suppose you have a list of 10000 voters in a precinct and you want to select a random sample of 20 of them for a survey. The **seq** operator can be used to generate a set of 10000 choices. The **sample** operator can be used to select some of these choices at random.

One way to connect the computations is by using objects to store the intermediate outputs.

```
> choices = seq(1, 10000)
> sample(choices, 20)
```

```
 [1] 7196 5352 6734 2438 9370 4713 6481 3549  593 3294 7815 6967 5097 3820
[15] 9170 6637 8801 2304 9919 4102
```

You can also pass the output of an operator *directly* as an argument to another operator. Here's another way to accomplish exactly the same thing as the above.

```
> sample(seq(1, 10000), 20)
 [1]   10 3029 9507 1037 9562 4057  786 7542 6190 2248 9237 3089 3216 8473
[15] 4951 8816 4473 7651 6449 8676
```

Numbers and Arithmetic

The language has a concise notation for arithmetic that looks very much like the traditional one:

```
> 7 + 2
[1] 9
> 3 * 4
[1] 12
> 5/2
[1] 2.5
> 3 - 8
[1] -5
> -3
[1] -3
> 5^2
[1] 25
```

Arithmetic operators, like any other operators, can be connected to form more complicated computations. For instance,

```
> 8 + 4/2
[1] 10
```

To a human reader, the command 8+4/2 might seem ambiguous. Is it intended to be (8+4)/2 or 8+(4/2)? The computer uses unambiguous rules to interpret the expression, but it's a good idea for you to use parethesis so that you can make sure that what you intend is what the computer carries out:

```
> (8 + 4)/2
[1] 6
```

Traditional mathematical notation uses superscripts and radicals to indicate exponentials and roots, e.g., 3^2 or $\sqrt{3}$ or $\sqrt[3]{8}$. This special typography doesn't work well with an ordinary keyboard, so R and most other computer languages uses a different notation:

```
> 3^2
[1] 9
> sqrt(3)
[1] 1.73
> 8^(1/3)
[1] 2
```

There is a large set of mathematical functions: exponentials, logs, trigonometric and inverse trigonometric functions, etc. Some examples:

Traditional	Computer
e^2	`exp(2)`
$\log_e(100)$	`log(100)`
$\log_{10}(100)$	`log10(100)`
$\log_2(100)$	`log2(100)`
$\cos(\frac{\pi}{2})$	`cos(pi/2)`
$\sin(\frac{\pi}{2})$	`sin(pi/2)`
$\tan(\frac{\pi}{2})$	`tan(pi/2)`
$\cos^{-1}(-1)$	`acos(-1)`

Numbers can be written in **scientific notation**. For example, the "universal gravitational constant" that describes the gravitational attraction between masses is 6.67428×10^{-11} (with units meters-cubed per kilogram per second squared). In the computer notation, this would be written G=6.67428e-11. The Avogradro constant, which gives the number of atoms in a mole, is $6.02214179 \times 10^{23}$ per mole, or 6.02214178e23.

The computer language does not directly support the recording of units. This is unfortunate, since in the real world numbers often have units and the units matter. For example, in 1999 the Mars Climate Orbiter crashed into Mars because the design engineers specified the engine's thrust in units of pounds, while the guidance engineers thought the units were newtons.

Computer arithmetic is accurate and reliable, but it often involves very slight rounding of numbers. Ordinarily, this is not noticeable. However, it can become apparent in some calculations that produce results that are zero. For example, mathematically $\sin(\pi) = 0$, however the computer does not duplicate this mathematical relationship exactly:

```
> sin(pi)
[1] 1.22e-16
```

Whether a number like this is properly interpreted as "close to zero," depends on the context and, for quantities that have units, on the units themselves. For instance, the unit "parsec" is used in astronomy in reporting distances between stars. The closest star to the sun is Proxima, at a distance of 1.3 parsecs. A distance of 1.22×10^{-16} parsecs is tiny in astronomy but translates to about 2.5 meters — not so small on the human scale.

In statistics, many calculations relate to probabilities which are always in the range 0 to 1. On this scale, `1.22e-16` is very close to zero.

There are two "special" numbers. `Inf` stands for ∞, as in

```
> 1/0
```

```
[1] Inf
```

`NaN` stands for "not a number," and is the result when a numerical operation isn't defined, for instance

```
> 0/0
```

```
[1] NaN
```

Aside. 1.2 Complex Numbers

Mathematically oriented readers will wonder why R should have any trouble with a computation like $\sqrt{-9}$; the result is the imaginary number $3i$. R works with complex numbers, but you have to tell the system that this is what you want to do. To calculate $\sqrt{-9}$, use `sqrt(-9+0i)`.

Types of Objects

Most of the examples used so far have dealt with numbers. But computers work with other kinds of information as well: text, photographs, sounds, sets of data, and so on. The word **type** is used to refer to the kind of information.

Modern computer languages support a great variety of types. It's important to know about the types of data because operators expect their input arguments to be of specific types. When you use the wrong type of input, the computer might not be able process your command.

For the purpose of starting with R, it's important to distinguish among three basic types:

numeric The numbers of the sort already encountered.

data frames Collections of data more or less in the form of a spreadsheet table. The Computation Technique section in Chapter 2 introduces the operators for working with data frames.

character Text data.

You indicate character data to the computer by enclosing the text in double quotation marks. For example:

```
> filename = "swimmers.csv"
```

There is something a bit subtle going on in the above command, so look at it carefully. The purpose of the command is to create an object, named `filename`, that stores a little bit of text data. Notice that the name of the object is not put in quotes, but the text characters are.

Whenever you refer to an object name, make sure that you don't use quotes, for example:

```
> filename
[1] "swimmers.csv"
```

If you make a command with the object name in quotes, it won't be treated as referring to an object. Instead, it will merely mean the text itself:

```
> "filename"
[1] "filename"
```

Similarly, if you omit the quotation marks from around text, the computer will treat it as if it were an object name and will look for the object of that name. For instance, the following command directs the computer to look up the value contained in an object named `swimmers.csv` and insert that value into the object `filename`.

```
> filename = swimmers.csv

Error in try(swimmers.csv) : object 'swimmers.csv' not found
```

As it happens, there was no object named `swimmers.csv` because it had not been defined by any previous assignment command. So, the computer generated an error.

For the most part, you will not need to use very many operators on text data; you just need to remember to include text, such as file names, in quotation marks, `"like this"`.

Reading Questions

1. How can a model be useful even if it is not exactly correct?

2. Give an example of a model used for classification.

3. Often we describe personalities as "patient," "kind," "vengeful," etc. How can these descriptions be used as models for prediction?

4. Give three examples of models that you use in everyday life. For each, say what is the purpose of the model and in what ways the representation differs from the real thing.

5. Make a sensible statement about how precisely these quantities are typically measured:

- The speed of a car.
- Your weight.
- The national unemployment rate.
- A person's intelligence.

6. Give an example of a controlled experiment. What quantity or quantities have been varied and what has been held constant?

7. Using one of your textbooks from another field, pick an illustration or diagram. Briefly describe the illustration and explain how this is a model, in what ways it is faithful to the system being described and in what ways it fails to reflect that system.

For exercises, see www.mosaic-web.org/StatisticalModeling/Exercises.

2

Data: Cases, Variables, Samples

The tendency of the casual mind is to pick out or stumble upon a sample which supports or defies its prejudices, and then to make it the representative of a whole class. — Walter Lippmann (1889-1974), journalist

The word "data" is plural. This is appropriate. Statistics is, at its heart, about variability: how things differ from one another.

Figure 2.1 shows a small collection of sea shells gathered during an idle quarter hour sitting at one spot on the beach on Malololailai island in Fiji. All the shells in the collection are similar: small disk-shaped shells with a hole in the center. But the shells also differ from one another in overall size and weight, in color, in smoothness, in the size of the hole, etc.

Any data set is something like the shell collection. It consists of **cases**: the objects in the collection. Each case has one or more attributes or qualities, called **variables**. This word "variable" emphasizes that it is differences or variation that is often of primary interest.

Usually, there are many possible variables. The researcher chooses those that are of interest, often drawing on detailed knowledge of the system that is under study. The researcher measures or observes the value of each variable for each case. The result is a **table**, also known as a **data frame**: a sort of spreadsheet. Within the data frame, each row refers to one case, each column to one variable.

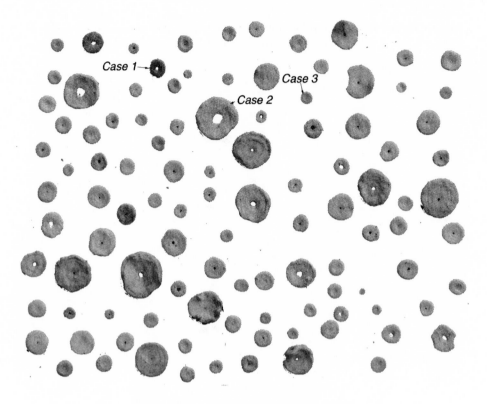

Figure 2.1: A collection of 103 sea shells.

A data frame for the sea shell collection might look like this:

Case	diameter	weight	color	hole
1	4.3 mm	0.010 mg	dark	medium
2	12.0 mm	0.050 mg	light	very large
3	3.8 mm	0.005 mg	light	none

and so on — there are 103 cases altogether

Each individual shell has a case number that identifies it; three of these are shown in the figure. These case numbers are arbitrary; the position of each case in the table — first, second, tenth, and so on — is of no significance. The point of assigning an identifying case number is just to make it easier to refer to individual cases later on.

If the data frame had been a collection of people rather than shells, the person's name or another identifying label could be used to identify the case.

There are many sorts of data that are recorded in different formats. For example, photographic images are stored as arrays of pixels without any reference to cases and variables. But the data frame format is very general and can be used to arrange all sorts of data, even if it is not the format always used in practice. Even data that seems at first not to be suitable to arrange as a data frame is often stored this way, for example the title/artist/genre/album organization found in music MP3 players or the geographic features (place locations and names, boundaries, rivers, etc.) found in geographic information systems (GIS).

2.1   Kinds of Variables

Most people tend to think of data as numeric, but variables can also be descriptions, as the sea shell collection illustrates. The two basic types of data are:

Quantitative: Naturally represented by a number, for instance diameter, weight, temperature, age, and so on.

Categorical: A description that can be put simply into words or categories, for instance male versus female or red vs green vs yellow, and so on. The value for each case is selected from a fixed set of possibilities. This set of possibilities are the **levels** of the categorical variable.

Categorical variables show up in many different guises. For example, a data frame holding information about courses at a college might have a variable `subject` with levels biology, chemistry, dance, economics, and so on. The variable `semester` could have levels Fall2008, Spring2009, Fall2009, and so on. Even the `instructor` is a categorical variable. The instructor's name or ID number could be used as the level of the variable.

Quantitative variables are numerical but they often have units attached to them. In the shell data frame, the variable `diameter` has been recorded in millimeters, while `weight` is given in milligrams. The usual practice is to treat quantitative variables as a pure number, without units being given explicitly. The information about the units — for instance that `diameter` is specified in millimeters — is kept in a separate place called a **code book**.

The code book contains a short description of each variable. For instance, the code book for the shell data might look like this:

Code book for shells from Malololailai island, collected on January 12, 2008.

`diameter`: the diameter of the disk in millimeters.

`weight`: the shell weight in milligrams.

`color`: a subjective description of the color. Levels: light, medium, and dark.

`hole`: the size of the inner hole. Levels: none, small, large, very large.

On the computer, a data frame is usually stored as a spreadsheet file, while the corresponding code book can be stored separately as a text file.

Sometimes quantitative information is represented by categories as in the `hole` variable for the sea shells. For instance, a data frame holding a variable `income` might naturally be stored as a number in, say, dollars per year. Alternatively, the variable might be treated categorically with levels of, say, "less than $10,000 per year," "between $10,000 and $20,000," and so on. Almost always, the genuinely quantitative form is to be preferred. It conveys more information even if it is not correct to the last digit.

The distinction between quantitative and categorical data is essential, but there are other distinctions that can be helpful even if they are less important.

Some categorical variables have levels that have a *natural* order. For example, a categorical variable for `temperature` might have levels such as "cold," "warm," "hot," "very hot." Variables like this are called **ordinal**. Opinion surveys often ask for a choice from an ordered set such as this: strongly disagree, disagree, no opinion, agree, strongly agree.

For the most part, this book will treat ordinal variables like any other form of categorical variable. But it's worthwhile to pay attention to the natural ordering of an ordinal variable. Indeed, sometimes it can be appropriate to treat an ordinal variable as if it were quantitative.

2.2   Data Frames and the Unit of Analysis

When collecting and organizing data, it's important to be clear about what is a case. For the sea shells, this is pretty obvious; each individual shell is an individual case. But in many situations, it's not so clear.

A key idea is the **unit of analysis**. Suppose, for instance, that you want to study the link between teacher pay, class size, and the performance of school children. There are all sorts of possibilities for how to analyze the data you collect. You might decide to compare different schools, looking at the average class size, average teacher pay, and average student performance in each school. Here, the unit of analysis is the school.

Or perhaps rather than averaging over all the classes in one school, you want to compare different classes, looking at the performance of the students in each class separately. The unit of analysis here is the class.

You might even decide to look at the performance of individual students, investigating how their performance is linked to the individual student's family income or the education of the student's parents. Perhaps even include the salary of student's teacher, the size of the student's class, and so on. The unit of analysis here is the individual student.

What's the difference between a unit of analysis and a case? A case is a row in a data frame. In many studies, you need to bring together different data frames, each of which may have a different notion of case. Returning to the teacher's pay example, one can easily imagine at least three different data frames being involved, with each frame storing data at a different level:

1. A frame with each class being a case and variables such as the size of the class, the school in which the class is taught, etc.

2. A frame with each teacher being a case and variables such as the teacher's salary, years of experience, advanced training, etc.

3. A frame with each student being a case and variables such as the student's test scores, the class that the student is in, and the student's family income and parent education.

Once you choose the unit of analysis, you combine information from the different data frames to carry out the data analysis, generating a single data frame in which cases are your chosen unit of analysis. The choice of the unit of analysis can be determined by many things, such as the availability of data. As a general rule, it's best to make the unit of analysis as small as possible. But there can be obstacles to doing this. You might find, for instance, that for privacy reasons (or less legitimate reasons of secrecy) the school district is unwilling to release the data at the individual student level, or even to release data on individual classes.

In the past, limitations in data analysis techniques and computational power provided a reason to use a coarse unit of analysis. Only a small amount of data could be handled effectively, so the unit of analysis was made large. For example, rather than using tens of thousand of individual students as the unit of analysis, a few dozen schools might be used instead. Nowadays these reasons are obsolete. The methods that will be covered in this book allow for a very fine unit of analysis. Standard personal computers have plenty of power to perform the required calculations.

2.3 Populations and Samples

A data frame is a collection, but a collection of what? Two important statistical terms are "population" and "sample." A **population** is the set of all the possible objects or units which might have been included in the collection. The root of the word "population" refers to people, and often one works with data frames in which the cases are indeed individual people. The statistical concept is broader; one might have a population of sea shells, a population of houses, a population of events such as earthquakes or coin flips.

A **sample** is a selection of cases from the population. The **sample size** is the number of cases in the sample. In Figure 2.1, the sample size is $n = 103$.

A **census** is a sample that contains the entire population. The most familiar sort of census is the kind to count the people living in a country. The United States and the United Kingdom have a census every ten years. Countries such as Canada, Australia, and New Zealand hold a census every five years.

Almost always, the sample is just a small fraction of the population. There are good reasons for this. It can be expensive or damaging to take a sample: Imagine a biologist who tried to use all the laboratory rats in the world for his or her work! Still, when you draw a sample, it is generally because you are interested in finding out something about the population rather than just the sample at hand. That is, you want the sample to be genuinely representative of the population. (In some fields, the ability to draw conclusions from a sample that can be generalized is referred to as **external validity** or **transferability**.)

The process by which the sample is taken is important because it controls what sorts of conclusions can legitimately be drawn from the sample. One of the most important ideas of statistics is that a sample will be representative of the population if the sample is collected at random. In a **simple random sample**, each member of the population is equally likely to be included in the sample.

Ironically, taking a random sample, even from a single spot on the beach, requires organization and planning. The sea shells were collected haphazardly, but this is not a genuinely random sample. The bigger shells are much easier to see and pick up than the very small ones, so there is reason to think that the small shells are under-represented: the collection doesn't have as big a proportion of them as in the population. To make the sample genuinely random, you need to have access in some way to the entire population so that you can pick any member with equal probability. For instance, if you want a sample of students at a particular university, you can get a list of all the students from the university registrar and use a computer to pick randomly from the list. Such a list of the entire set of possible cases is called a **sampling frame**.

In a sense, the sampling frame is the *definition* of the population for the purpose of drawing conclusions from the sample. For instance, a researcher studying cancer treatments might take the sampling frame to be the list of all the patients who visit a particular clinic in a specified month. A random sample from that sampling frame can reasonably be assumed to represent that particular population, but not necessarily the population of all cancer patients.

You should always be careful to define your sampling frame precisely. If you decide to sample university students by picking randomly from those who enter the front door of the library, you will get a sample that might not be typical for *all* university students. There's nothing wrong with using the library students for your sample, but you need to be aware that your sample will be representative of just the library students, not necessarily all students.

When sampling at random, use formal random processes. For example, if you are sampling students who walk into the library, you can flip a coin to decide whether to include that student in your sample. When your sampling frame is in the form of a list, it's wise to use a computer random number generator to select the cases to include in the sample.

A **convenience sample** is one where the sampling frame is defined mainly in a way that makes it easy for the researcher. For example, during lectures I often sample from the set of students in my class. These students — the ones who take statistics courses from me — are not necessarily representative of all university students. It might be fine to take a convenience sample in a quick, informal, preliminary study. But don't make the mistake of assuming that the convenience sample is representative of the population. Even if you believe it yourself, how will you convince the people who are skeptical about your results?

When cases are selected in an informal way, it's possible for the researcher to introduce a non-representativeness or **sampling bias**. For example, in deciding which students to interview who walk into the library, you might consciously or subconsciously select those who seem most approachable or who don't seem to be in a hurry.

There are many possible sources of sampling bias. In surveys, sampling bias can come from non-response or self-selection. Perhaps some of the students whom you selected randomly from the people entering the library have declined to participate in your survey. This **non-response** can make your sample non-representative. Or, perhaps some people whom you didn't pick at random have walked up to you to see what you are up to and want to be surveyed themselves. Such **self-selected** people are often different from people whom you would pick at random.

In a famous example of self-selection bias, the newspaper columnist Ann Landers asked her readers, "If you had it to do over again, would you have children?" Over 70% of the respondents who wrote in said "No." This result is utterly different from what was found in surveys on the same question done with a random sampling methodology: more than 90% said "Yes." Presumably the people who bothered to write were people who had had a particularly bad experience as parents whereas the randomly selected parents are representative of the whole population. Or, as Ann Landers wrote, "[T]he hurt, angry, and disenchanted tend to write more readily than the contented ...." (See [7].)

Non-response is often a factor in political polls, where people don't like to express views that they think will be unpopular.

It's hard to take a genuinely random sample. But if you don't, you have no guarantee that your sample is representative. Do what you can to define your sampling frame precisely and to make your selections as randomly as possible from that frame. By using formal selection procedures (e.g., coin flips, computer random number generators) you have the opportunity to convince skeptics who might otherwise wonder what hidden biases were introduced by informal selections. If you believe that your imperfect selection may have introduced biases — for example the suspected under-representation of small shells in my collection

— be up-front and honest about it. In surveys, you should keep track of the non-response rate and include that in whatever report you make of your study.

Example 2.1: Struggling for a Random Sample   Good researchers take great effort to secure a random sample. One evening I received a phone call at home from the state health department. They were conducting a survey of access to health care, in particular how often people have illnesses for which they don't get treatment. The person on the other end of the phone told me that they were dialing numbers randomly, checked to make sure that I live in the area of interest, and asked how many adults over age 18 live in the household. "Two," I replied, "Me and my wife." The researcher asked me to hold a minute while she generated a random number. Then the researcher asked to speak to my wife. "She isn't home right now, but I'll be happy to help you," I offered. No deal.

The sampling frame was adults over age 18 who live in a particular area. Once the researcher had made a random selection, as she did after asking how many adults are in my household, she wasn't going to accept any substitutes. It took three follow-up phone calls over a few days — at least that's how many I answered, who knows how many I wasn't home for — before the researcher was able to contact my wife. The researcher declined to interview me in order to avoid self-selection bias and worked hard to contact my wife — the randomly selected member of our household — in order to avoid non-response bias.

2.4   Longitudinal and Cross-Sectional Samples

DATA FILE
Cherry-
Blosssom-
2008.csv

Data are often collected to study the links between different traits. For example, the data in the following table are a small part of a larger data set of the speeds of runners in a ten-mile race held in Washington, D.C. in 2008. The variable time gives the time from the start gun to the finish line, in seconds.

Name	Age	Time	Sex
A. Renee Callahan	42	112.4	F
Aaron Alton	34	89.3	M
Cristine Doran	25	87.8	F
Ed Donahoe	58 D	77.3	M
Amy Lewis	30	94.0	F

... and so on.

Such data might be used to study the link between age and speed, for example to find out at what age people run the fastest and how much they slow down as they age beyond that.

This sample is a **cross section**, a snapshot of the population that includes people of different ages. Each person is included only once.

Another type of sample is **longitudinal**, where the cases are tracked over time, each person being included more than once in the data frame. A longitudinal data set for the runners looks like this:

DATA FILE
Cherry-
Blosssom-
Long.csv

Name	Year of Birth	Age	Time	Sex	Year
a. renee callahan	1966	37	103.3	F	2003
a. renee callahan	1966	42	112.4	F	2008
aaren pastor	1991	14	94.4	F	2005
aaren pastor	1991	15	74.8	F	2006
aaron alton	1974	31	86.9	M	2005
aaron alton	1974	32	92.5	M	2006
aaron alton	1974	33	92.4	M	2007
aaron alton	1974	34	89.3	M	2008

... and so on.

The individual runners have been tracked from year to year, so each individual person shows up in multiple rows.

If your concern is to understand how individual change as they age, it's best to collect data that show such change in individuals. Using cross-sectional data to study a longitudinal problem is risky. Suppose, as seems likely, that younger runners who are slow tend to drop out of racing as they age, so the older runners who do participate are those who tend to be faster. This could bias your estimate of how running speed changes with age.

2.5 Computational Technique

2.5.1 Reading Tabular Data into R

Data used in statistical modeling are usually organized into tables, often created using spreadsheet software. Most people presume that the same software used to create a table of data should be used to display and analyze it. This is part of the reason for the popularity of spreadsheet programs such as Excel and Google Spreadsheets.

For serious statistical work, it's helpful to take another approach that strictly separates the processes of data collection and of data analysis: use one program to create data files and another program to analyze the data stored in those files. By doing this, one guarantees that the original data are not modified accidentally in the process of analyzing them. This also makes it possible to perform many different analyses of the data; modelers often create and compare many different models of the same data.

Reading Tabular Data into R

Data is central to statistics, and the tabular arrangement of data is very common. Accordingly, R provides a large number of ways to read in tabular data. These vary depending on how the data are stored, where they are located, etc. To help keep things as simple as possible, the mosaic package in R provides an operator, fetchData() that allows you to access data files in tabular format on your computer as well as data stored on repositories such as the one associated with this book or one that a course instructor might set up for his or her students.

To use fetchData(), as well as a variety of other operators that you will encounter later, you need to load the mosaic package.

```
> require(mosaic)
```

You need do this only once in each session of R, and on systems such as RStudio the package will generally be reloaded automatically. (If you get an error message, it's likely that the mosaic package has not been installed on your system. Use the package installation menu in R to install mosaic, after which the require() function will load the package.)

DATA FILE
swim100m.csv

Reading in a data table that's been connected with fetchData() is simply a matter of knowing the name of the data set. For instance, one data table used in examples in this book is **swim100m.csv**. To read in this data table and create an object in R that contains the data, use a command like this:

```
> swim = fetchData("swim100m.csv")
```

The csv part of the name in "swim100m.csv" indicates that the file has been stored in a particular data format, **comma-separated values** that is handled by spreadsheet software as well as many other kinds of software.

The part of this command that requires creativity is choosing a name for the R object that will hold the data. In the above command it is called **swim**, but you might prefer another name, e.g., **s** or **sdata** or even **ralph**. Of course, it's sensible to choose names that are short, easy to type and remember, and remind you what the contents of the object are about.

To help you identify data tables that can be accessed through fetchData(), examples in this book will be marked with a flag containing the name of the file containing the data file. The files themselves are either built in to the mosaic package or available automatically through the web site for this book.

Data Frames

The type of R object created by fetchData() is called a **data frame** and is essentially a tabular layout. To illustrate , here are the first several cases of the **swim** data frame created by the previous use of fetchData():

```
> head(swim)

  year time sex
1 1905 65.8   M
2 1908 65.6   M
3 1910 62.8   M
4 1912 61.6   M
5 1918 61.4   M
6 1920 60.4   M
```

Note that the head() function, one of several functions that operate on data frames, takes the R object that you created, not the quoted name of the data file.

Data frames, like tabular data generally, involve variables and cases. In R, each of the variables is given a name. You can refer to the variable by name in a couple of different ways. To see the variable names in a data frame, something you might want to do to remind yourself of how names a spelled and capitalized, use the names() function:

```
> names(swim)

[1] "year" "time" "sex"
```

Another way to get quick information about the variables in a data frame is with summary():

```
> summary(swim)

     year            time        sex
 Min.   :1905   Min.   :47.8   F:31
 1st Qu.:1924   1st Qu.:53.6   M:31
 Median :1956   Median :56.9
 Mean   :1952   Mean   :59.9
 3rd Qu.:1976   3rd Qu.:65.2
 Max.   :2004   Max.   :95.0
```

To see how many cases there are in a data frame, use nrow():

```
> nrow(swim)

[1] 62
```

Variables in Data Frames

Perhaps the most common operation on a data frame is to refer to the values in a single variable. The two ways you will most commonly use involve functions with a **data=** argument and the direct use of the **$** notation.

Most of the statistical modeling functions you will encounter in this book are designed to work with data frames and allow you to refer directly to variables within a data frame. For instance:

```
> mean( year, data=swim )
```

```
[1] 1952
> min( year, data=swim )
[1] 1905
```

The **data=** argument tells the function which data frame to pull the variable from. Leaving off that argument leads to an error:

```
> mean( year )

Error in mean(year) :
    error in evaluating the argument 'x', object 'year' not found
```

Of course, you know that the variable **year** is defined within the data frame **swim**, but you have to give this information to the function mean() explicitly, otherwise it doesn't know where to find the variable.

Take note that many long-time users of R use the **$** notation, like this:

```
> mean( swim$year )
```

Think of this as referring to the variable by both its family name (the data frame's name,"swim") and its given name ("year"), something like Einstein$Albert.

The advantage of the **data=** approach becomes evident when you construct statements that involve more than one variable within a data frame. For instance, here's a calculation of the mean year separately for the different sexes:

```
> mean( year ~ sex, data=swim )

    F    M
1951 1954
```

You will see much more of the ~ ("tilde") starting in Chapter 4. It's the R notation for "modeled by," or "broken down by," or "versus."

Both the mean() and min() functions have been arranged by the mosaic package to look in the data frame when interpreting variables, but not all R functions — particularly older ones — are designed this way. For instance:

```
> sqrt(year, data=swim )

Error in try(sqrt(year, data = swim)) : object 'year' not found
```

When you encounter a function that can't handle the **data=** format, you can use the special with() function that instructs any function to refer to a data frame:

```
> with( data=swim, sqrt(year) )

 [1] 43.6 43.7 43.7 43.7 43.8 43.8 43.8 43.9 44.0 44.0 44.0 44.1 44.1 44.1 44.2
[16] 44.2 44.3 44.3 44.4 44.4 44.4 44.4 44.4 44.5 44.5 44.6 44.6 44.6 44.7 44.7
[31] 44.7 43.7 43.7 43.7 43.7 43.8 43.8 43.9 43.9 43.9 43.9 43.9 43.9 44.0 44.0
[46] 44.0 44.2 44.2 44.3 44.3 44.3 44.4 44.4 44.4 44.5 44.5 44.5 44.6 44.6 44.7
[61] 44.7 44.8
```

Adding a New Variable

Sometimes you will compute a new quantity from the existing variables and want to treat this as a new variable. Adding a new variable to a data frame can be done with the `transform()` function. For instance, here is how to create a new variable in `swim` that holds the `time` converted from minutes to units of seconds:

```
> swim = transform( swim, minutes = time/60 )
```

The new variable, `minutes`, appears just like the old ones:

```
> names(swim)
[1] "year"    "time"    "sex"     "minutes"
```

You could also, if you want, redefine an existing variable, for instance:

```
> swim = transform( swim, time=time/60 )
```

Such assignment operations do not change the original file from which the data were read, only the data frame in the current session of R. This is an advantage, since it means that your data in the data file stay in their original state and therefore won't be corrupted by operations made during analysis.

Again, be aware that many long-time R users use the `$` notation instead of `transform()` for adding a new variable to a data frame, like this:

```
> swim$minutes = with(swim, time/60)
```

2.5.2 Sampling from a Sample Frame

Much of statistical analysis is concerned with the consequences of drawing a sample from the population. Ideally, you will have a sampling frame that lists every member of the population from which the sample is to be drawn. With this in hand, you could treat the individual cases in the sampling frame as if they were cards in a deck of hands. To pick your random sample, shuffle the deck and deal out the desired number of cards.

When doing real work in the field, you would use the randomly dealt cards to locate the real-world cases they correspond to. Sometimes in this book, however, in order to let you explore the consequences of sampling, you will select a sample from an existing data set. The `deal()` function performs this, taking as an argument the data frame to be used in the selection and the number of cases to sample.

For example, the `kidsfeet.csv` data set has $n = 39$ cases.

DATA FILE
kidsfeet.csv

```
> kids = fetchData("kidsfeet.csv")
> nrow(kids)
[1] 39
```

Here's how to take a random sample of five of the cases:

```
> deal( kids, 5 )
```

	name	birthmonth	birthyear	length	width	sex	biggerfoot	domhand
26	Glen	7	88	27.1	9.4	B	L	R
28	David	12	87	25.5	9.5	B	R	R
37	Teshanna	3	88	26.0	9.0	G	L	R
15	Julie	11	87	26.0	9.3	G	L	R
4	Josh	1	88	25.2	9.8	B	L	R

The results returned by deal() will never contain the same case more than once, just as if you were dealing cards from a shuffled deck. In contrast, resample replaces each case after it is dealt so that it can appear more than once in the result. You wouldn't want to do this to select from a sampling frame, but it turns out that there are valuable statistical uses for this sort of **sampling with replacement**. You'll make use of re-sampling in Chapter 5.

```
> resample( kids, 5 )
```

	name	birthmonth	birthyear	length	width	sex	biggerfoot	domhand
15	Julie	11	87	26.0	9.3	G	L	R
31	Danielle	6	88	24.0	9.3	G	L	R
29	Mike	11	88	24.2	8.9	B	L	R
38	Hayley	1	88	21.6	7.9	G	R	R
29.1	Mike	11	88	24.2	8.9	B	L	R

Notice that Mike was sampled twice.

Reading Questions

1. What are the two major different kinds of variables?

2. How are variables and cases arranged in a data frame?

3. How is the relationship between these things: population, sampling frame, sample, census?

4. What's the difference between a longitudinal and cross-sectional sample?

5. Describe some types of sampling that lead to the sample potentially being unrepresentative of the population?

For exercises, see www.mosaic-web.org/StatisticalModeling/Exercises.

Describing Variation

Variation itself is nature's only irreducible essence. Variation is the hard reality, not a set of imperfect measures for a central tendency. Means and medians are the abstractions. — Stephen Jay Gould (1941-2002), paleontologist and historian of science

A statistical model partitions variation. People describe the partitioning in different ways depending on their purposes and the conventions of the field in which they work: explained variation versus unexplained variation; described variation versus undescribed; predicted variation versus unpredicted; signal versus noise; common versus individual. This chapter describes ways to quantify variation in a single variable. Once you can quantify variation, you can describe how models divide it up.

To start, consider a familiar situation: the variation in human heights. Everyone is familiar with height and how heights vary from person to person, so variation in height provides a nice example to compare intuition with the formal descriptions of statistics. Perhaps for this reason, height was an important topic for early statisticians. In the 1880s, Francis Galton, one of the pioneers of statistics, collected data on the heights of about 900 adult children and their parents in London. Figure 3.1 shows part of his notebook.

Galton was interested in studying the relationship between a full-grown child's height and his or her mother's and father's height. One way to study this relationship is to build a model that accounts for the child's height — the **response variable** — by one or more **explanatory variables** such as mother's height or father's height or the child's sex. In later chapters you will construct such models. For now, though, the objective is to describe and quantify how the response variable varies across children without taking into consideration any explanatory variables.

Figure 3.1: Part of Francis Galton's notebook recording the heights of parents and their adult children. [8]

Galton's height measurements are from about 200 families in the city of London. In itself, this is an interesting choice. One might think that the place to start would be with exceptionally short or tall people, looking at what factors are associated with these extremes.

Adult humans range in height from a couple of feet to about nine feet. (See Figure 3.2.) One way to describe variation is by the **range of extremes**: an interval that includes every case from the smallest to the largest.

What's nice about describing variation through the extremes is that the range includes every case. But there are disadvantages. First, you usually don't always have a **census**, measurements on the entire population. Instead of a census, you typically have only a **sample**, a subset of the population. Usually only a small proportion of the population is included in a sample. For example, of the millions of people in London, Galton's sample included only 900 people. From such a sample, Galton would have had no reason to believe the either the tallest or shortest person in London, let alone the world, happened to be included.

A second disadvantage of using the extremes is that it can give a picture that is untypical. The vast majority of adults are between $4\frac{1}{2}$ feet and 7 feet tall. Indeed, an even narrower range — say 5 to $6\frac{1}{2}$ feet — would give you a very good idea of typical variation in heights. Giving a comprehensive range — 2 to 9 feet — would be misleading in important ways, even if it were literally correct.

A third disadvantage of using the extremes is that even a single case can have a strong influence on your description. There are about six billion people on earth. The discovery of even a single, exceptional 12-foot person would cause you substantially to alter your description of heights even though the population — minus the one new case — remains unchanged.

It's natural for people to think about variation in terms of records and extremes. People are used to drawing conclusions from stories that are newsworthy and

Figure 3.2: Some extremes of height. Angus McAskill (1825-1863) and Charles Sherwood Stratton (1838-1883). McAskill was 7 feet 9 inches tall. Stratton, also known as Tom Thumb, was 2 feet 6 inches in height.

exceptional; indeed, such anecdotes are mostly what you read and hear about. In statistics, however, the focus is usually on the unexceptional cases, the typical cases. With such a focus, it's important to think about **typical variation** rather than extreme variation.

3.1   Coverage Intervals

One way to describe typical variation is to specify a fraction of the cases that are regarded as typical and then give the **coverage interval** or range that includes that fraction of the cases.

Imagine arranging all of the people in Galton's sample of 900 into order, the way a school-teacher might, from shortest to tallest. Now walk down the line, starting at the shortest, counting heads. At some point you will reach the person at position 225. This position is special because one quarter of the 900 people in line are shorter and three quarters are taller. The height of the person at position 225 — 64.0 inches — is the 25th **percentile** of the height variable in the sample.

Continue down the line until you reach the person at position 675. The height of this person — 69.7 inches — is the 75th percentile of height in the sample.

Position in list k	Height (inches)	# of previous cases $k-1$	Percentile
1	59.0	0	0
2	61.5	1	10
3	62.0	2	20
4	63.0	3	30
5	64.7	4	40
6	65.5	5	50
7	68.0	6	60
8	69.0	7	70
9	72.0	8	80
10	72.0	9	90
11	72.0	10	100

Table 3.1: Finding sample percentiles by sorting and counting.

The range from 25th to 75th percentile is the **50-percent coverage interval**: 64.0 to 69.7 inches in Galton's data. Within this interval is 50% of the cases.

For most purposes, a 50% coverage interval excludes too much; half the cases are outside of the interval.

Scientific practice has established a convention, the **95-percent coverage interval** that is more inclusive than the 50% interval but not so tied to the extremes as the 100% interval. The 95% coverage interval includes all but 5% of the cases, excluding the shortest 2.5% and the tallest 2.5%.

To calculate the 95% coverage interval, find the 2.5 percentile and the 97.5 percentile. In Galton's height data, these are 60 inches and 73 inches, respectively.

There is nothing magical about using the coverage fractions 50% or 95%. They are just conventions that make it easier to communicate clearly. But they are important and widely used conventions.

To illustrate in more detail the process of finding coverage intervals, let's look at Galton's data. Looking through all 900 cases would be tedious, so the example involves just a few cases, the heights of 11 randomly selected people:

```
72.0 62.0 68.0 65.5 63.0 64.7 72.0 69.0 61.5 72.0 59.0
```

Table 3.1 puts these 11 cases into sorted order and gives for each position in the sorted list the corresponding percentile. For any given height in the table, you can look up the percentile of that height, effectively the fraction of cases that came previously in the list. In translating the position in the sorted list to a percentile, convention puts the smallest case at the 0th percentile and the largest case at the 100th percentile. For the kth position in the sorted list of n cases, the percentile is taken to be $(k-1)/(n-1)$.

With $n = 11$ cases in the sample, the sorted cases themselves stand for the 0th, 10th, 20th, ..., 90th, and 100th percentiles. If you want to calculate a percentile that falls in between these values, you (or the software) interpolate between the samples. For instance, the 75th percentile would, for $n = 11$, be taken as half-way between the values of the 70th and 80th percentile cases.

Coverage intervals are found from the tabulated percentiles. The 50% coverage interval runs from the 25th to the 75th percentile. Those exact percentiles happen not be be in the table, but you can estimate them. Take the 25th percentile to be half way between the 20th and 30th percentiles: 62.5 inches. Similarly, take the 75th percentile to be half way between the 70th and 80th percentiles: 70.5 inches.

Thus, the 50% coverage interval for this small subset of $N = 11$ cases is 62.5 to 70.5 inches. For the complete set of $N = 900$ cases, the interval is 64 to 69 inches — not exactly the same, but not too much different. In general you will find that the larger the sample, the closer the estimated values will be to what you would have found from a census of the entire population.

This small $N = 11$ subset of Galton's data illustrates a potential difficulty of a 95% coverage interval: The values of the 2.5th and 97.5th percentiles in a small data set depend heavily on the extreme cases, since interpolation is needed to find the percentiles. In larger data sets, this is not so much of a problem.

A reasonable person might object that the 0th percentile of the sample is probably not the 0th percentile of the population; a small sample almost certainly does not contain the shortest person in the population. There is no good way to know whether the population extremes will be close to the sample extremes and therefore you cannot demonstrate that the estimates of the extremes based on the sample are valid for the population. The ability to draw demonstrably valid inferences from sample to population is one of the reasons to use a 50% or 95% coverage interval rather than the range of extremes.

Different fields have varying conventions for dividing groups into parts. In the various literatures, one will read about **quintiles** (division into 5 equally sized groups, common in giving economic data), **stanines** (division into 9 unevenly sized groups, common in education testing), and so on.

In general-purpose statistics, it's conventional to divide into four groups: **quartiles**. The dividing point between the first and second quartiles is the 25th percentile. For this reason, the 25th percentile is often called the "first quartile." Similarly, the 75th percentile is called the "third quartile."

The most famous percentile is the 50th: the **median**, which is the value that half of the cases are above and half below. The median gives a good representation of a typical value. In this sense, it is much like the **mean**: the average of all the values.

Neither the median nor the mean describes the variation. For example, knowing that the median of Galton's sample of heights is 66 inches does not give you any indication of what is a typical range of heights. In the next section, however, you'll see how the mean can be used to set up an important way of measuring variation: the typical distance of cases from the mean.

Aside. 3.1 What's Normal?

You've just been told that a friend has hypernatremia. Sounds serious. So you look it up on the web and find out that it has to do with the level of sodium in the blood:

> For adults and older children, the normal range [of sodium] is 137 to 145 millimoles per liter. For infants, the normal range is somewhat lower, up to one or two millimoles per liter from the adult range. As soon as a person has more than 145 millimoles per liter of blood serum, then he has hypernatremia, which is too great a concentration of sodium in his blood serum. If a person's serum sodium level falls below 137 millimoles per liter, then they have hyponatremia, which is too low a concentration of sodium in his blood serum. [From http://www.ndif.org/faqs.]

You wonder, what do they mean by "normal range?" Do they mean that your body stops functioning properly once sodium gets above 145 millimoles per liter? How much above? Is 145.1 too large for the body to work properly? Is 144.9 fine?

Or perhaps "normal" mean a coverage interval? But what kind of coverage interval: 50%, 80%, 95%, 99%, or somethings else? And in what population? Healthy people? People who go for blood tests? Hospitalized people?

If 137 to 145 were a 95% coverage interval for healthy people, then 19 of 20 healthy people would fall in the 137 to 145 range. Of course this would mean that 1 out of 20 healthy people would be out of the normal range. Depending on how prevalent sickness is, it might even mean that most of the people outside of the normal range are actually healthy.

People frequently confuse "normal" in the sense of "inside a 95% coverage interval" with "normal" in the sense of "functions properly." It doesn't help that publications often don't make clear what they mean by normal. In looking at the literature, the definition of hypernatremia as being above 145 millimoles of sodium per liter appears in many places. Evidently, a sodium level above 145 is very uncommon in healthy people who drink normal amounts of water, but it's hard to find out from the literature just how uncommon it is.

3.2 The Variance and Standard Deviation

The 95% and 50% coverage intervals are important descriptions of variation. For constructing models, however, another format for describing variation is more widely used: the variance and standard deviation.

To set the background, imagine that you have been asked to describe a variable in terms of a *single* number that typifies the group. Think of this as a very simple model, one that treats all the cases as exactly the same. For human heights, for instance, a reasonable model is that people are about 5 feet 8 inches tall (68 inches).

If it seems strange to model every case as the same, you're right. Typically you will be interested in relating one variable to others. To model height, depending on your purposes, you might consider explanatory variables such as age and sex as pediatricians do when monitoring a child's growth. Galton, who was interested in what is now called genetics, modeled child's height (when grown to adulthood) using sex and the parents' heights as explanatory variables. One can also imagine using economic status, nutrition, childhood illnesses, participation in sports, etc. as explanatory variables. The next chapter will introduce such models. At this point, though, the descriptions involve only a single variable — there are no other variables that might distinguish one case from another. So the only possible model is that all cases are the same.

Any given individual case will likely deviate from the single model value. The value of an individual can be written in a way that emphasizes the common model value shared by all the cases and the deviation from that value of each individual:

individual case = model value + deviation of that case.

Writing things in this way partitions the description of the individual into two pieces. One piece reflects the information contained in the model. The other piece — the deviation of each individual — reflects how the individual is different from the model value.

As the single model value of the variable, it's reasonable to choose the mean. For Galton's height data, the mean is 66.7 inches. Another equally good choice would be the *median*, 66.5 inches. (Chapter 8 deals with the issue of how to choose the "best" model value, and how to define "best.")

Once you have chosen the model value, you can find how much each case deviates from the model. For instance, Figure 3.3 shows a group of nine brothers. Each brother's height differs somewhat from the model value; that difference is the deviation for that person.

In the more interesting models of later chapters, the model values will differ from case to case and so part of the variation among individual cases will be captured by the model. But here the model value is the same for all cases, so the deviations encompass all of the variation.

The word "deviation" has a negative connotation: a departure from an accepted norm or behavior. Indeed, in the mid-1800s, early in the history of statistics, it

Figure 3.3: The heights of nine brothers were recorded on a tintype photograph in the 1880s. The version here has been annotated to show the mean height and the individual deviations from the mean.

Height (inches)	Model Value (inches)	Residual (inches)	Square-Residual (inches^2)
72.0	66.25	5.75	33.06
62.0	66.25	-4.25	17.06
68.0	66.25	1.75	3.05
65.5	66.25	-0.75	0.56
63.0	66.25	-3.25	10.56
64.7	66.25	-1.55	2.40
72.0	66.25	5.75	33.06
69.0	66.25	2.75	7.56
61.5	66.25	-4.75	22.56
72.0	66.25	5.75	33.06
59.0	66.25	-7.25	52.56

Sum of Squares: 216.5

Table 3.2: Calculation of the sum of squares of the residuals for the subset of $N = 11$ cases from Galton's data used in Table 3.1. (For this small subset, the mean height is 66.25 inches, somewhat different from the mean of 66.7 inches in the complete set.)

was widely believed that "normal" was best quantified as a single model value. The deviation from the model value was seen as a kind of mistake or imperfection. Another, related word from the early days of statistics is "error." Nowadays, though, people have a better understanding that a range of behaviors is normal; normal is not just a single value or behavior.

The word **residual** provides a more neutral term than "deviation" or "error" to describe how each individual differs from the model value. It refers to what is left over when the model value is taken away from the individual case. The word "deviation" survives in statistics in a technical terms such as **standard deviation**, and **deviance**. Similarly, "error" shows up in some technical terms such as **standard error**.

Any of the measures from Section 3.1 can be used to describe the variation in the residuals. The range of extremes is from -10.7 inches to 12.3 inches. These numbers describe how much shorter the shortest person is from the model value and how much taller the tallest. Alternatively, you could use the 50% interval

(-2.7 to 2.8 inches) or the 95% interval (-6.7 to 6.5 inches). Each of these is a valid description.

In practice, instead of the coverage intervals, a very simple, powerful, and perhaps unexpected measure is used: the **mean square** of the residuals. To produce this measure, add up the square of the residuals for the individual cases. This gives the **sum of squares** of the residuals as shown in Table 3.2. Such sums of squares will show up over and over again in statistical modeling.

It may seem strange to square the residuals. Squaring the residuals changes their units. For the height variable, the residuals are naturally in inches (or centimeters or meters or any other unit of length). The sum of squares, however is in units of square-inches, a bizarre unit for relating information about height. A good reason to compute the square is to emphasize the interest in *how far* each individual is from the mean. If you just added up the raw residuals, negative residuals (for those cases below the mean) would tend to cancel out positive residuals (for those cases above the mean). By squaring, all the negative residuals become positive square-residuals. It would also be reasonable do this by taking an absolute value rather than squaring, but the operation of squaring captures in a special way important properties of the potential randomness of the residuals.

Finding the sum of squares is an intermediate step to calculating an important measure of variation: the **mean square**. The mean square is intended to report a typical square residual for each case. The obvious way to get this is to divide the sum of squares by the number of cases, N. This is not exactly what is done by statisticians. For reasons that you will see later, they divide by $N - 1$ instead. (When N is big, there is no practical difference between using N and $N - 1$.) For the subset of the Galton data in Table 3.2, the mean square residual is 21.65 square-inches.

Later in this book, mean squares will be applied to all sorts of models in various ways. But for the very simple situation here — the every-case-the-same model — the mean square has a special name that is universally used: the **variance**.

The variance provides a compact description of how far cases are, on average, from the mean. As such, it is a simple measure of variation.

It is undeniable that the unfamiliar units of the variance — squares of the natural units — make it hard to interpret. There is a simple cure, however: take the square root of the variance. This is called, infamously to many students of statistics, the **standard deviation**. For the Galton data in Table 3.2, the standard deviation is 4.65 inches (the square-root of 21.65 square-inches).

The term "standard deviation" might be better understood if "standard" were replaced by a more contemporary equivalent word: "typical." The standard deviation is a measure of how far cases typically deviate from the mean of the group.

Historically, part of the appeal of using the standard deviation to describe vari-

Height (inches)

Figure 3.4:   A rug plot of Galton's height data. Each case is one tick mark.

ation comes from the ease of calculating it using arithmetic. Percentiles require more tedious sorting operations. Nowadays, computers make it easy to calculate 50% or 95% intervals directly from data. Still, standard deviations remain an important way of describing variation both because of historical convention and, more important for this book, because of its connection to concepts of modeling and randomness encountered in later chapters.

3.3   Displaying Variation

One of the best ways to depict variation is graphically. This takes advantage of the human capability to capture complicated patterns at a glance and to discern detail. There are several standard formats for presenting variation; each has its own advantages and disadvantages.

A simple but effective display plots out each case as a point on a number line. This **rug plot** is effectively a graphical listing of the values of the variable, case-by-case.

From the rug plot of Galton's heights in Figure 3.4, you can see that the shortest person is about 56 inches tall, the tallest about 79 inches. You can also see that there is a greater density in the middle of the range. Unfortunately, the rug plot also suppresses some important features of the data. There is one tick at each height value for which there is a measurement, but that one tick might correspond to many individuals. Indeed, in Galton's data, heights were rounded off to a quarter of an inch, so many different individuals have exactly the same recorded height. This is why there are regular gaps between the tick marks.

DATA FILE
galton.csv

Another simple display, the **histogram**, avoids this overlap by using two different axes. As in the rug plot, one of the axes shows the variable. The other axis displays the number of individual cases within set ranges, or "bins," of the variable.

Number of individuals in each rank 1   0   0   1   5   7   7 22 25 26 27 17 11 17   4   4   1
Heights in feet and inches to which
ranks correspond 4:10 4:11 5.0 5:1 5:2 5:3 5:4 5:5 5:6 5:7 5:8 5:9 5:10 5:11 6:0 6:1 6:2

Figure 3.5: A histogram arrangement published in 1914 of the student body of Connecticut Agricultural College (now the Univ. of Connecticut) grouped by height. [9] (See also [10].)

Figure 3.5 shows a "living histogram," made by arranging people by height. The people in each "bar" fall into a range of values, the **bin** range, which in Figure 3.5 is one inch wide. If a different bin width had been chosen, say 1 cm, the detailed shape of the histogram would be different, but the overall shape — here, peaked in the center, trailing off to the extremes — would be much the same.

Histograms have been a standard graphical format for more than a century, but even so they are often not interpreted correctly. Many people wrongly believe that variation in the data is reflected by the uneven height of the bars. Rather, the variation is represented by the *width* of the spread measured from side to side, not from bottom to top.

The histogram format tends to encourage people to focus on the irregularity in bar height, since so much graphical ink is devoted to distinguishing between the heights of neighboring bars. The graphically busy format also makes it difficult to compare the distribution of two groups, especially when the groups are very different in size.

A more modern format for displaying distributions is a **density plot**. To understand a density plot, start with the idea of a rug plot, as in Figure 3.4. The "density" of points in the rug plot reflects how close together the cases are. In places where the cases are very close, the density is high. Where the cases are spread out far from one another, the density is low. In the density plot, a smooth curve is used to trace how the density varies from place to place. Unlike the histogram, the density plot does not divide the cases into rigid bins.

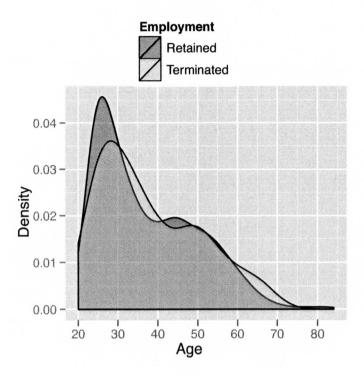

Figure 3.6: The age distribution of employees at a national firm whose employment was terminated, compared to the age distribution for those who were retained.

The height of the density-plot curve is scaled so that the overall area under the curve is always exactly 1. This choice makes it possible to interpret the area under a part of the curve as the fraction of cases that lie in that plot.

Since the density plot is a smooth curve, and since the area is scaled to 1, it's feasible to compare different groups. Consider, for example, a dataset reflecting the ages of employees at a national firm. Due to an economic slowdown, the firm "terminated" about 10% of its employees. Some of those who were terminated felt that they were being discriminated against on the basis of age. One way to examine this issue is to compare the distribution of ages of those who were terminated to those who were not. Figure 3.6 overlays density plots of age for the two groups. Note that the densities are similar for the two groups, even though the number of people in the two groups is very different.

The first thing to notice about the density distribution in Figure 3.6 is that in both groups there are many more employees in their 20s than older employees — the density falls off fairly steadily with age. This sort of distribution is called **skew right**, since the long "tail" of the distribution runs to the right. In contrast, the histogram of heights (Figure 3.5 is symmetric, peaked in the center and falling off similarly both to the left and the right. The density plots also shows that employees range in age from about 20 years to 80 years — consistent with what we know about people's career patterns.

The densities of the terminated and retained groups are roughly similar, suggesting that there is no night-and-day difference between the two groups. The graph does suggest that the retained employees are somewhat more likely to be in their 20s than the fired employees, and that the fired employees are more likely to be in their 60s than the retained employees. There seems to be a hump in the age distribution of the retained employees in their 40s, and a corresponding dip in the terminated employees in their 40s. Later chapters will deal with the question of whether such "small" differences are consistent or inconsistent with the inevitable random fluctuations that appear in data, or whether they are strong enough to suggest a systematic effect.

It takes a bit of thought to understand the units of measuring density. In general, the word "density" refers to an amount per unit length, or area, or volume. For example, the mass-volume density of water is the mass of water per unit of volume, typically given as kilograms per liter. The sort of density used for density plots is the fraction-of-cases per unit of the measured variable.

To see how this plays out in Figure 3.6, recall that the unit of the measured variable, age, is in years, so the units of the density axis is "per year". The area of each of the large grid rectangles in the plot is 10 years × 0.01 per year = 0.1. If you count the number grid rectangles under each of the curves, taking the fractional part of each rectangle that is covered in part, you will find approximately 10 covered rectangles, giving an overall area of 0.1 × 10 = 1.0. Indeed, the units on the "density" axis are always scaled so that the area under the density curve is exactly 1.

3.3.1   Shapes of Distributions

A very common form for the density of variables is the bell-shaped pattern seen in Figure 3.5: the individuals are distributed with most near the center and fewer and fewer near the edges. The pattern is so common that a mathematical idealization of it is called the **normal distribution**.

Don't be mislead by the use of the word "normal." Although the bell-shaped distribution is common, other shapes of distributions also often occur, such as the **right skew** distribution seen in the age distribution of employees in Figure 3.6. It's easy to imagine how such a distribution arose for ages of employees: a company starts with a few employees and hires younger employees as it grows. The growing company hires more and more employees each year, creating a large population of young workers compared to the small group of old-timers who started with the company when it was small.

It's tempting to focus on the details of a distribution, and sometimes this is

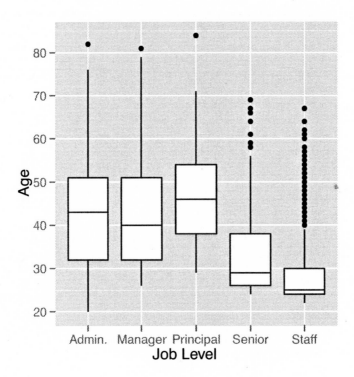

Figure 3.7: Side-by-side boxplots comparing the ages of the terminated and retained employees of different levels of employees.

appropriate. For example, it's probably not a coincidence that there is a dip in the terminated employee age distribution just after age 40; the U.S. the Age Discrimination in Employment Act of 1967 prohibits discrimination against those 40 and older, so a company seeking to stay in compliance with the Act would understandably be more likely to fire a 39-year old than a 41-year old.

But usually, distributions are examined for their gross or coarse characteristics: the location of their center, their width, whether they are skew or symmetric, etc. A nice graphical device for emphasizing such broad characteristics is the **box plot**. The box plot shows the minimum first quartile, median, third quartile, and maximum. Figure 3.7 shows a box plot of the employee age versus termination data. Note that the variable itself is being plotted on the vertical axis, contrasting with the other graphical depictions where the variable has been plotted on the horizontal axis.

The stylized display of the box plot is most useful when comparing the distribution of a variable across two or more different groups, as in Figure 3.7. In that bar plot, you can see that employees at the "Principal" level tend to be somewhat older than other employees, that "Staff" tend to be the youngest, and that "Senior" employees are not so senior. You can also see that the age distribution for Staff is skewed toward higher ages, meaning that while most Staff are young — the median age is only 25, and three-quarters of staff are 30 or younger — there are several staff aged 40 and above, marked as individual dots to indicate that they fall quite far from the typical pattern: they are **outliers**. Notice also that a 50-year old is regarded as an outlier among the Staff, but is quite in the middle for Principals.

3.4   Categorical Variables

All of the measures of variation encountered so far are for quantitative variables; the kind of variable for which it's meaningful to average or sort.

Categorical variables are a different story. One thing to do is to display the variation using tables and bar charts. For example, in the employment data, the number of employees at each level can be shown concisely with a table.

	Level
Admin.	266
Manager	245
Principal	121
Senior	261
Staff	337

The same information, in graphical form, takes up more space, and should perhaps be considered a decorative technique rather than an efficient way to inform.

3.4.1   Quantifying Categorical Variation

For a quantitative variable, such as Age in the employment data, there are several good choices for describing the variation:

The standard deviation, 12.3 years.

The variance, 151.833 square-years, which is just the square of the standard deviation.

The interquartile interval, 19

But when it comes to categorical variables, giving a numerical summary for variation is a more difficult matter. Recall that for quantitative variables, one can define a "typical" value, e.g., the mean or the median. It makes sense to measure residuals as how far an individual value is from the typical value, and to quantify variation as the average size of a residual. This led to the variance and the standard deviation as measures of variation.

For a categorical variable like sex, concepts of mean or median or distance or size don't apply. Neither F nor M is typical and in-between doesn't really make sense. Even if you decided that, say, M is typical — there are somewhat more of them in Galton's data — how can you say what the "distance" is between F and M?

Statistics textbooks hardly ever give a quantitative measure of variation in categorical variables. That's understandable for the reasons described above. But it's also a shame because many of the methods used in statistical modeling rely on quantifying variation in order to evaluate the quality of models.

There are quantitative notions of variation in categorical variables. You won't have use for them directly, but they are used in the software that fits models of categorical variables.

Solely for the purposes of illustration, here is one measure of variation in categorical variables with two levels, say F and M as in sex in Galton's data. Two-level variables are important in lots of settings, for example diagnostic models of whether or not a patient has cancer or models that predict whether a college applicant will be accepted.

Imagine that altogether you have N cases, with k being level F and $N - k$ being level M. (In Galton's data, N is 898, while $k = 433$ and $N - k = 465$.)

A simple measure of variation in two-level categorical variables is called, somewhat awkwardly, the **unalikeability**. This is

$$\text{unalikeability} = 2\frac{k}{N}\frac{N-k}{N}.$$

Or, more simply, if you write the proportion of level F as p_F, and therefore the proportion of level M as $1 - p_F$,

$$\text{unalikeability} = 2p_F(1 - p_F).$$

For instance, in the variable sex, $p_F = \frac{433}{898} = 0.482$. The unalikeability is therefore $2 \times 0.482 \times .518 = 0.4993$.

Some things to notice about unalikeability: If all of the cases are the same (e.g., all are F), then the unalikeability is zero — no variation at all. The highest possible level of unalikeability occurs when there are equal numbers in each level; this gives an unalikeability of 0.5.

Where does the unalikeability come from? One way to think about unalikeability is as a kind of numerical trick. Pretend that the level F is 1 and the level M is 0 — turn the categorical variable into a quantitative variable. With this transformation, `sex` looks like 0 1 1 1 0 0 1 1 0 1 0 and so on. Now you can quantify variation in the ordinary way, using the variance. It turns out that the unalikeability is exactly twice the variance.

Here's another way to think about unalikeability: although you can't really say *how far* F is from M, you can certainly see the difference. Pick two of the cases at random from your sample. The unalikeability is the probability that the two cases will be different: one an M and the other an F.

There is a much more profound interpretation of unalikeability that is introduced in Chapter 16, which covers modeling two-level categorical variables. For now, just keep in mind that you can measure variation for any kind of variable and use that measure to calculate how much of the variation is being captured by your models.

3.5 Computational Technique

As a setting to illustrate computer techniques for describing variability, take the data that Galton collected on the heights of adult children and their parents. The file **galton.csv** stores these data in a modern, case/variable format.

DATA FILE
galton.csv

```
> require(mosaic)
> galton = fetchData("galton.csv")
```

3.5.1 Simple Statistical Calculations

Simple numerical descriptions are easy to compute. Here are the mean, median, standard deviation and variance of the children's heights (in inches).

```
> mean(height, data=galton)
[1] 66.8
> median(height, data=galton)
[1] 66.5
> sd(height, data=galton)
[1] 3.58
> var(height, data=galton)
[1] 12.8
```

Notice that the variance function (`var()`) returns the square of the standard deviation (`sd()`). Having both is merely a convenience.

A percentile tells where a given value falls in a distribution. For example, a height of 63 inches is on the short side in Galton's data:

```
> pdata(63, height, data=galton)
```

```
[1] 0.192
```

Only about 19% of the cases have a height less than or equal to 63 inches. The pdata() function takes one or more values as a first argument and finds where they fall in the distribution of values in the second argument.

A quantile refers to the same sort of calculation, but inverted. Instead of giving a value in the same units as the distribution, you give a probability: a number between 0 and 1. The qdata() function then calculates the value whose percentile would be that value:

```
> qdata(0.20, height, data=galton)
 20%
63.5
```

Remember that the probability is given as a number between 0 and 1, so use 0.50 to indicate that you want the value which falls at the 50th percentile.

- The 25th and 75th percentile in a single command — in other words, the 50 percent coverage interval:

  ```
  > qdata(c(0.25, 0.75), height, data=galton)
   25%  75%
  64.0 69.7
  ```

- The 2.5th and 97.5th percentile — in other words, the 95 percent coverage interval:

  ```
  > qdata(c(0.025, 0.975), height, data=galton)
   2.5% 97.5%
     60    73
  ```

The interquartile range is the width of the 50 percent coverage interval: the difference between the 75th and 25th percentiles.

```
> diff( qdata(c(0.25, 0.75), height, data=galton))
75%
5.7
```

This is quite verbose, so many people prefer to use the IQR() function.

```
> with(data=galton, IQR(height))
[1] 5.7
```

IQR() is not part of the mosaic system, so with() is used to direct it to the data set that height is coming from.

Some other useful operators are min(), max(), and range().

3.5.2   Simple Statistical Graphics

There are several basic types of statistical graphics to display the distribution of a variable: histograms, density plots, and boxplots. These work in a manner that's similar to mean(), range() and so on, but there is one new element of R syntax. The ~ ("tilde") sign is used in R to denote relationships and models. You can read it as "modeled by" or "broken down by." In graphics, it can be interpreted as meaning "versus", as in "plot y versus x," and signifies which quantity goes on which axis. In graphics, the quantity being plotted on the x-axis *follows* the ~.

Histograms and Distributions

Constructing a histogram involves dividing the range of a variable up into bins and counting how many cases fall into each bin. This is done in an almost entirely automatic way:

```
> histogram( ~ height, data=galton )
```

When constructing a histogram, R makes an automatic but sensible choice of the number of bins. If you like, you can control this yourself. For instance:

```
> histogram( ~ height, data=galton, breaks=25 )
```

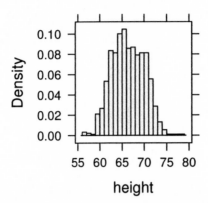

The horizontal axis of the histogram is always in the units of the variable. For the histograms above, the horizontal axis is in "inches" because that is the unit of the `height` variable in the **galton** dataset.

The vertical axis is conventionally drawn in one of three ways: controlled by an optional argument named **type**.

Absolute Frequency or Counts A simple count of the number of cases that falls into each bin. This mode is set with **type="count"** as in

```
> histogram( ~ height, data=galton, type="count")
```

Relative Frequency The vertical axis is scaled so that the height of the bar give the proportion of cases that fall into the bin. This is the default.

Density The vertical axis *area* of the bar gives the relative proportion of cases that fall into the bin. Set **type="density"** as in

```
> histogram( ~ height, data=galton, type="density" )
```

In a density plot, areas can be interpreted as probabilities and the area under the entire histogram is equal to 1.

Other useful optional arguments set the labels for the axes and the graph as a whole and color the bars. For example,

```
> histogram(~height, data=galton, type="density",
      xlab="Height (inches)",
      main="Distribution of Heights",
      col="gray")
```

Distribution of Heights

The above command is so long that it has been broken into several lines for display purposes. R ignores the line breaks, holding off on executing the command until it sees the final closing parentheses. Notice the use of quotation marks to delimit the labels and names like `"blue"`.

Density Plots

A **density plot** avoids the need to create bins and plots out the distribution as a continuous curve. Making a density plot involves two operators. The **density** operator performs the basic computation which is then displayed using either the `plot` or the `lines` operator. For example:

```
> densityplot( ~ height, data=galton )
```

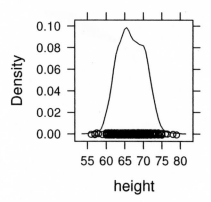

If you want to suppress the rug-like plotting of points at the bottom of the graph, use

```
> densityplot( ~ height, data=galton, plot.points=FALSE )
```

Box-and-Whisker Plots

Box-and-whisker plots are made with the **bwplot** command:

```
> bwplot( ~ height, data=galton )
```

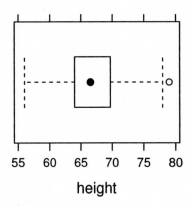

The median is represented by the heavy dot in the middle. Outliers, if any, are marked by dots outside the whiskers.

The real power of the box-and-whisker plot is for comparing distributions. This will be raised again more systematically in later chapters, but just to illustrate, here is how to compare the heights of males and females:

```
> bwplot(height ~ sex, data=galton)
```

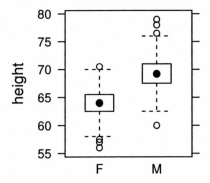

Notice that `sex` is displayed on the x-axis and therefore follows the modeling ˜.

3.5.3 Displays of Categorical Variables

For categorical variables, it makes no sense to compute descriptive statistics such as the mean, standard deviation, or variance. Instead, look at the number of cases at each level of the variable.

```
> tally( ˜ sex, data=galton)
    F    M Total
  433  465   898
```

Proportions can be found in a similar way:

```
> tally ( ˜ sex, data=galton, format="proportion")
    F     M Total
0.482 0.518 1.000
```

Note that the variable, in this case `sex`, follows the ˜. That's because the data set is being broken down by the variable.

Reading Questions

1. What is the disadvantage of using a 100% coverage interval to describe variation?

2. In describing a sample of a variable, what is the relationship between the variance and the standard deviation?

3. What is a residual?

4. What's the difference between "density" and "frequency" in displaying a variable with a histogram?

5. What's a normal distribution?

6. Here is the graph showing boxplots of height broken down according to sex as well as for both males and females together.

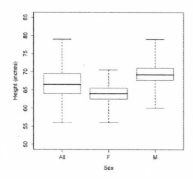

Which components of the boxplot for "All" match up exactly with the boxplot for "M" or "F"? Explain why.

7. Variables typically have units. For example, in Galton's height data, the height variable has units of inches. Suppose you are working with a variable in units of degrees celsius. What would be the units of the standard deviation of a variable? Of the variance? Why are they different?

For exercises, see www.mosaic-web.org/StatisticalModeling/Exercises.

r = run[run$sex == "F"),]
  or run[with(run, sex = "F")]

4

Group-wise Models

Seek simplicity and distrust it. — Alfred North Whitehead (1861-1947), mathematician and philosopher

This chapter introduces a simple form of statistical model based on separating the cases in your data into different groups. Such models are very widely used and will seem familiar to you, even obvious. They can be useful in very simple situations, but can be utterly misleading in others. Part of the objective of this chapter is to guide you to understand the serious limitations of such models and to critique the inappropriate, though all too common, use of group-wise models.

4.1 "Grand" and Group-wise Models

Consider these two statements:

> *Adults are about 67 inches tall.*[1]

and

> *Worldwide per-capita income in 2010 was about $12,000 per year.*

Such statements lump everybody together into one group.

You're also familiar with statements that divide things up into separate groups. For example:

---

[1] 1.70 meters in metric units.

Women are about 64 inches tall; men are about 69 inches tall.

and this sort of information about per-capita income:

Per-capita Income in 2010

Country	Amount	Country	Amount
Qatar	$88,559	Tajikistan	$1935
Luxembourg	$81,383	Bangladesh	$1572
Singapore	$56,522	Haiti	$1165
United States	$47,284	Afghanistan	$907
Switzerland	$41,663	Zimbabwe	$434

Source: International Monetary Fund
World Economic Outlook Database - April 2011

These sorts of statements, either in the **grand mean** form that puts everyone into the same group, or **group-wise mean** form where people are divided up into several groups, are very common.

People are so used to this sort of division by sex or citizenship that it's easy to miss that the point that these are only some of many possible variables that might be informative. For instance, other variables that might also contribute to account for variation in people's height are nutrition, parents' height, ethnicity, etc.

It's understandable to interpret such statements as giving "facts" or "data," not as models. But they are representations of the situation which are useful for some purposes and not for others: in other words, models.

The group-wise income model, for instance, accounts for some of the person-to-person variation in income by dividing things up country by country. In contrast, the corresponding "grand" model is simply that per capita income worldwide is $12,000 — everybody in one group! The group-wise model is much more informative because there is so much spread: some people are greatly above the mean, some much, much lower, and a person's country accounts for a lot of the variation.

The idea of averaging income by countries is just one way to display how income varies. There are many other ways that one might choose to account for variation in income. For example, income is related to skill level, to age, to education, to the political system in force, to the natural resources available, to health status, and to the population level and density, among many other things. Accounting for income with these other variables might provide different insights into the sources of income and to the association of income with other outcomes of interest, e.g., health. The table of country-by-country incomes is a statistical model in the sense that it attempts to explain or account for variation in income.

These examples have all involved situation where the cases are people, but in general you can divide up the cases in your data, whatever they be, into groups as you think best. The simplest division is really no division at all, putting every case into the same group. This might descriptively be called **all-cases-the-same** models, but you will usually hear them referred to by the statistic on which they are often based: the **grand mean** or the grand median. Here, "grand" is just a way of distinguishing them from group-wise quantities: grand versus group.

Given an interest in using models to account for variation, an all-cases-the-same model seems like a non-contender from the start — if everybody is the same, there is no variation. Even so, grand models are important in statistical modeling; they providing a starting point for measuring variation.

4.2 Accounting for Variation

Models explain or account for some (and sometimes all) of the case-to-case variation. If cases don't vary one from the other, there is nothing to model!

It's helpful to have a way to measure the "amount" of variation in a quantity so that you can describe how much of the overall variation a model accounts for. There are several such standard measures, described in Chapter 3:

- the standard deviation

- the variance (which is just the standard deviation squared)

- the inter-quartile interval

- the range (from minimum to maximum)

- coverage intervals, such as the 95% coverage intervals

Each of these ways of measuring variation has advantages and disadvantages. For instance, the inter-quartile interval is not much influenced by extreme values, whereas the range is completely set by them. So the inter-quartile interval has advantages if you are interested in describing a "typical" amount of variation, but disadvantages if you do not want to leave out even a single case, no matter how extreme or non-typical.

It turns out that the variance in particular has a property that is extremely advantageous for describing how much variation a model accounts for: the variance **partitions the variation** between that explained or accounted for by a model, and the remaining variation that remains unexplained or unaccounted for. This latter is called the **residual variation**.

To illustrate, consider the simple group-wise mean model, "Women are 64.1 inches tall, while men are 69.2 inches tall." How does this model account for variation?

Measuring the person-to-person variation in height by the variance, gives a variation of 12.8 square-inches. That's the total variation to be accounted for.

Now imagine creating a new data set that replaces each person's actual height with what the model says. So all men would be listed at a height of 69.2 inches, and all women at a height of 64.1 inches. Those model values also have a variation, which can be measured by their variance: 6.5 square inches.

Now consider the residual, the difference between the actual height and the heights according to the model. A women who is 67 inches tall would have a residual of 2.9 inches — she's taller by 2.9 inches than the model says. Each person has his or her own residual in a model. Since these vary from person to person, they also have a variance, which turns out to be 6.3 inches for this group-wise model of heights.

Notice the simple relationship among the three variances:

$$\begin{array}{ccccc} \text{Overall} & & \text{Model} & & \text{Residual} \\ 12.8 & = & 6.5 & + & 6.3 \end{array}$$

This is the partitioning property of the variance: the overall case-by-case variation in a quantity is split between the variation in the model values and the variation in the residuals.

You might wonder why it's the variance — the square of the standard deviation, with it's funny units (square inches for height!) — that works for partitioning. What about the standard deviation itself or the IQR or other ways of describing variation? As it happens, the variance, uniquely, has the partitioning property. It's possible to calculate any of the other measures of variation, but they won't generally be such that the variation in the model values plus the variation in the residuals gives exactly the variation in the quantity being modeled. It's this property that leads to the variance being an important measure, even though the standard deviation contains the same information and has more natural units.

The reason the variance is special can be explained in different ways, but for now it suffices to point out an analogous situation that you have seen before. Recall the Pythagorean theorem and the way it describes the relationship between the sides of a right triangle: if a and b are the lengths of the sides adjoining the right angle, and c is the length of the hypotenuse, then $a^2 + b^2 = c^2$. One way to interpret this is that sides a and b partition the hypotenuse, but only when you measure things in terms of square lengths rather than the length itself.

To be precise about the variance and partitioning ... the variance has this property of partitioning for a certain kind of model — groupwise means and the generalization of that called **linear, least-squares models** that are the subject of later chapters — but those models are by far the most important. For other kinds of models, such as **logistic models** described in Chapter 16 there are other measures of variation that have the partitioning property.

Aside. 4.1 The Geometry of Partitioning

The idea of **partitioning** is to divide the overall variation into parts: that accounted for by the model and that which remains: the residual.

This is done by assigning to each case a model value. The difference between the actual value and the model value is the residual. Naturally, this means that the model value *plus* the residual add up to the actual value. One way to think of this is in terms of a triangle: the model value is one side of the triangle, the residual is another side, and the actual values are the third side.

For reasons to be described in Chapter 8 it turns out that this triangle involve a right angle between the residuals and the model values. As such, the Pythagorean theorem applies and the square of the triangle side lengths add in the familiar way:

$$\text{Model values}^2 + \text{Residuals}^2 = \text{Actual values}^2.$$

4.3 Group-wise Proportions

It's often useful to consider proportions broken down, group by group. For example, In examining employment patterns for workers, it makes sense to consider mean or median wages in different groups, mean or median ages, and so on. But when the question has to do with employment termination — whether or not a person was fired — the appropriate quantity is the proportion of workers in each group who were terminated. For instance, in the job termination data introduced on page 60, About 10% of employees were terminated. This differs from job level to job level, as seen in the table below. For instance, fewer than 2% of Principals (the people who run the company) were terminated. Staff were the most likely to be terminated.

	Administrative	Manager	Principal	Senior	Staff
Retained	91.73	91.84	98.35	90.04	88.43
Terminated	8.27	8.16	1.65	9.96	11.57

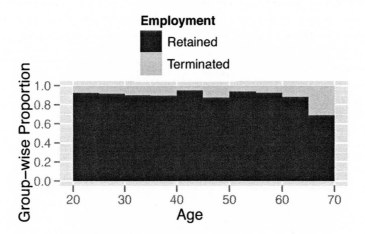

Figure 4.1: The proportion of workers who were terminated broken into groups according to age.

Figure 4.1 shows another way of looking at the termination data: breaking down the groups according to age and, within each group, showing the fraction of workers who were terminated. The graph suggests that workers in their late 60's were substantially more likely to be fired. This might be evidence for age discrimination, but there might be other reasons for the pattern. For instance, it could be that those employees in their 60s were people who failed to be promoted in the past, or who were making relatively high salaries, or who were planning to retire soon. A more sophisticated model would be needed to take such factors into account.

4.4   What's the Precision?

The main point of constructing group-wise models is to be able to support a claim that the groups are different, or perhaps to refute such a claim. In thinking about differences, it's helpful to distinguish between two sorts of criteria:

- Whether the difference is substantial or important in terms of the phenomenon that you are studying. For example, Administrative workers in the previous example were terminated at a rate of 8.27%, whereas Managers were terminated at a rate of 8.16%. This hardly makes a difference.

- How much evidence there is for any difference at all. This is a more subtle point.

In most settings, you will be working with *samples* from a population rather than the population itself. In considering a group difference, you need to take into account the random nature of the sampling process, which leads to some randomness is the group-wise statistics. If different cases had been included in the sample, the results would be different.

Quantifying and interpreting this **sampling variability** is an important component of statistical reasoning. The techniques to do so are introduced in Chapter 5 and then expanded in later chapters. But before moving on to the techniques for quantifying sampling variability, consider the common format for presenting it: the **confidence interval**.

A confidence interval is a way of expressing the precision or repeatability of a statistic, how much variation would likely be present across the possible different random samples from the population. In format, it is a form of coverage interval, typically taken at the 95% level, and looks like this:

$$68.6 \pm 3.3$$

The first number, 68.6 here, is called the **point estimate**, and is the statistic itself. The second number, the **margin of error**, reflects how precise the point estimate is. There is a third number, sometimes stated explicitly, sometimes left implicit, the **confidence level**, which is the level of the coverage interval, typically 95%.

Like other coverage intervals, a confidence interval leaves out the extremes. You can think of this as arranging the confidence interval to reflect what *plausibly* might happen, rather than the full extent of the possibilities, no matter how extreme or unlikely.

4.5 Misleading Group-wise Models

Group-wise models appear very widely, and are generally simple to explain to others and to calculate, but this does not mean they serve the purposes for which they are intended. To illustrate, consider a study done in the early 1970s in Whickham, UK, that examined the health consequences of smoking. [11] The method of the study was simple: interview women to find out who smokes and who doesn't. Then, 20 years later, follow-up to find out who is still living.

DATA FILE
whickham.csv

Examining the data file `whickham.csv` shows that, after 20 years, 945 women in the study were still alive out of 1315 total: a proportion of 72%. Breaking this proportion into group-wise into smokers and non-smokers gives

Non-smokers : 68.6% were still alive.

Smokers : 76.1% were still alive.

Before drawing any conclusions, you should know what is the precision of those estimates. Using techniques to be introduced in the next chapter, you can calculate a 95% confidence interval on each proportion:

Non-smokers : $68.6 \pm 3.3\%$ were still alive.

Smokers : $76.1 \pm 3.7\%$ were still alive.

The 95% confidence interval on the difference in proportions is 7.5 ± 5.0 percentage points. That is, the data say that smokers were more likely than non-smokers to have stayed alive through the 20-year follow up period.

Perhaps you are surprised by this. You should be. Smoking is convincingly established to increase the risk of dying (as well as causing other health problems such as emphysema).

The problem isn't with the data. The problem is with the group-wise approach to modeling. Comparing the smokers and non-smokers in terms of mortality doesn't take into account the other differences between those groups. For instance, at the time the study was done, many of the older women involved had grown up at a time when smoking was uncommon among women. In contrast, the younger women were more likely to smoke. You can see this in the different ages of the two groups:

Among non-smokers the average age is 48.7 ± 1.3.

Among smokers the average age is 44.7 ± 1.4.

You might think that the difference of 4 years in average ages is too small to matter. But it does, and you can see the difference when you use modeling techniques to incorporate both age and smoking status as explaining mortality.

Since age is related to smoking, the question the group-wise model asks is, effectively, "Are younger smokers different in survival than older non-smokers?" This is probably not the question you want to ask. Instead, a meaningful question would be, "**Holding other factors constant**, are smokers different in survival than non-smokers?"

You will often see news reports or political claims that attempt to account for or dismiss differences by appealing to "other factors." This is a valuable form of argument, but it ought to be supported by quantitative evidence, not just an intuitive sense of "small" or "big." The modeling techniques introduced in the following chapters enable you to do consider multiple factors in a quantitative way.

A relatively simple modeling method called **stratification** can illustrate how this is possible.

Rather than simply dividing the Whickham data into groups of smokers and non-smokers, divide it as well by age. Here's a table of survival percentages done this way:

	Age Group			
	18-30	31-40	41-53	54-64
Non-Smokers	98.2	95.5	87.6	66.9
Smokers	97.6	94.1	80.2	58.1

Within each age group, smokers are less likely than non-smokers to have been alive at the 20-year follow-up, especially in the older groups. By comparing people of similar ages — stratifying or **disaggregating** the data by age — the model is effectively "holding age constant."

You may rightly wonder whether the specific choice of age groups plays a role in the results. You also might wonder whether it's possible to extend the approach to more than one stratifying variable, for instance, not just smoking status but overall health status. The following chapters will introduce modeling techniques that let you avoid having to divide variables like age into discrete groups and that allow you to include multiple stratifying variables.

4.6 Computational Technique

Calculating means and other simple statistics is a matter of using the right function in R. The mosaic package — which you should load in to R as shown in Section 2.5.1 — makes it straightforward to calculate either a "grand" statistic or a "group-wise" statistic. To illustrate:

Load the mosaic package, needed only once per session:

```
> require(mosaic)
```

Read in data you are interested in analyzing, for instance the Cherry-Blossom 2008 data described earlier:

```
> runners = fetchData("Cherry-Blossom-2008.csv")
> names( runners )
[1] "position" "division" "total"    "name"     "age"      "place"    "net"
[8] "gun"      "sex"
```

DATA FILE
Cherry-
Blosssom-
2008.csv

Calculate a grand mean on the "gun" time — the time from the start of the race, signalled by a gun, and when each runner crossed the finish line:

```
> mean( gun, data=runners )
[1] 93.7
```

Other "grand" statistics include:

```
> median( gun, data=runners )
[1] 93.7
> sd( gun, data=runners )
[1] 15
```

To tell R that you want to break the statistics down by groups, use the ~ notation, pronounced "**tilde.**" You will be using this notation frequently in building models. It means, "model by" or "broken down by" or "versus."

```
> mean( gun ~ sex, data=runners )
   F    M
98.8 88.3
```

Other statistics work the same way, for instance,

```
> sd( gun ~ sex, data=runners )
   F    M
13.3 14.7
```

Another example ... wage broken down by sector of the economy, using data :

```
> cps = fetchData("cps.csv")
> mean( wage ~ sector, data=cps )

clerical    const   manag   manuf    other     prof   sales  service
    7.42     9.50   12.70    8.04     8.50    11.95    7.59     6.54
```

DATA FILE
whickham.csv

In the Whickham smoking data example, the outcome for each person was not a number but a category: Alive or Dead at the time of the follow-up.

```
> w = fetchData("whickham.csv")
> names(w)
[1] "outcome" "smoker"  "age"
> with( w, levels(outcome) )
[1] "Alive" "Dead"
```

To find the proportion of people who were alive at the end of the 20-year follow-up period, you can use a computational trick. Convert the outcome variable to **TRUE** or **FALSE** to indicate whether an individual is alive, then take the mean of the true/false values. R, like many computer languages, treats **TRUE** as 1 and **FALSE** as 0 for the purposes of doing arithmetic.

```
> mean( outcome=="Alive", data=w )
[1] 0.719
```

Here's the breakdown according to smoking status:

```
> mean( outcome=="Alive" ~ smoker, data=w )
   No   Yes
0.686 0.761
```

A more meaningful question is whether smokers are different from non-smokers when holding other variables constant, such as age. To address this question, you need to add age into the model.

It might be natural to consider each age — 35, 36, 37, and so on — as a separate group, but you won't get very many members of each group. And, likely, the data for 35 year-olds has quite a lot to say about 36 year-olds, so it doesn't make sense to treat them as completely separate groups.

You can use the cut() function to divide up a quantitative variable into groups. You get to specify the breaks between groups. Using transform(), you can add the new variable to an existing data frame.

```
> w = transform(w, ageGroups=cut(age,breaks=c(0,30,40,53,64,75,100)))
> mean( outcome=="Alive" ~ ageGroups, data=w )

  (0,30]   (30,40]   (40,53]   (53,64]   (64,75]  (75,100]
   0.979     0.948     0.832     0.625     0.201     0.000
> mean( outcome=="Alive" ~ smoker + ageGroups, data=w )

   No.(0,30]    Yes.(0,30]    No.(30,40]   Yes.(30,40]    No.(40,53]   Yes.(40,53]
       0.982         0.976         0.955         0.941         0.876         0.802
  No.(53,64]   Yes.(53,64]    No.(64,75]   Yes.(64,75]  No.(75,100] Yes.(75,100]
       0.669         0.581         0.214         0.158         0.000         0.000
```

The mean has been calculated group-by-group. This is a very widely used technique, but there is a better approach that will be introduced in later chapters: use quantitative variables directly without dividing them into groups.

4.6.1 Model Values and Residuals

A group-wise model tells you the model value for each group. There is additional information that you will want to generate about models. Two fundamental aspects of a model are the **fitted model values** for each case and the **residual** for each case. To make it easy to do these calculations, R has a set of modeling functions that keep track of the data used in creating the model. Later chapters will introduce the lm() function — l for "linear", m for "model" — that is central to statistical modeling. To create a model based on groupwise means, use the mm() function — the first m for means, the second m for "model." mm() does the same sorts of calculations as mean(), but packages up its results in a different way:

```
> kids = fetchData("kidsfeet.csv")
> mod = mm( width ~ sex, data=kids )
> mod

Groupwise Model
Coefficients:
   B    G
9.19 8.78
```

The fitted() function takes as an argument a model such as generated by mm().
fitted() computes the fitted model value for each case in the data used to fit the
model. To do this, fitted() takes each case in turn, figures out which group it
belongs to and the corresponding model value, and then returns the set of model
value for each of the cases. For example:

```
> fitted( mod )
 [1] 9.19 9.19 9.19 9.19 9.19 9.19 9.19 8.78 8.78 9.19 9.19 9.19 9.19 9.19 8.78
[16] 8.78 8.78 8.78 8.78 8.78 9.19 9.19 8.78 8.78 8.78 9.19 8.78 9.19 9.19 9.19
[31] 8.78 8.78 8.78 9.19 9.19 8.78 8.78 8.78 8.78
```

The residuals are found by subtracting the case-by-case model value from the
actual values for each case. This is accomplished by the resid() function, which
works in much the same way as fitted():

```
> resid(mod)
 [1] -0.790 -0.390  0.510  0.610 -0.290  0.510  0.410  0.016  0.516 -0.390
[11]  0.610 -0.290 -0.090  0.610  0.516 -0.884 -0.084  0.016  0.216  0.716
[21]  0.010 -0.590 -0.484  0.216 -0.684  0.210  0.716  0.310 -0.290  0.110
[31]  0.516 -0.184 -0.184 -0.190 -0.590 -0.284  0.216 -0.884  0.016
```

For each case, adding the residual to the fitted value will produce the value of
the response variable.

The var() function calculates variance. There is a simple additive relationship
among the variances of the response variable, the model's fitted values, and the
corresponding residual values:

```
> var( width, data=kids )  # overall variation
[1] 0.2597
> var( fitted(mod) ) # variation in model values
[1] 0.04222
> var( resid(mod) ) # residual variation
[1] 0.2175
```

Reading Questions

1. Which is larger: variance of residuals, variance of the model values, or the variance
   of the actual values?

2. How can a difference in group means clearly shown by your data nonetheless be
   misleading?

3. What does it mean to partition variation? What's special about the variance —
   the square of the standard deviation — as a way to measure variation?

For exercises, see www.mosaic-web.org/StatisticalModeling/Exercises.

5

Confidence Intervals

It's easy enough to calculate the mean or median within groups. Often the point of doing this is to support a claim that the groups are different, for instance that men are on average taller than women.

Less obvious to those starting out in statistics is the idea that a quantity such as the mean or median itself has limited precision. This isn't a matter of the calculation itself. If the calculation has been done correctly, the resulting quantity is exactly right. Instead the limited precision arises from the sampling process that was used to collect the data. The exact mean or median relates to the particular sample you have collected. Had you collected a different sample, it's likely that you would have gotten a somewhat different value for the quantities you calculate, the so-called **sampling variability**. One purpose of statistical inference is to characterize sampling variability, that is, to provide a quantitative meaning for "somewhat different value."

5.1 The Sampling Distribution

An estimate of the limits to precision that stem from sampling variability can be made by simulating the sampling process itself. To illustrate, consider again the data in `Cherry-Blossom-2008.csv`. These data give the running times of all 12,302 participants in a ten-mile long running race held in Washington, DC in March 2008.

DATA FILE
Cherry-
Blosssom-
2008.csv

Suppose want to describe how women's running times differ from men's. If you had to go out and collect your own data, you would likely take a random sample from the sampling frame. Suppose, for instance, that you collect a sample of size $n = 200$ runners and calculate the group-wise mean running time for men and women. The results will be that men took, on average, about 88 minutes to run

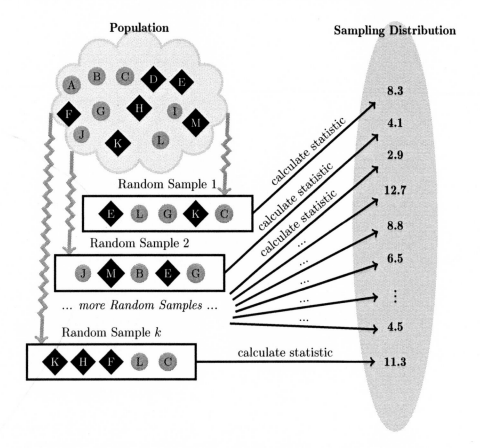

Figure 5.1: The sampling distribution reflects how the sample statistics would vary from one random sample to the next.

the 10 miles, while women took about 99 minutes. If you were to take another random sample of $n = 200$, you would get a somewhat different answer, perhaps 86 minutes for men and 98 for women. Each new random sample of $n = 200$ will generate a new result.

The **sampling distribution** describes how different the answers stemming from different random samples will be. The word "random" is very important here. Random sampling helps to ensure that the sample is representative of the population.

The process of generating the sampling distribution is shown in Figure 5.1. Take a random sample from the sampling frame and calculate the statistic of interest. (In this case, that's the mean running time for men and for women.) Do this many times. Because of the random sampling process, you'll get somewhat different results each time. The spread of those results indicates the limited precision that arises from sampling variability.

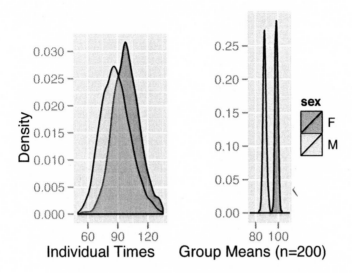

Figure 5.2: Comparing the distribution of the population of individuals (left) to the sampling distribution of the means of men's and women's running times for a sample of size $n = 200$ (right).

Historically, the sampling distribution was approximated using algebraic techniques. But it's perfectly feasible to use the computer to repeat the process of random sampling many times and to generate the sampling distribution through a simulation.

The sampling distribution depends on both the data and on the statistic being calculated. Figure 5.2 shows both the distribution of individual running times — the data themselves! — and the sampling distribution for the means of men's and women's running time for a sample of size $n = 200$.

Notice that the sampling distribution for $n = 200$ is much narrower than the individual data. That's because, in taking the mean, the fast running times tend to cancel out the slow running times.

The usual way to quantify the precision of a measurement is called a **confidence interval**. This is commonly written in either of two equivalent ways:

Plus-and-minus format 98.8 ± 1.7 minutes with 95% confidence

Range format 97.1 to 100.5 minutes with 95% confidence.

If the sample size had been smaller, the confidence interval would be bigger; that is, smaller samples result in less precise estimates. Figure 5.3 shows the sampling distribution for the mean of the running times for samples of size $n = 50$ and

Figure 5.3: The sampling distributions of the mean of men's and women's running time for $n = 50$ and $n = 800$. A larger sample size gives a more precise estimate of the mean.

$n = 800$. Notice that when $n = 50$, the sampling distribution is wide — the men's mean and the women's mean overlap somewhat. This is because $n = 50$ cases don't allow a very precise statement to be made about the means. For instance, the 95% confidence interval for women is 98.8 ± 5.3 minutes and for men it's 88.2 ± 5.8 minutes. In contrast, when $n = 800$, the sampling distribution is very narrow. All that data results in a very precise estimate: for women 98.8 ± 1.3 minutes and 88.2 ± 1.4 minutes for men.

The logic of sampling distributions and confidence intervals applies to any statistic calculated from a sample, not just the means used in these examples but also proportions, medians, standard deviations, inter-quartile intervals, etc.

5.2   The Resampling Distribution & Bootstrapping

The construction of the sampling distribution by repeatedly collecting new samples from the population is theoretically sound but has a severe practical shortcoming: It's hard enough to collect a single sample of size n, but infeasible to repeat that work multiple times to sketch out the sampling distribution. And, if you were able to increase the number of cases in your sample, you would have included the new cases in your original sample: n would have been bigger to give you better precision.

For almost all practical work, you need to estimate the properties of the sampling distribution from your *single* sample of size n.

Aside. 5.1 Precision and Sample Size

In keeping with the Pythagorean principle, it's the square of the precision that behaves in a simple way, just as it's the square of triangle edge lengths that add up in the Pythagorean relationship. As a rule, the square width of the sampling distribution scales with $1/n$, that is,

$$\text{width}^2 \propto \frac{1}{n}.$$

Taking square roots leads to the simple relationship of width with n:

$$\text{width} \propto \frac{1}{\sqrt{n}}.$$

To improve your precision by a factor of two, you will need 4 times as much data. For ten times better precision, you'll need 100 times as much data.

One way to do this is called **bootstrapping**. The word itself is not very illuminating. It's drawn from the phrase, "He pulled himself up by his own bootstraps," said of someone who improves himself through his own efforts, without assistance.

To carry out a statistical bootstrap, you substitute your sample itself in place of the overall sampling frame, creating a hypothetical population that is easy to draw new samples from — Use the computer! — and can in many circumstances, be used to generate an approximation to the sampling distribution. The simple idea behind bootstrapping is to use the sample itself to stand for the population.

5.2.1   Re-sampling

The sample is already in hand, in the form of a data frame, so it's easy to draw cases of it. Such new samples, taken from your original sample, not from the population, are called **resamples**: sampling from the sample.

Figure 5.4 illustrates how re-sampling works. There is just one sample drawn — with actual labor and expense — from the real population. Thereafter, the sample itself is used as a stand-in for the population and new samples are drawn from the sample.

Will such resamples capture the sampling variation that would be expected if you were genuinely drawing new samples from the population? An objection might come to mind: If you draw n cases out of a sample consisting of n cases, the resample will look exactly like the sample itself. No variability. This problem is easily overcome by **sampling with replacement**.

Whenever a case is drawn from the sample to put in a resample, the case is put back so that it is available to be used again. This is not something you would do when collecting the original sample; in sampling (as opposed to re-sampling) you

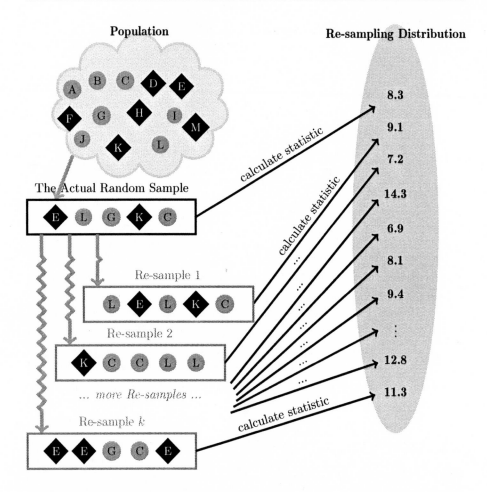

Figure 5.4: Re-sampling draws randomly from the sample to create new samples. Compare this process to the hypothetical sampling-distribution process in Figure 5.1.

don't use a case more than once.

The resamples in Figure 5.4 may seem a bit odd. They often repeat cases and omit cases. And, of course, any case in the population that was not included in the sample cannot be included in any of the resamples. Even so, the resamples do the job; they simulate the variation in model coefficients introduced by the process of random sampling.

5.2.2 The Re-Sampling Distribution

It's important to emphasize what the resamples do not and cannot do: they don't construct the sampling distribution. The resamples merely show what the

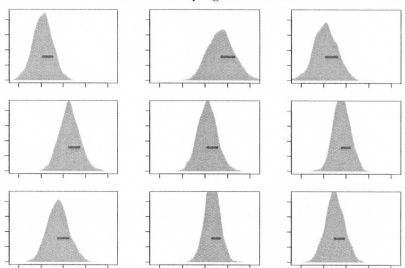

Figure 5.5: Top: A sampling distribution reflecting variation when sampling from the population. Below: Several re-sampling distributions, each constructed from an individual sample from the population. The location of the center of the re-sampling distributions doesn't always match the population-based sampling distribution. Instead, the center corresponds to the particular sample from which the re-samples are drawn. But the width of the re-sampling distributions are a good match to the width of the population-based sampling distribution.

sampling distribution would look like *if the population looked like your sample*. The center of the re-sampling distribution from any given sample is generally not aligned exactly with the center of the population-based sampling distribution. However, in practice, the width of the re-sampling distribution is a good match to the width of the sampling distribution. The re-sampling distribution is adequate for the purpose of finding standard errors and margins of error.

Figure 5.5 shows an experiment to demonstrate this. At the top of the figure is the sampling distribution on the age coefficient in the running model. This was found by drawing 1000 genuine repeated samples of size $n = 100$ from the population. The remaining panels show re-sampling distributions, each panel based on a single genuine sample of size $n = 100$ from the population and then drawing 1000 resamples from that sample. The re-sampling distribution varies from sample to sample. Sometimes it's to the left of the sampling distribution, sometimes to the right, occasionally well aligned. Consistently, however, the re-sampling distributions have a standard error that is a close match to the standard error of the sampling distribution.

The process of finding confidence intervals via re-sampling is called **bootstrapping**.

Example 5.1: The Precision of Grades

The "grade-point average" is widely used to describe a student's academic performance. Grading systems differ from place to place. In the United States, it's common to give letter grades with A the best grade, and descending through B, C, and D, and with E or F representing failure. You can't average letters, so they are converted to numbers (i.e., A=4, B=3, and so on) and the numbers are averaged.

An individual typically sees his or her own grades in isolation, but institutions have large collections of information about those grades, including other information such as the instructor's identity, the size of the class, etc. Here is of part of such an institutional database from a college with an enrollment of about 2000 students. This shows the information for a single student, ID 31509. Of course, the database contains information for many other students as well.

DATA FILE
grades.csv

sessionID	grade	sid	grpt	dept	level	sem	enroll	iid
C1959	B+	S31509	3.33	Q	300	FA2001	13	i323
C2213	A-	S31509	3.66	i	100	SP2002	27	i209
C2308	A	S31509	4.00	O	300	SP2002	18	i293
C2344	C+	S31509	2.33	C	100	FA2001	28	i140
C2562	A-	S31509	3.66	Q	300	FA2002	22	i327
C2585	A	S31509	4.00	O	200	FA2002	19	i310
C2737	A	S31509	4.00	q	200	SP2003	11	i364
C2851	A	S31509	4.00	O	300	SP2003	14	i308
C2928	B+	S31509	3.33	O	300	FA2003	22	i316
C3036	B+	S31509	3.33	q	300	FA2003	21	i363
C3443	A	S31509	4.00	O	200	FA2004	17	i300

(The course name and other identifying information such as the department and instructor have been coded for confidentiality.)

The student's grade-point average is just the mean of the fourth column: 3.60.

What's rarely or ever reported is the precision of this number. A simple 95% confidence interval on the mean of these 11 grades is 3.6 ± 0.3, that is, 3.3 to 3.9. It's important to keep in mind that this confidence interval reflects the individual grades and the amount of grade data. A grade-point average of 3.6 does not by any means always come with a margin of error of ± 0.3 — the size of the margin of error depends on the line-by-line variability within the grade data and on the number of grades. More data gives more precise estimates.

5.3   The Confidence Level

In constructing a confidence interval, a choice is made about how to describe the sampling distribution (or, in practice, the re-sampling distribution). The conventional choice is a 95% coverage interval — the top and bottom limits that cover 95% of the distribution.

When constructing a confidence interval, the amount of coverage is called a **confidence level** and is often indicated with a phrase like "at 95% confidence." The choice of 95% is conventional and uncontroversial, but sometimes people choose for good reasons or bad to use another level such as 99% or 90%.

Why not 100%? Because a 100% confidence interval would be too broad to be useful. In theory, 100% confidence intervals tend to look like $-\infty$ to ∞. No information there! Complete confidence comes at the cost of complete ignorance.

The 95% confidence level is standard in contemporary science; it's a convention. For that reason alone, it is a good idea to use 95% so that the people reading your work will tend to interpret things correctly.

The vocabulary of "confidence interval" and "confidence level" can be a little misleading. Confidence in everyday meaning is largely subjective, and you often hear of people being "over confident" or "lacking self-confidence." It might be better if a term like "sampling precision interval" were used. In some fields, the term "error bar" is used informally, although "error" itself may have nothing to do with it; the precision stems from sampling variation.

5.4   Interpreting Confidence Intervals

Confidence intervals are easy to construct, whether by bootstrapping or other techniques. The are also very easy to misinterpret. One of the most common misinterpretations is to confuse the statement of the confidence interval with a statement about the individuals in the sample. For example, consider the confidence interval for the running times of men and women. Using the Cherry-Blossom data (with more than 12,000 runners), the 95% confidence interval for the mean of women's times is 98.77 ± 0.35 minutes and for men it is 88.3 ± 0.36.

Do those confidence intervals suggest to you that men are consistently faster than women, for example that most men are faster than most women? There's no justification for such a belief in the data themselves. Figure 5.2 (left) shows the distribution of running times broken down by sex; there is a lot of overlap.

Confidence intervals are often mistaken for being about individuals — the "typical" person, when a mean is involved — but they are really about the strength of evidence, about the precision of an estimate. There is a lot of evidence in the Cherry-Blossom data that the mean running times for men and women differ; with so much data, you can make a very precise statement about the means as shown by the narrow confidence interval. But the confidence interval does not tell you how much a typical individual differs from the mean.

Another tempting statement is, "If I repeated my study with a different random sample, the new result would be within the margin of error of the original result." But that statement isn't correct mathematically, unless your point estimate happens to align perfectly with the population parameter — and there's no reason to think this is the case.

Treat the confidence interval just as an indication of the precision of the measurement. If you do a study that finds a statistic of 17 ± 6 and someone else does a study that gives 23 ± 5, then there is little reason to think that the two studies are inconsistent. On the other hand, if your study gives 17 ± 2 and the other study is 23 ± 1, then something seems to be going on; you have a genuine disagreement on your hands.

5.5   Confidence Intervals from Census Data

Recall the distinction between a **sample** and a **census**. A census involves every member of the population, whereas a sample is a subset of the population.

The logic of statistical inference applies to samples and is based on the variation introduced by the sampling process itself. Each possible sample is somewhat different from other possible samples. The techniques of inference provide a means to quantify "somewhat" and a standard format for communicating the imprecision that necessarily results from the sampling process.

But what if you are working with the population: a census not just a sample? For instance, the employment termination data is based on every employee at the firm, not a random sample.

One point of view is that statistical inference for a census is meaningless: the population is regarded as fixed and non random, so the population parameters are also fixed. It's sampling from the population that introduces random variation.

A different view, perhaps more pragmatic, considers the population itself as a hypothetically random draw from some abstract set of possible populations. For instance, in the census data, the particular set of employees was influenced by a host of unknown random factors: someone had a particularly up or down day when being interviewed, an employee became disabled or had some other life-changing event.

Similarly, in the grade-point average data, you might choose to regard the set of courses taken by a student as fixed and non-random. If so, the idea of sampling precision doesn't make sense. On the other hand, it's reasonable to consider that course choice and grades are influenced by random factors: schedule conflicts, what your friend decided to take, which instructor was assigned, which particular questions were on the final exam, and so on.

You can certainly calculate the quantities of statistical inference from the complete population, using the internal, case-by-case variation as a stand-in for the hypothetical random factors that influenced each case in the population. Interpreting confidence intervals from populations in the same way as confidence intervals can provide a useful indication of the strength of evidence, and, indeed is recognized by courts when dealing with claims of employment discrimination. It does, however, rely on an untestable hypothesis about internal variation, which might not always be true.

Compare, for example, two possible extreme scenarios of course choice and grades. In one, students select courses on their own from a large set of possibilities. In the other scenario, every student takes exactly the same sequence of courses from the same instructors. In the first, it's reasonable to calculate a confidence interval on the grade-point average and use this interval to compare the performance of two students. In the second scenario, since the students have all been in exactly the same situation, there might not be a good justification for constructing a confidence interval as if the data were from a random sample. For instance, there might be substantial internal variation because different instructors have different grading standards. But since every student had the same set of instructors, that variation shouldn't be included in estimating sampling variation and confidence intervals.

The reality, for courses and grades at least, is usually somewhere between the two scenarios. The modeling techniques described in later chapters provide an approach to pulling apart the various sources of variation, rather than ascribing all of it to randomness and including all of it in the calculation of confidence intervals.

5.6 Computational Technique

Again, you will need the `mosaic` package in R, which provides some of the basic operators for constructing sampling and resampling distributions.

```
> require(mosaic)
```

The examples will be based on the Cherry-Blossom 2008 data described earlier:

DATA FILE
Cherry-
Blosssom-
2008.csv

```
> runners = fetchData("Cherry-Blossom-2008.csv")
> names( runners )
[1] "position" "division" "total"    "name"     "age"      "place"
[7] "net"      "gun"      "sex"
```

5.6.1   Finding a Sampling Distribution through Bootstrapping

Your data are typically a sample from a population. Collecting the sample is usually hard work. Just to illustrate the context of a sampling distribution, here is a simulation of selecting a sample of size $n = 100$ from the population of runners. It's essential to keep in mind that **you do not usually** pull out your sample using the computer in this way. Instead, you go into the field or laboratory and collect your data.

```
> mysamp = deal( runners, 100 ) # A Simulation of sampling
```

Now that you have a sample, you can calculate the sample statistic that's of interest to you. For instance:

```
> mean( gun ~ sex, data=mysamp )
    F     M
96.73 86.56
```

Note that the results are slightly different from those found above using the whole population. That's to be expected, since the sample is just a random part of the population. But ordinarily, you will not know what the population values are; all you have to work with is your sample.

Theoretically, the sampling distribution reflects the variation from one randomly dealt sample to another, where each sample is taken from the population. In practice, your only ready access to the population is through your sample. So, to simulate the process of random sampling, re-sampling is used and the re-sampling distribution is used as a convenient approximation to the sampling distribution.

Re-sampling involves drawing from the set of cases in your sample with replacement. To illustrate, consider this example of a very small, simple set: the numbers 1 to 5:

```
> nums = c(1,2,3,4,5)
> nums

[1] 1 2 3 4 5
```

Each resample of size n consists of n members from the set, but in any one resample each member might appear more than once and some might not appear at all. Here are three different resamples from **nums**:

```
> resample(nums)

[1] 1 1 4 5 4
```

```
> resample(nums)
[1] 4 2 3 4 2
> resample(nums)
[1] 5 2 2 1 1
```

To use resampling to estimate the sampling distribution of a statistic, you apply the calculation of the statistic to a resampled version of your sample. For instance, here are the group-wise means from one resample of the running sample:

```
> mean( gun ~ sex, data=resample(mysamp) )
    F     M
98.57 84.94
```

And here is another:

```
> mean( gun ~ sex, data=resample(mysamp) )
    F     M
95.04 87.97
```

The bootstrap procedure involves conducting many such trials and examining the variation from one trial to the next.

The do() function lets you automate the collection of multiple trials. For instance, here are five trials carried out using do():

```
> do(5) * mean( gun ~ sex, data=resample(mysamp) )
      F     M
1 97.50 88.61
2 97.97 84.30
3 97.25 87.32
4 95.56 86.76
5 95.90 86.87
```

Typically, you will use several hundred trials for bootstrapping. The most common way to summarize the variation in bootstrap trials, you can calculate a 95% coverage interval. (When applied to a sampling distribution, the coverage interval is called a **confidence interval**.)

To do the computation, give a name to the results of the repeated bootstrap trials, here it's called **trials**:

```
> trials = do(500) * mean( gun ~ sex, data=resample(mysamp) )
> trials
      F     M
1 94.44 84.61
2 98.56 88.37
3 98.65 87.12
4 96.34 88.84
5 96.28 84.43
6 94.49 89.38
... for 500 rows altogether ...
```

Computing the coverage intervals can be done using `qdata()` on the columns, or, for convenience, use the `confint()` function.

```
> confint(trials)
  name lower upper
1    F 93.66 99.62
2    M 82.18 90.74
```

The idea of sampling distributions is based on drawing at random from the population, not resampling. Ordinarily, you can't do this calculation since you don't have the population at hand. But in this example, we happen to have the data for all runners. Here's the population-based confidence interval for the mean running time, with sample size $n = 100$, broken down by sex:

```
> trials = do(500) * mean( gun ~ sex, data=deal(runners,100) )
> confint(trials)
  name lower  upper
1    F 95.06 102.53
2    M 84.16  92.23
```

The output of `confint()` shows the lower and upper limits of the confidence interval for each of the groups. The labels on the columns indicate the confidence level. By default, the interval is at the 95% level, and so the interval runs from the 2.5 percentile to the 97.5 percentile.

Historically, statisticians have been concerned with very small samples: say $n = 2$ or $n = 3$. Even in this era of huge data sets, such small sample sizes often are encountered in laboratory experiments, etc. Bootstrapping cannot work well with such small samples, and other techniques are needed to simulate sampling variability. Many of these techniques are based in algebra and probability theory, and give somewhat complex formulas for calculating confidence intervals from data. The formulas are often found in textbooks, but for most of the modeling techniques you will use in later chapters, appropriate formulas for confidence intervals have been implemented in software. For other modeling techniques, bootstrapping is used to find the confidence intervals. But keep in mind that bootstrapping can only be effective when the sample size n is one or two dozen or larger.

5.6.2   Computing Grade-Point Averages

The grade-point average is a kind of group-wise mean, where the group is an individual student. This is not the usual way of looking at things for a student, who sees only his or her own grades. But institutions have data on many students.

The data files **grades.csv** and **courses.csv** are drawn from an institutional database at a college. They give the grades for more than 400 students who graduated in year 2005. Another file, **grade-to-number.csv**, gives the rules used by the institution in converting letter grades to numbers.

The data files are part of a **relational data base**, a very important way of managing large amounts of data used by private and public institutions, corporations and governments — it's the basis for a multi-billion dollar segment of the economy. Ordinarily, relational data bases are queried using special-purpose computer languages that sort, extract, and combine the data. Here are the R commands for converting the letter grades to numbers and extracting the data for one student:

```
> grades = fetchData("grades.csv")
> gp = fetchData("grade-to-number.csv")
> all.students = merge(grades, gp)
> one.student = subset( all.students, sid=="S31200" )

> one.student

      grade    sid    sessionID gradepoint
5196      C S31200 session2324       2.00
5039     B- S31200 session3809       2.66
5488     D+ S31200 session2331       1.33
5395     C+ S31200 session3546       2.33
... for 14 cases altogether ...
```

Calculating the mean grade-point for the one student is a simple matter:

```
> mean( gradepoint, data=one.student )

[1] 2.186
```

It's equally straightforward to calculate the grade-point averages for all students as individuals:

```
> mean( gradepoint ~ sid, data=all.students )

S31185 S31188 S31191 S31194 S31197
 2.413  3.018  3.212  3.359  3.356
... for 443 cases altogether ...
```

Bootstrapping can be used to find the confidence interval on the grade-point average for each student:

```
> trials = do(100)*mean(gradepoint ~ sid, data=resample(all.students) )

> confint(trials)

    name 2.5 % 97.5 %
1 S31185 1.568  2.979
2 S31188 2.571  3.432
3 S31191 3.034  3.455
4 S31194 3.059  3.641
5 S31197 3.193  3.482
... for 443 students altogether ...
```

It's important to point out that there are other methods for calculating confidence intervals that are based on the standard deviation of the data. Formulas and procedures for such methods are given in just about every standard introductory statistics book and would certainly be used instead of bootstrapping in a simple calculation of the sort illustrated here.

However, such formulas don't go to the heart of the problem: accounting for variation in the grades and the contribution from different sources of that variation. For example, some of the variation in this student's grades might be due systematically to improvement over time or due to differences between instructor's practices. The modeling techniques introduced in the following chapters provide a means to examine and quantify the different sources of variation.

Reading Questions

- What is a sampling distribution? What sort of variation does it reflect?
- What is resampling and bootstrapping?
- What is the difference between a "confidence interval" and a "coverage interval?"

For exercises, see www.mosaic-web.org/StatisticalModeling/Exercises.

6

The Language of Models

I do not believe in things. I believe only in their relationships. —
Georges Braque (1882-1963) cubist painter

Mathematicians do not study objects, but relations among objects. —
Henri Poincaré (1854-1912) mathematician

Chapter 4 is concerned with model forms based on division into groups. Those
models are very common, but their utility is limited: the models can be misleading
because they fail to take into concern multiple factors that can shape outcomes,
not just simple membership in a group. This chapter starts down the path toward
more sophisticated models. The point of departure will be a set of concepts and a
notation for describing models that are more general and therefore more flexible
than simple group-wise models.

One October I received a bill from the utility company: $52 for natural gas for the
month. According to the bill, the average outdoor temperature during October
was 49°F (9.5°C).

I had particular interest in this bill because two months earlier, in August, I replaced the old furnace in our house with a new, expensive, high-efficiency furnace
that's supposed to be saving gas and money. This bill is the first one of the
heating season and I want to know whether the new furnace is working.

To be able to answer such questions, I keep track of my monthly utility bills.
The `gasbill` variable shows a lot of variation: from $3.42 to $240.90 per month.
The 50% coverage interval is $21.40 to $117.90. The mean bill is $77.85. Judging
from this, the $52 October bill is low. It looks like the new furnace is working!

DATA FILE
`utilities.csv`

Perhaps that conclusion is premature. My new furnace is just one factor that
can influence the gas bill. Some others: the weather, the price of natural gas

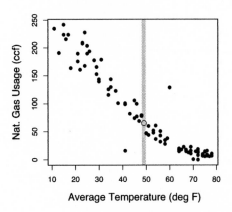

Figure 6.1: Monthly natural gas usage versus average outdoor temperature during the month.

(which fluctuates strongly from season to season and year to year), the thermostat setting, whether there were windows or doors left open, how much gas we use for cooking, etc. Of all the factors, I think the weather and the price of natural gas are the most important. I'd like to take these into account when judging whether the $52 bill is high or low.

Rather than looking at the bill in dollars, it makes sense to look at the quantity of gas used. After all, the new furnace can only reduce the amount of gas used, it doesn't influence the price of gas. According to the utility bill, the usage in October was 65 ccf. ("ccf" means cubic feet, one way to measure the quantity of gas.) The variable ccf gives the historical values from past bills: the range is 0 to 242 ccf, so 65 ccf seems perfectly reasonable, but it's higher than the median monthly usage, which is 51 ccf. Still, this doesn't take into account the weather.

Now it is time to build a model: a representation of the utility data for the purpose of telling whether 65 ccf is low or high given the temperature. The variable temperature contains the average temperature during the billing period.

A simple graph of ccf versus temperature will suffice. (See Figure 6.1.) The open point shows the October bill (49 deg. and 65 ccf). The gray line indicates which points to look at for comparison, those from months near 49 degrees.

The graph suggests that 65 ccf is more or less what to expect for a month where the average temperature is 49 degrees. The new furnace doesn't seem to make much of a difference.

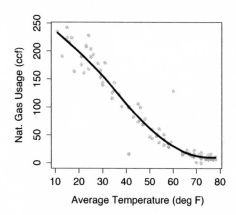

Figure 6.2: A model of natural gas usage versus outdoor temperature.

6.1   Models as Functions

Figure 6.1 gives a pretty good idea of the relationship between gas usage and temperature.

The concept of a **function** is very important when thinking about relationships. A function is a mathematical concept: the relationship between an **output** and one or more **inputs**. One way to talk about a function is that you plug in the inputs and receive back the output. For example, the formula $y = 3x + 7$ can be read as a function with input x and output y. Plug in a value of x and receive the output y. So, when x is 5, the output y is 22.

One way to represent a function is with a formula, but there are other ways as well, for example graphs and tables. Figure 6.2 shows a function representing the relationship between gas usage and temperature. The function is much simpler than the data. In the data, there is a scatter of usage levels at each temperature. But in the function there is only one output value for each input value.

Some vocabulary will help to describe how to represent relationships with functions.

- The **response variable** is the variable whose behavior or variation you are trying to understand. On a graph, the response variable is conventionally plotted on the vertical axis.

- The **explanatory variables** are the other variables that you want to use to explain the variation in the response. Figure 6.1 shows just one explanatory variable, `temperature`. It's plotted on the horizontal axis.

- **Conditioning on explanatory variables** means taking the value of the explanatory variables into account when looking at the response variables. When in Figure 6.1 you looked at the gas usage for those months with a temperature near 49°, you were conditioning gas usage on temperature.

- The **model value** is the output of a function. The function — called the **model function** — has been arranged to take the explanatory variables as inputs and return as output a typical value of the response variable. That is, the model function gives the typical value of the response variable *conditioning on* the explanatory variables. The function shown in Figure 6.2 is a model function. It gives the typical value of gas usage conditioned on the temperature. For instance, at 49°, the typical usage is 65 ccf. At 20°, the typical usage is much higher, about 200 ccf.

- The **residuals** show how far each case is from its model value. For example, one of the cases plotted in Figure 6.2 is a month where the temperature was 13° and the gas usage was 191 ccf. When the input is 13°, the model function gives an output of 228 ccf. So, for that case, the residual is $191 - 228 = -37$ ccf. Residuals are always "actual value minus model value."

  Graphically, the residual for each case tells how far above the model function that case is. A negative residual means that the case is below the model function.

The idea of a function is fundamental to understanding statistical models. Whether the function is represented by a formula or a graph, the function takes one or more inputs and produces an output. In the statistical models in this book, that output is the model value, a "typical" or "ideal" value of the response variable at given levels of the inputs. The inputs are the values explanatory variables.

The model function describes how the typical value of the response variable depends on the explanatory variables. The output of the model function varies along with the explanatory variables. For instance, when temperature is low, the model value of gas usage is high. When temperature is high, the model value of gas usage is low. The idea of "depends on" is very important. In some fields such as economics, the term **dependent variable** is used instead of "response variable." Other phrases are used for this notion of "depends on," so you may hear statements such as these: "the value of the response *given* the explanatory variables," or "the value of the response *conditioned on* the explanatory variables."

The model function describes a relationship. If you plug in values for the explanatory variables for a given case, you get the model value for that case. The model value is usually different from one case to another, at least so long as the values of the explanatory variables are different. When two cases have exactly the same values of the explanatory values, they will have exactly the same model value even though the actual response value might be different for the two cases.

The residuals tell how each case differs from its model value. Both the model values and the residuals are important. The model values tell what's typical or average. The residuals tell how far from typical an individual case is likely to be. This might remind you of the mean and standard deviation.

As already said, models partition the variation in the response variable. Some of the variability is explained by the model, the remainder is unexplained. The model values capture the "deterministic" or "explained" part of the variability of the response variable from case to case. The residuals represent the "random" or "unexplained" part of the variability of the response variable.

6.2 Model Functions with Multiple Explanatory Variables

Historically, women tended to be paid less than men. To some extent, this reflected the division of jobs along sex lines and limited range of jobs that were open to women — secretarial, nursing, school teaching, etc. But often there was simple discrimination; an attitude that women's work wasn't as valuable or that women shouldn't be in the workplace. Over the past thirty or forty years, the situation has changed. Training and jobs that were once rarely available to women — police work, management, medicine, law, science — are now open to them.

Surveys consistently show that women tend to earn less than men: a "wage gap." To illustrate, consider data from one such survey, the Current Population Survey (CPS) from 1985. In the survey data, each case is one person. The variables are the person's hourly wages at the time of the survey, age, sex, marital status, the sector of the economy in which they work, etc.

DATA FILE
cps.csv

One aspect of these data is displayed by plotting wage versus sex, as in Figure 6.3. The model plotted along with the data show that typical wages for men are higher than for women.

The situation is somewhat complex since the workforce reflected in the 1985 data is a mixture of people who were raised in the older system and those who were emerging in a more modern system. A woman's situation can depend strongly on when she was born. This is reflected in the data by the age variable.

There are other factors as well. The roles and burdens of women in family life remain much more traditional than their roles in the economy. Perhaps marital status ought to be taken into account. In fact, there are all sorts of variables that you might want to include — job type, race, location, etc.

A statistical model can include multiple explanatory variables, all at once. To illustrate, consider explaining wage using the worker's age, sex, and marital status.

In a typical graph of data, the vertical axis stands for the response variable and the horizontal axis for the explanatory variable. But what do you do when

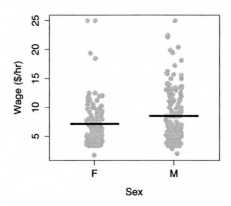

Figure 6.3: Hourly wages versus sex from the Current Population Survey data of 1985.

there is more than one explanatory variable? One approach, when some of the explanatory variables are categorical, is to use differing symbols or colors to represent the differing levels of the categories. The left panel in Figure 6.4 shows wages versus age, sex, and marital status plotted out this way.

The first thing that might be evident from the scatter plot is that not very much is obvious from the data on their own. There does seem to be a slight increase in wages with age, but the cases are scattered all over the place.

The model, shown as the continuous curves in the figure, simplifies things. The relationships shown in the model are much clearer. You can see that wages tend to increase with age, up until about age 40, and they do so differently for men and for women and differently for married people and single people.

Models can sometimes reveal patterns that are not evident in a graph of the data. This is a great advantage of modeling over simple visual inspection of data. There is a real risk, however, that a model is imposing structure that is not really there on the scatter of data, just as people imagine animal shapes in the stars. A skeptical approach is always warranted. Much of the second half of the book is about ways to judge whether the structure suggested by a model is justified by the data.

There is a tendency for those who first encounter models to fix attention on the clarity of the model and ignore the variation around the model. This is a mistake. Keep in mind the definition of statistics offered in the first chapter:

> *Statistics is the explanation of variation in the context of what remains unexplained.*

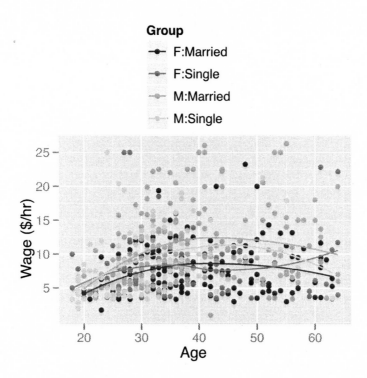

Figure 6.4: Hourly wages versus age, sex, and marital status. It's hard to see a pattern among the data points; the models (shown as smooth curves) suggest that wages increase until age 40, then level off.

The scatter of the wage data around the model is very large; this is a very important part of the story. The scatter suggests that there might be other factors that account for large parts of person-to-person variability in wages, or perhaps just that randomness plays a big role.

Compare the broad scatter of wages to the rather tight way the gas usage in Figure 6.1 is modeled by average temperature. The wage model is explaining only a small part of the variation in wages, the gas-usage model explains a very large part of the variation in those data.

Adding more explanatory variables to a model can sometimes usefully reduce the size of the scatter around the model. If you included the worker's level of education, job classification, age, or years working in their present occupation, the unexplained scatter might be reduced. Even when there is a good explanation for the scatter, if the explanatory variables behind this explanation are not included in the model, the scatter due to them will appear as unexplained variation. (In the gas-usage data, it's likely that wind velocity, electricity usage that supplements gas-generated heat, and the amount of gas used for cooking and hot water would explain a lot of the scatter. But these potential explanatory variables were not measured.)

6.3   Reading a Model

There are two distinct ways that you can read a model.

Read out the model value. Plug in specific values for the explanatory variables and read out the resulting model value. For the model in Figure 6.1, an input temperature of 35° produces a predicted output gas usage of 125 ccf. For the model in Figure 6.4 a single, 30-year old female has a model value of $8.10 per hour. (Remember, the model is based on data from 1985!)

Characterize the relationship described by the model. In contrast to reading out a model value for some specific values of the explanatory variables, here interest is in the overall relationship: how gas usage depends on temperature; how wages depend on sex or marital status or age.

Reading out the model value is useful when you want to make a prediction (What would the gas usage be if the temperature were 10 degrees?) or when you want to compare the actual value of the response variable to what the model says is a typical value. (Is the gas usage in the 49° month lower than expected, perhaps due to my new furnace?).

Characterizing the relationship is useful when you want to make statements about broad patterns that go beyond individual cases. Is there really a connection between marital status and wage? Which way does it go?

The "shape" of the model function tells you about such broad relationships. Reading the shape from a graph of the model is not difficult.

For a quantitative explanatory variable, e.g., temperature or age, the model form is a continuous curve or line. An extremely important aspect of this curve is its slope. For the model of gas usage in Figure 6.2, the slope is down to the right: a negative slope. This means that as temperature increases, the gas usage goes down. In contrast, for the model of wages in Figure 6.4, the slope is up to the right: a positive slope. This means that as age increases, the wage goes up.

The slope is measured in the usual way: rise over run. The numerical size of the slope is a measure of the strength of the relationship, the sign tells which way the relationship goes. Some examples: For the gas usage model in Figure 6.2 in winter-like temperatures, the slope is about −4 ccf/degree. This means that gas usage can be expected to go down by 4 ccf for every degree of temperature increase. For the model of wages in Figure 6.4, the slope for single females is about 0.20 dollars-per-hour/year: for every year older a single female is, wages typically go up by 20 cents-per-hour.

Slopes have units. These are always the units of the response variable divided by the units of the explanatory variable. In the wage model, the response has units of dollars-per-hour while the explanatory variable `age` has units of years. Thus the units of the slope are dollars-per-hour/year.

For categorical variables, slopes don't apply. Instead, the pattern can be described in terms of *differences*. In the model where wage is explained only by sex, the difference between typical wages for males and females is 2.12 dollars per hour.

When there is more than one explanatory variable, there will be a distinct slope or difference associated with each.

When describing models, the words used can carry implications that go beyond what is justified by the model itself. Saying "the difference between typical wages" is pretty neutral: a description of the pattern. But consider this statement: "Typical wages go up by 20 cents per hour for every year of age." There's an implication here of **causation**, that as a person ages his or her wage will go up. That might in fact be true, but the data on which the model is based were not collected in a way to support that claim. Those data don't trace people as they age; they are not longitudinal data. Instead, the data are a snapshot of different people at different ages: cross-sectional data. It's dangerous to draw conclusions about changes over time from cross-sectional data of the sort in the CPS data set. Perhaps people's wages stay the same over time but that the people who were hired a long time ago tended to start at higher wages than the people who have just been hired.

Consider this statement: "A man's wage rises when he gets married." The model in Figure 6.4 is consistent with this statement; it shows that a married man's typical wage is higher than an unmarried man's typical wage. But does marriage cause a higher wage? It's possible that this is true, but that conclusion isn't justified from the data. There are other possible explanations for the link between marital status and wage. Perhaps the men who earn higher wages are more attractive candidates for marriage. It might not be that marriage causes higher wages but that higher wages cause marriage.

To draw compelling conclusions about causation, it's important to collect data in an appropriate way. For instance, if you are interested in the effect of marriage on wages, you might want to collect data from individuals both before and after marriage and compare their change in wages to that over the same time period in individuals who don't marry. As described in Chapter 18, the strongest evidence for causation involves something more: that the condition be imposed experimentally, picking the people who are to get married at random. Such an experiment is hardly possible when it comes to marriage.

6.4   Choices in Model Design

The suitability of a model for its intended purpose depends on choices that the modeler makes. There are three fundamental choices:

1. The data.

2. The response variable.

3. The explanatory variables.

6.4.1   The Data

How were the data collected? Are they a random sample from a relevant sampling frame? Are they part of an experiment in which one or more variables were intentionally manipulated by the experimenter, or are they observational data? Are the relevant variables being measured? (This includes those that may not be directly of interest but which have a strong influence on the response.) Are the variables being measured in a meaningful way? Start thinking about your models and the variables you will want to include while you are still planning your data collection.

When you are confronted with a situation where your data are not suitable, you need to be honest and realistic about the limitations of the conclusions you can draw. The issues involved will be discussed starting in Chapter 10.

6.4.2   The Response Variable

The appropriate choice of a response variable for a model is often obvious. The response variable should be the thing that you want to predict, or the thing whose variability you want to understand. Often, it is something that you think is the effect produced by some other cause.

For example, in examining the relationship between gas usage and outdoor temperature, it seems clear that gas usage should be the response: temperature is a major determinant of gas usage. But suppose that the modeler wanted to be able to measure outdoor temperature from the amount of gas used. Then it would make sense to take temperature as the response variable.

Similarly, wages make sense as a response variable when you are interested in how wages vary from person to person depending on traits such as age, experience, and so on. But suppose that a sociologist was interested in assessing the influence of income on personal choices such as marriage. Then the marital status might be a suitable response variable, and wage would be an explanatory variable.

Most of the modeling techniques in this book require that the response variable be quantitative. The main reason is that there are straightforward ways to measure variation in a quantitative variable and measuring variation is key to assessing the reliability of models. There are, however, methods for building models with a categorical response variable. (One of them, logistic regression, is the subject of Chapter 16.)

6.4.3   The Explanatory Variables

Much of the thought in modeling goes into the selection of explanatory variables and later chapters in this book describes several ways to decide if an explanatory variable ought to be included in a model.

Of course, some of the things that shape the choice of explanatory variables are obvious. Do you want to study sex-related differences in wage? Then sex had better be an explanatory variable. Is temperature a major determinant of the usage of natural gas? Then it makes sense to include it as an explanatory variable.

You will see situations where including an explanatory variable hurts the model, so it is important to be careful. (This will be discussed in Chapter 12.) A much more common mistake is to leave out explanatory variables. Unfortunately, few people learn the techniques for handling multiple explanatory variables and so your task will often need to go beyond modeling to include explaining how this is done.

When designing a model, you should think hard about what are potential explanatory variables and be prepared to include them in a model along with the variables that are of direct interest.

6.5   Model Terms

Once the modeler has selected explanatory variables, a choice must be made about **model terms**.

Notice that the models in the preceding examples have graphs of different shapes. The gas-usage model is a gentle curve, the wage-vs-sex model is just two values, and the more elaborate wage model is four lines with different slopes and intercepts.

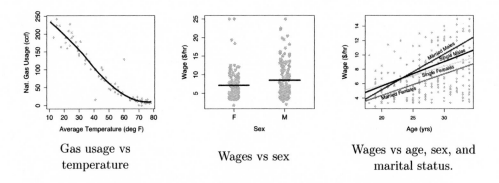

| Gas usage vs temperature | Wages vs sex | Wages vs age, sex, and marital status. |

The modeler determines the shape of the model through his or her choice of **model terms**. The basic idea of a model term is that explanatory variables can be included in a model in more than one way. Each kind of term describes a different way to include a variable in the model.

You need to learn to describe models using model terms for several reasons. First, you will communicate in this language with the computers that you will use to perform the calculations for models. Second, when there is more than one explanatory variable, it's hard to visualize the model function with a graph. Knowing the language of model terms will help you "see" the shape of the function even when you can't graph it. Third, model terms are the way to talk about "parts" of models. In evaluating a model, statistical methods can be used to take the model apart and describe the contribution of each part. This analysis — the word "analysis" literally means to loosen apart — helps the modeler to decide which parts are worth keeping.

There are just a few basic kinds of models terms. They will be introduced by example in the following sections

1. the intercept term : a sort of "baseline" that is included in almost every model.

2. main terms : the effect of explanatory variables directly.

3. interaction terms : how different explanatory variables modulate the relationship of each other to the response variable.

4. transformation terms : simple modifications of explanatory variables.

Models almost always include the intercept term and a main term for each of the explanatory variables. Transformation and interaction terms can be added to create more expressive or flexible shapes.

To form an understanding of how different kinds of terms contribute to the overall "shape" of the model function, it's best to look at the different shape functions

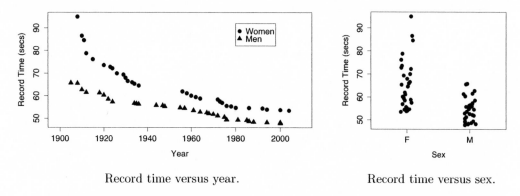

Record time versus year.   Record time versus sex.

Figure 6.5: World record swimming times in the 100 meter freestyle.

that result from including different model terms. The next section illustrates this. Several differently shaped models are constructed of the same data plotted in Figure 6.5. The data are the record `time` (in seconds) for the 100 meter freestyle race along with the `year` in which the record was set and the `sex` of the swimmer. The response variable will be `time`, the explanatory variables will be `year` and `sex`.

DATA FILE
`swim100m.csv`

Figure 6.5 shows some obvious patterns, seen most clearly in the plot of time versus year. The record time has been going down over the years. This is natural, since setting a new record means beating the time of the previous record. There's also a clear difference between the men's and women's records; men's record times are faster than women's, although the difference has decreased markedly over the years.

The following models may or may not reflect these patterns, depending on which model terms are included.

6.5.1 The Intercept Term (and no other terms)

The **intercept term** is included in almost every statistical model. The intercept term is a bit strange because it isn't something you measure; it isn't a variable. (The term "intercept" will make sense when model formulas are introduced in the next chapter.)

The figure below shows the swimming data with a simple model consisting only of the intercept term.

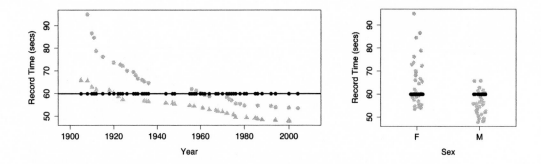

The model value for this model is exactly the same for every case. In order to create model variation from case to case, you would need to include at least one explanatory variable in the model.

6.5.2   Intercept and Main Terms

The most basic and common way to include an explanatory variable is as a main effect. Almost all models include the intercept term and a main term for each of the explanatory variables. The figures below show three different models each of this form:

The intercept and a main term from year.   This produces model values that vary with year, but show no difference between the sexes. This is because sex has not been included in the model.

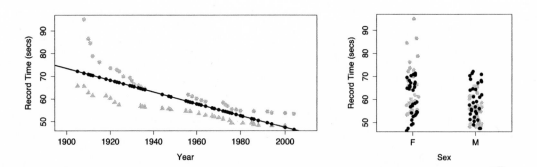

The model values have been plotted out as small black dots. The model pattern is evident in the left graph: swim time versus year. But in the right graph — swim time versus sex — it seems to be all scrambled. Don't be confused by this. The right-hand graph doesn't include year as a variable, so the dependence of the model values on year is not at all evident from that graph. Still, each of the model value dots in the left graph occurs in the right graph at exactly the same *vertical* coordinate.

The intercept and a main term from sex.   This produces different model values for each level of sex.

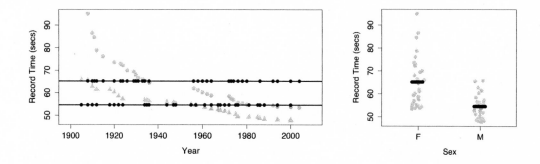

There is no model variation with year because year has not been included in the model.

The intercept and main terms from sex and from year.   This model gives dependence on both sex and year.

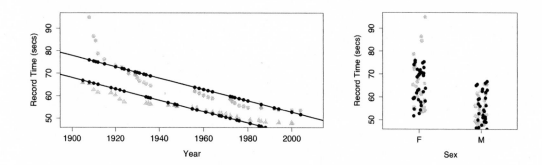

Note that the model values form two parallel lines in the graph of time versus year: one line for each sex.

6.5.3   Interaction Terms

Interaction terms combine two other terms, typically two main terms. An interaction term can describe how one explanatory variable modulates the role of another explanatory variable in modeling the relationship of both with the response variable.

In the graph, including the interaction term between sex and year produces a model with two non-parallel lines for time versus year. (The model also has the main terms for both sex and year and the intercept term, as always.)

 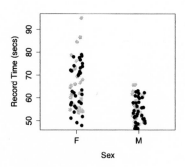

One way to think about the meaning of the interaction term in this model is that it describes how the effect of sex changes with year. Looking at the model, you can see how the difference between the sexes changes over the years; the difference is getting smaller. Without the interaction term, the model values would be two *parallel* lines; the difference between the lines wouldn't be able to change over the years.

Another, equivalent way to put things is that the interaction term describes how the effect of year changes with sex. The effect of year on the response is reflected by the slope of the model line. Looking at the model, you can see that the slope is different depending on sex: steeper for women than men.

For most people, it's surprising that one term — the interaction between sex and year — can describe both how the effect of year is modulated by sex, and how the effect of sex is modulated by year. But these are just two ways of looking at the same thing.

A common misconception about interaction terms is that they describe how one explanatory variable affects another explanatory variable. Don't fall into this error. Model terms are always about how the response variable depends on the explanatory variables, not how explanatory variables depend on one another. An interaction term between two variables describes how two explanatory variables combine jointly to influence the response variable.

Once people learn about interaction terms, they are tempted to include them everywhere. After all, it's natural to think that world record swimming times would depend differently on year for women than for men. Of course wages might depend differently on age for men and women! Regretably, the uncritical use of interaction terms can lead to poor models. The problem is not the logic of interaction, the problem is in the data. Interaction terms can introduce a problem called **multi-collinearity** which can reduce the reliability of models. (See Chapter 12.) Fortunately, it's not hard to detect multi-collinearity and to drop interaction terms if they are causing a problem. The model diagnostics that will be introduced in later chapters will make it possible to play safely with interaction terms.

6.5.4   Transformation Terms

A **transformation term** is a modification of another term using some mathematical transformation. Transformation terms only apply to quantitative variables. Some common transformations are x^2 or $\sqrt{x}$ or $\log x$, where the quantitative explantory variable is x.

A transformation term allows the model to have a dependence on x that is not a straight line. The graph shows a model that includes these terms: an intercept, main effects of sex and year, an interaction between sex and year, and a year-squared transformation term.

Adding in the year-squared term provides some curvature to the model function.

Aside. 6.1 Are swimmers slowing down?

Look carefully at the model with a year-squared transformation term. You may notice that, according to the model, world record times for men have been getting worse since about year 1990. This is, of course, nonsense. Records can't get worse. A new record is set only when an old record is beaten. The model doesn't know this common sense about records — the model terms allow the model to curve in a certain way and the model curves in exactly that way. What you probably want out of a model of world records is a slight curve that's constrained never to slope upward. There is no elementary way to do this. Indeed, it is an unresolved problem in statistics how best to include in a model additional knowledge that you might have such as "world records can't get worse with time."

6.5.5   Main Effects without the Intercept

It's possible to construct a model with main terms but no intercept terms. If the explanatory variables are all quantitative, this is almost always a mistake. The figure, which plots the model function for swim `time` modeled by `age` with no intercept term, shows why.

 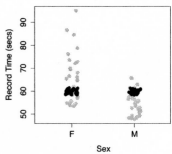

The model function is sloping slightly upward rather than falling as the data clearly indicate. This is because, without an intercept term, the model line is forced to go through the origin. The line is sloping upward so that it will show a `time` of zero in the hypothetical `year` zero! Silly. It's no wonder that the model function fails to look anything like the data.

Never leave out the intercept unless you have a very good reason. Indeed, statistical software typically includes the intercept term by default. You have to go out of your way to tell the software to exclude the intercept.

6.6   Standard Notation for Describing Model Design

There is a concise notation for specifying the choices made in a model design, that is, which is the response variable, what are the explanatory variables, and what model terms to use. This notation, introduced originally in [12], will be used throughout the rest of this book and you will use it in working with computers.

To illustrate, here is the notation for some of the models looked at earlier in this chapter:

- `ccf` $\sim 1 +$ `temperature`

- `wage` $\sim 1 +$ `sex`

- `time` $\sim 1 +$ `year` $+$ `sex` $+$ `year:sex`

The ~ symbol (pronounced "tilde") divides each statement into two parts. On the left of the tilde is the name of the response variable. On the right is a list of model terms. When there is more than one model term, as is typically the case, the terms are separated by a + sign.

The examples show three types of model terms:

1. The symbol 1 stands for the intercept term.

2. A variable name (e.g., sex or temperature) stands for using that variable in a main term.

3. An interaction term is written as two names separated by a colon, for instance year:sex.

Although this notation looks like arithmetic or algebra, IT IS NOT. The plus sign does not mean arithmetic addition, it simply is the divider mark between terms. In English, one uses a comma to mark the divider as in "rock, paper, and scissors." The modeling notation uses + instead: "rock + paper + scissors." So, in the modeling notation 1 + age does NOT mean "arithmetically add 1 to the age." Instead, it means "two model terms: the intercept and age as a main term."

Similarly, don't confuse the tilde with an algebraic equal sign. The model statement is not an equation. So the statement wage ~ 1 + age does *not* mean "wage equals 1 plus age." Instead it means, "wage is the response variable and there are two model terms: the intercept and age as a main term."

In order to avoid accidentally leaving out important terms, the modeling notation includes some shorthand. Two main points will cover most of what you will do:

- You don't have to type the 1 term; it will be included by default. So, wage ~ age is the same thing as wage ~ 1 + age.

  On those very rare occasions when you might want to insist that there be no intercept term, you can indicate this with a minus sign: wage ~ age - 1.

- Almost always, when you include an interaction term between two variables, you will also include the main terms for those variables. The * sign can be used as shorthand. The model wage ~ 1 + sex + age + sex:age can be written simply as wage ~ sex * age.

6.7 Computational Technique

At the core of the language of modeling is the notation that uses the tilde character (~) to identify the response variable and the explanatory variables. This notation is incorporated into many of operators that you will use.

DATA FILE
utilities.csv

To illustrate the computer commands for modeling and graphically displaying relationships between variables, use the utilities data set:.

```
> require(mosaic)
> utils = fetchData("utilities.csv")
```

Some of the following examples make particular use of these variables

- ccf — the natural gas usage in cubic feet during the billing period.

- month — the month coded as 1 to 12 for January to December.

- temp — the average temperature during the billing period.

DATA FILE
cps.csv

Another illustrative example uses Current Population Survey wage data:

```
> cps = fetchData("cps.csv")
```

and focuses on the variables wage, sex, and sector.

6.7.1 Bi-variate Plots

The basic idea of a bi-variate (two variable) plot is to examine one variable as it relates to another. The conventional format is to plot the response variable on the vertical axis and an explanatory variable on the horizontal axis.

Quantitative Explanatory Variable

When the explanatory variable is quantitative, a scatter-plot is an appropriate graphical format. In the scatter plot, each case is a single point.

The basic computer operator for making scatter plots is `xyplot()`:

```
> xyplot(ccf ~ temp, data=utils)
```

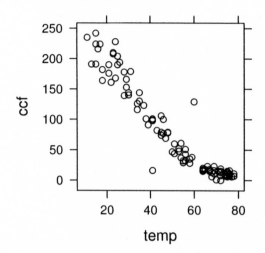

The first argument is a model formula written using the " $\sim$ " modeling notation. This formula, `ccf ~ temp` is pronounced "ccf versus temperature."

In order to keep the model notation concise, the model formula has left out the name of the data frame to which the variables belong. Instead, the frame is specified in the **data** argument. Since **data** has been set to be **utils**, the formula `ccf~temp` is effectively translated to `utils$ccf~utils$temp`.

You can specify the labels by hand, if you like. For example,

```
> xyplot( ccf ~ temp, data=utils,
      xlab="Temperature (deg F)",
      ylab="Natural Gas Usage (ccf)")
```

Categorical Explanatory Variable

When the explanatory variable is categorical, an appropriate format of display is the box-and-whiskers plot, made with the **bwplot** operator. Here, for example, is the `wage` versus `sex` from the Current Population Survey:

```
> bwplot( wage ~ sex, data=cps)
```

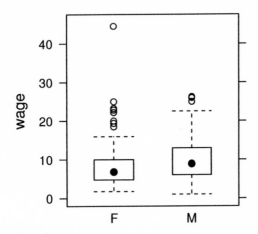

Notice that the outliers are setting the overall vertical scale for the graph and obscuring the detail at typical wage levels. You can use the `ylim` argument to set the scale of the y-axis however you want. For example:

```
> bwplot(wage~sector, data=cps, ylim=c(0,30) )
```

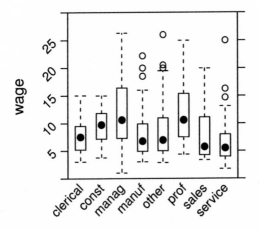

You can also make side-by-side density plots which show more detail than the box-and-whisker plots. For instance:

```
> densityplot( ~ wage, groups=sex, data=cps, auto.key=TRUE )
```

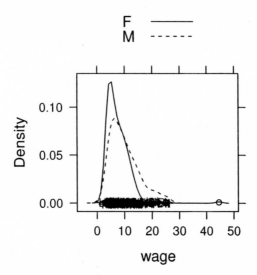

It seems a bit odd to have the notation ~wage — nothing is in the role of the response variable. This idiosyncratic notation perhaps is meant to reflect that wage is on the horizontal axis.

Multiple Explanatory Variables

The two-dimensional nature of paper or the computer screen lends itself well to displaying two variables: a response versus a single explanatory variable. Sometimes it is important to be able to add an additional explanatory variable. The graphics system gives a variety of options in this regard:

Coding the additional explanatory variable using color or symbol shapes. This is done by using the **groups** argument set to the name of the additional explanatory variable. For example:

```
> xyplot(wage ~ age, groups=sex, data=cps,
    auto.key=TRUE)
```

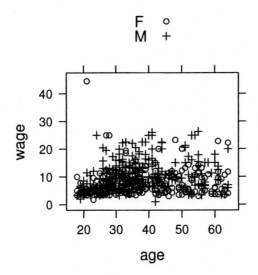

Splitting the plot into the groups defined by the additional explanatory variable. This is done by including the additional variable in the model formula using a | separator. For example:)

```
> xyplot(wage ~ age | sex, data=cps)
```

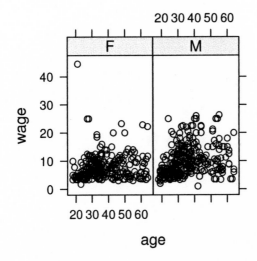

6.7.2   Fitting Models and Finding Model Values

The lm operator (short for "Linear Model") will translate a model design into fitted model values.   It does this by "fitting" the model to data, a process that will be explained in later chapters. For now, focus on how to use `lm` to compute the fitted model values.

The `lm` operator uses the same model language as in the book. To illustrate, consider the world-record swim-times data :

```
> swim = fetchData("swim100m.csv")
```

To construct the model `time ~ 1` for the swim data:

```
> mod1 = lm( time ~ 1, data=swim)
```

Here the model has been given a name, `mod1`, so that you can refer to it later. You can use any name you like, so long as it is valid in R.

DATA FILE
swim100m.csv

Once the model has been constructed, the fitted values can be found using the `fitted` operator:

```
> fitted(mod1)

    1    2    3    4    5    6    7    8    9   10   11   12
 59.9 59.9 59.9 59.9 59.9 59.9 59.9 59.9 59.9 59.9 59.9 59.9
 ... for 62 cases altogether ...
```

There is an individual fitted model value for each case. Of course, in this model all the model values are exactly the same since the model `time ~ 1` treats all the cases as exactly the same.

In later chapters you'll see how to analyze the model values, make predictions from the model, and assess the contribution of each model term. For now, just look at the model values by plotting them out along with the data used. I'll plot out both the data values and the model values versus `year` just to emphasize that the model values are the same for every case:

```
> xyplot( time + fitted(mod1) ~ year, data=swim)
```

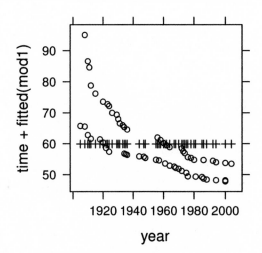

Pay careful attention to the syntax used in the above command. There are two quantities to the left of the ~. This is not part of the modeling language, where there is always a single response variable. Instead, it is a kind of shorthand, telling **xyplot** that it should plot out *both* of the quantities on the left side against the quantity on the right side. Of course, if you wanted to plot just the model values, without the actual data, you could specify the formula as **fitted(mod1)~year**.

Here are more interesting models:

```
> mod2 = lm( time ~ 1+year, data=swim)
> mod3 = lm( time ~ 1+sex, data=swim)
> mod4 = lm( time ~ 1+sex+year, data=swim)
> mod5 = lm( time ~ 1+year+sex+year:sex, data=swim)
```

You can, if you like, compare the fitted values from different models on one plot:

```
> xyplot( fitted(mod5) + fitted(mod3) ~ year, data=swim,
    auto.key=TRUE)
```

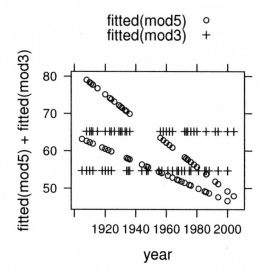

Interactions and Main Effects

Typically a model that includes an interaction term between two variables will include the main terms from those variables too. As a shorthand for this, the modeling language has a `*` symbol. So, the formula `time~year+sex+year:sex` can also be written `time~year*sex`.

Transformation Terms

Transformation terms such as squares can also be included in the model formula. To mark the quantity clearly as a single term, it's best to wrap the term with `I()` as follows:

```
> mod7 = lm( time ~ year + I(year^2) + sex, data=swim)
```

Another way to accomplish this, for polynomials, is to use the operator `poly` as in the model formula `time~poly(year,2)+sex`.

Here's a plot of the result:

```
> xyplot( time + fitted(mod7) ~ year, data=swim)
```

Reading Questions

- What is an "explanatory variable" and how does it differ from a "response variable?"

- What is the difference between a "model term" and a "variable?"

- Why are there sometimes multiple model terms in a model?

- What is an interaction term and how does it differ from a variable?

- In graphs of the model response value versus an explanatory variable, quantitative explanatory variables are associated with slopes and categorical explanatory variables are associated with step-like differences. Explain why.

- How can models be useful that fail to represent the actual causal connections (if any) between variables? Give an example.

For exercises, see www.mosaic-web.org/StatisticalModeling/Exercises.

7

Model Formulas and Coefficients

> *All economical and practical wisdom is an extension or variation of the following arithmetical formula: $2 + 2 = 4$. Every philosophical proposition has the more general character of the expression $a + b = c$. We are mere operatives, empirics, and egotists, until we learn to think in letters instead of figures.* — Oliver Wendell Holmes, Jr. (1841-1935), jurist

The previous chapter presents models as graphs. The response variable is plotted on the vertical axis and one of the explanatory variables on the horizontal axis. Such a visual depiction of a model is extremely useful, when it can be made. In such a graph, the relationship between the response and explanatory variables can be seen as slopes or differences; interactions can be seen as differences between slopes; the match or mismatch between the data and the model can be visualized easily.

A graph is also a useful mode of communicating; many people have the graph-reading skills needed to interpret the sorts of models in the previous chapter, or, at least, to get an impression of what the models are about.

Presenting models via a graph is, regrettably, very limiting. The sorts of models that can be graphed effectively have only one or two explanatory variables, whereas often models need many more explanatory variables. (There are models with thousands of explanatory variables, but even a model with only three or four explanatory variables can be impossible to graph in an understandable way.) Even when a model is simple enough to be graphed, it's helpful to be able to quantify the relationships. Such quantification becomes crucial when you want to characterize the reliability of a model or draw conclusions about the strength of the evidence to support the claim of a relationship shown by a model.

This chapter introduces important ways to present models in a non-graphical way as formulas and as coefficients.

7.1   The Linear Model Formula

Everyone who takes high-school algebra encounters this equation describing a straight-line relationship:

$$y = mx + b$$

The equation is so familiar to many people that they automatically make the following associations: x and y are the variables, m is the slope of the line, b is the y-intercept — the place the line crosses the y axis.

The straight-line equation is fundamental to statistical modeling, although the nomenclature is a little different. To illustrate, consider this model of the relationship between an adult's height and the height of his or her mother, based on Galton's height data:

DATA FILE
galton.csv

$$\underset{\text{Values}}{\text{Model}} \; \text{height} = 46.7 + 0.313 \, \text{mother}$$

This is a model represented not as a graph but as a **model formula**. Just reading the model in the same way as $y = mx + b$ shows that the intercept is 46.7 and the slope is 0.313. That is, if you make a graph of the model values of the response variable `height` (of the adult child) against the values of the explanatory variable `mother`, you will see a straight line with that slope and that intercept.

To find the model value given by the formula, just plug in numerical values for the explanatory variable. So, according to the formula, a mother who is 65 inches tall will have children with a typical height of $46.7 + 0.313 \times 65$, giving 67.05 inches.

You can also interpret the model in terms of the relationship between the child's height and the mother's height. Comparing two mothers who differ in height by one inch, their children would typically differ in height by 0.313 inches.

In the design language, the model is specified like this:

$$\text{height} \sim 1 + \text{mother}$$

There is a simple correspondence between the model design and the model formula. The model formula takes each of the terms in the model design and multiplies it by a number. The intercept term is multiplied by 46.7 and the `mother` term is multiplied by 0.313. Such numbers have a generic name: **model coefficients**. Instead of calling 0.313 the "slope," it's called the "coefficient on the term `mother`." Similarly, 46.7 could be the "coefficient on the intercept term," but it seems more natural just to call it the intercept.

Where did these precise values for the coefficients come from? A process called **fitting the model to the data** finds coefficients that bring the model values from the formula to correspond as closely as possible to the response values in the data. As a result, the coefficients that result from fitting a given model design will depend on the data to which the model is fitted. Chapter 8 describes the fitting process in more detail.

7.2   Linear Models with Multiple Terms

It's easy to generalize the linear model formula to include more than one explanatory variable or additional terms such as interactions. For each term, just add a new component to the formula. For example, suppose you want to model the child's height as a function of **both** the mother's and the father's height. As a model design, take

$$\text{height} \sim 1 + \text{mother} + \text{father}$$

Here is the model formula for this model design fitted to Galton's data:

$$\underset{\text{Values}}{\text{Model}} \quad \text{height} = 22.3 + 0.283 \ \text{mother} + 0.380 \ \text{father}$$

As before, each of the terms has its own coefficient. This same pattern of terms and coefficients can be extended to include as many variables as you like.

Interaction terms also fit into this framework. Suppose you want to fit a model with an interaction between the father's height and the mother's height. The model design is

$$\text{height} \sim 1 + \text{mother} + \text{father} + \text{father:mother}$$

For Galton's data, the formula that corresponds to this design is

$$\underset{\text{Values}}{\text{Model}} \quad \text{height} = 132.3 - 1.43 \ \text{mother} - 1.21 \ \text{father} + 0.0247 \ \text{father} \times \text{mother}$$

The formula follows the same pattern as before: a coefficient multiplying the value of each term. So, to find the model value of height for a child whose mother is 65 inches tall and whose father is 67 inches tall, multiply the coefficient by the value of corresponding term: $132.34 - 1.429 \times 65 - 1.206 \times 67 + 0.0247 \times 65 \times 67$ giving 66.1 inches. The term father $\times$ mother may look a little odd, but it just means to multiply the mother's height by the father's height.

Aside. 7.1 Interpreting Interaction Terms

The numerics of interaction terms are easy. You just have to remember to multiply the coefficient by the product of all the variables in the term. Multiply the coefficient times the values of all the variables in the interaction term. The meaning of interaction terms is somewhat more difficult. Many people initially mistake interaction terms to refer to a relationship between two variables. For instance, they would (wrongly) think that an interaction between mother's and father's heights means that, say, tall mothers tend to be married to tall fathers. Actually, interaction terms do not describe the relationship between the two variables, they are about *three* variables: how one explanatory variable modulates the effect of another on the response.

A model like `height ~ 1+mother+father` captures some of how a child's height varies with the height of either parent. The coefficient on mother (when fitting this model to Galton's data) was 0.283, indicating that an extra inch of the mother's height is associated with an extra 0.283 inches in the child. This coefficient on `mother` doesn't depend on the father's height; the model provides no room for it to do so.

Suppose that the relationship between the mother's height and her child's height is potentiated by the father's height. This would mean that if the father is very tall, then the mother has even more influence on the child's height than for a short father. That's an interaction.

To see this sort of effect in a model, you have to include an interaction term, as in the model `height ~ 1+mother+father+mother:father`. The coefficients from fitting this model to Galton's data allow you to compare what happens when the father is very short (say, 60 inches) to when the father is very tall (say, 75 inches). With a short father, an extra inch in the mother is associated with an extra 0.05 inches in the child. With a tall father, an extra inch in the mother is associated with an extra 0.42 inches in the child.

The interaction term can also be read the other way: the relationship between a father's height and the child's height is greater when the mother is taller.

Of course, this assumes that the model coefficients can be taken at face value as reliable. Later chapters will deal with how to evaluate the strength of the evidence for a model. It will turn out that Galton's data do not provide good evidence for an interaction between mother's and father's heights in determining the child's height.

7.3   Formulas with Categorical Variables

Since quantitative variables are numbers, they can be reflected in a model formula in a natural, direct way: just multiply the value of the model term by the coefficient on that term.

Categorical variables are a little different. They don't have numerical values. It doesn't mean anything to multiply a category name by a coefficient.

In order to include a categorical variable in a model formula, a small translation is necessary. Suppose, for example, that you want to model the child's height by both its father's and mother's height and also the sex of the child. The model design is nothing new: just include a model term for sex.

$$\text{height} \sim 1 + \text{mother} + \text{father} + \text{sex}$$

The corresponding model formula for this design on the Galton data is

$$\underset{\text{Values}}{\overset{\text{Model}}{}} \text{height} = 15.3 + 0.322 \ \text{mother} + 0.406 \ \text{father} + 5.23 \ \text{sex}\mathbf{M}$$

Interpret the quantitative terms in the ordinary way. The new term, 5.23 sex**M**, means "add 5.23 whenever the case has level M on sex." This is a very roundabout way of saying that males tend to be 5.23 inches taller than females, according to the model.

Another way to think about the meaning of sex**M** is that it is a new quantitative variable, called an **indicator variable**, that has the numeric value 1 when the case is level M in variable sex, and numeric value 0 otherwise.

A categorical variable will have one indicator variable for each level of the variable. Thus, a variable language with levels Chinese, English, French, German, Hindi, etc. has a separate indicator variable for each level.

For the sex variable, there are two levels: F and M. But notice that there is only one coefficient for sex, the one for sex**M**. Get used to this. Whenever there is an intercept term in a model, at least one of the indicator variables from any categorical variable will be left out. The level that is omitted is a **reference level**. Chapter 8 explains why things are done this way.

7.4   Coefficients and Relationships

One important purpose for constructing a model is to study the relationships implied by your data between the explanatory variables and the response. Measurement of the size of a relationship, often called the **effect size**, is based on comparing changes.

To illustrate, consider again this model of height:

$$\substack{\text{Model} \\ \text{Values}} \quad \texttt{height} = 15.3 + 0.322\,\texttt{mother} + 0.406\,\texttt{father} + 5.23\,\texttt{sex}\mathbf{M}$$

What's the relationship between `height` and `father`? One way to answer this question is to pose a hypothetical situation. Suppose that the value of `father` changed by one unit — that is, the father got taller. How much would this change the model value of `height`.

Working through the arithmetic of the formula shows that a one-inch increase in `father` leads to a 0.406 increase in the model value of `height`. That's a good way to describe the size of the relationship.

Similarly, the formula indicates that a 1 inch change in `mother` will correspond to a 0.322 increase in the model value of `height`.

More generally, the size of a relationship between a quantitative explanatory variable and the quantitative response variable is measured using a concept from calculus: the **derivative** of the response variable with respect to the explanatory variable. For those unfamiliar with calculus, the derivative reflects the same idea as above: making a small change in the explanatory variable and seeing how much the model value changes.

For categorical explanatory variables, such as `sex`, the coefficient on each level indicates how much difference there is in the model value between the reference level and the level associated with the coefficient. In the above model, the reference level is F, so the coefficient 5.23 on `sex`**M** means that the model value for M is 5.23 inches larger than for F; more simply stated, males are, according to the model, 5.23 inches taller than females. To avoid leading to a mis-interpretation, it's better to say that the model formula indicates that males are, **on average**, 5.23 inches taller than females.

The sign of a coefficient tells which way the relationship goes. If the coefficient on `sex`**M** had been −5.23, it would mean that males are typically shorter than females. If the coefficient on `mother` had been −0.322, then taller mothers would have shorter children.

When there is an interaction or a transformation term in a model, the effect size cannot be easily read off as the coefficients. Those familiar with calculus may recognize the connection to the *partial derivative* in this approach of comparing model values due to a change of inputs. Chapter 10 will consider the issues in more detail, particularly the matter of **holding constant** other variables or **adjusting** for other variables.

7.5   Model Values and Residuals

If you plug in the values of the explanatory variables from your data, the model formula gives, as an output, the model values. It's rarely the case that the model values are an exact match with the actual response variable in your data. The difference is the *residual*.

For any one case in the data, the residual is always defined in terms of the actual response variable and the model value that arises when that case's values for the explanatory variables are given as the input to the model formula. For instance, if you are modeling `height`, the residuals are

$$\texttt{height} = \underset{\text{Values}}{\overset{\text{Model}}{}} \texttt{height} + \text{residuals}$$

The residuals are always defined in terms of a particular data set and a particular model. Each case's residual would likely change if the model were altered or if another data set were used to fit the model.

7.6   Coefficients of Basic Model Designs

The presentation of a linear model as a set of coefficients is a compact shorthand for the complete model formula. It often happens that for some purposes, interest focuses on a single coefficient of interest. In order to help you to interpret coefficients correctly, it is helpful to see how they relate to some basic model designs. Often, the interpretation for more complicated designs is not too different.

To illustrate how basic model designs apply generally, I will use A to stand for a generic response variable, B to stand for a quantitative explanatory variable, and G for a categorical explanatory variable. As always, 1 refers to the intercept term.

Model A ~ 1

The model A ~ 1 is the simplest of all. There are no explanatory variables; the only term is the intercept. Think of this model as saying that all the cases are the same. In fitting the model, you are looking for a single value that is as close as possible to each of the values in A.

The coefficient from this model is the mean of A. The model values are the same for every case: the mean of all the samples. This is sometimes called the **grand mean** to distinguish it from group means, the mean of A for different groups.

DATA FILE
galton.csv

Example 7.1: The mean height of all the cases in Galton's height data — the "grand mean" — is the coefficient on the model `height ~ 1`. Fitting this model to Galton's data gives this coefficient:

Model Term	Coefficient
Intercept	66.7607

Thus, the mean height is 66.76 inches.

DATA FILE
cps.csv

Example 7.2: The mean wage earned by all of the people in the Current Population Survey is given by the coefficient of the model `wage ~ 1`. Fitting the model to the CPS gives:

Model Term	Coefficient
Intercept	9.024

Thus, the mean wage is $9.02 per hour.

Model A ~ 1+G

The model `A ~ 1+G` is also very simple. The categorical variable G can be thought of as dividing the data into groups, one group for each level of G. There is a separate model value for each of the groups.

The model values are the group-wise means: separate means of A for the cases in each group. The model coefficients, however, are not exactly these group-wise means. Instead, the coefficient of the intercept term is the mean of one group, which can be called the **reference group** or **reference level**. Each of the other coefficients is the *difference* between its group's mean and the mean of the reference group.

Example 7.3: Calculate the group-wise means of the heights of men and women in Galton's data by fitting the model `height ~ sex`.

Model Term	Coefficient
Intercept	64.11
sex**M**	5.12

The mean height for the reference group, women, is 64.11 inches. Men are taller by 5.12 inches. In the standard form of a model report, the identity of the reference group is not stated explicitly. You have to figure it out from which levels of the variable are missing.

By suppressing the intercept term, you change the meaning of the remaining coefficients; they become simple group-wise means rather than the difference of the mean from a reference group's mean. Here's the report from fitting the model height ~ sex - 1.

Model Term	Coefficient
sex**F**	64.11
sex**M**	69.23

It might seem obvious that this simple form is to be preferred, since you can just read off the means without doing any arithmetic on the coefficients. That can be the case sometimes, but almost always you will want to include the intercept term in the model. The reasons for this will become clearer when hypothesis testing is introduced in later chapters.

Example 7.4:   Calculate group-wise means of wages in the different sectors of the economy by fitting the model wage ~ sector:

Model Term	Coefficient
Intercept	7.42
sector**const**	2.08
sector**manag**	4.69
sector**manuf**	0.61
sector**other**	1.08
sector**prof**	4.52
sector**sales**	0.17
sector**service**	-0.89

There are eight levels of the sector variable, so the model has 8 coefficients. The coefficient of the intercept term gives the group-wise mean of the reference group. The reference group is the one level that isn't listed explicitly in the other coefficients; it turns out to be the clerical sector. So, the mean wage of clerical workers is $7.42 per hour. The other coefficients give the *difference* between the mean of the reference group and the means of other groups. For example, workers in the construction sector make, on average $2.08 per hour more than clerical workers. Similarly, service sector works make 89 cents per hour *less* than clerical workers.

Model A ~ 1+B

Model A ~ 1+B is the basic straight line relationship. The two coefficients are the intercept and the slope of the line. The slope tells what change in A corresponds to a one-unit change in B.

Example 7.5:   The model wage ~ 1+educ shows how workers wages are different for people with different amounts of education (as measured by years in school). Fitting this model to the Current Population Survey data gives the following coefficients:

Model Term	Coefficient
Intercept	−0.69
educ	0.74

According to this model, a one-year increase in the amount of education that a worker received is associated with a 74 cents per hour increase in wages. (Remember, these data are from 1985.)

It may seem odd that the intercept coefficient is negative. Nobody is paid a negative wage. Keep in mind that the intercept of a straight line $y = mx + b$ refers to the value of y when $x = 0$. The intercept coefficient −0.69, tells the typical wage for workers with zero years of education. There are no workers in the data set with zero years; only three workers have less than five years. In this data set, the intercept is an **extrapolation** outside of the range of the data.

Model A ~ 1 + G + B

The model A ~ 1 + G + B gives a straight-line relationship between A and B, but allows different lines for each group defined by G. The lines are different only in their intercepts; all of the lines have the same slope.

The coefficient labeled "intercept" is the intercept of the line for the reference group. The coefficients on the various levels of categorical variable G reflect how the intercepts of the lines from those groups differ from the reference group's intercept.

The coefficient on B gives the slope. Since all the lines have the same slope, a single coefficient will do the job.

Example 7.6:   Wages versus educational level for the different sexes: wage ~ 1 + educ + sex The coefficients are

DATA FILE
cps.csv

Model Term	Coefficient
Intercept	-1.92773
sexM	2.27
educ	0.74

The `educ` coefficient tells how education is associated with wages. The `sexM` coefficient says that men tend to make $2.27 more an hour than women when comparing men and women with the same amount of education. Chapter 10 will explain why the inclusion of the `educ` term allows this comparison *at the same level* of education.

Note that the model A ~ 1 + G + B is the same as the model A ~ 1 + B + G. The order of model terms doesn't make a difference.

Model A ~ 1 + G + B + G:B

The model A ~ 1 + G + B + G:B is also a straight-line model, but now the different groups defined by G can have different slopes and different intercepts. (The interaction term G:B says how the slopes differ for the different group. That is, thinking of the slope as effect of B on A, the interaction term G:B tells how the effect of B is modulated by different levels of G.)

Example 7.7:   Here is a model describing wages versus educational level, separately for the different sexes: `wage ~ 1 + sex + educ + sex:educ`

Model Term	Coefficient
Intercept	-3.10
sexM	4.20
educ	0.83
sexM:educ	-0.15

Interpreting these coefficients: For women, an extra year of education is associated with an increase of wages of 83 cents per hour. For men, the relationship is weaker: an increase in education of one year is associated with only an increase of wages of only $0.831 - 0.148$ or 68 cents per hour.

7.7   Coefficients have Units

A common convention is to write down coefficients and model formulas without being explicit about the units of variables and coefficients. This convention is unfortunate. Although leaving out the units leads to neater tables and simpler-looking formulas, the units are fundamental to interpreting the coefficients. Ignoring the units can mislead severely.

To illustrate how units come into things, consider the model design wages ~ 1 + educ + sex. Fitting this model design to the Current Population Survey gives this model formula:

$$\underset{\text{Values}}{\text{Model}} \quad \text{wage} = \text{-1.93} + 0.742 \text{ educ} + 2.27 \text{ sex}\mathbf{M}$$

A first glance at this formula might suggest that sex is more strongly related than educ to wage. After all, the coefficient on educ is much smaller than the coefficient on sex**M**. But this interpretation is invalid, since it doesn't take into account the units of the variables or the coefficients.

The response variable, wage, has units of dollars-per-hour. The explanatory variable educ has units of years. The explanatory variable sex is categorical and has no units; the indicator variables for sex are just zeros and ones: pure numbers with no units.

The coefficients have the units needed to transform the quantity that they multiply into the units of the response variable. So, the coefficient on educ has units of "dollars-per-hour per year." This sounds very strange at first, but remember that the coefficient will multiply a quantity that has units of years, so the product will be in units of dollars-per-hour, just like the wage variable. In this formula, the units of the intercept coefficient and the coefficient on sex**M** both have units of dollars-per-hour, because they multiply something with no units and need to produce a result in terms of dollars-per-hour.

A person who compares 0.742 dollars-per-hour per year with 2.27 dollars per hour is comparing apples and oranges, or, in the metric-system equivalent, comparing meters and kilograms. If the people collecting the data had decided to measure education in months rather than in years, the coefficient would have been a measly $0.742/12 = 0.0618$ even though the relationship between education and wages would have been exactly the same.

7.8   Untangling Explanatory Variables

One of the advantages of using formulas to describe models is the way they facilitate using multiple explanatory variables. Many people assume that they can study relationships one variable at a time, even when they know there are influences from multiple factors. Underlying this assumption is a belief that influences add up in a simple way. Indeed model formulas without interaction terms actually do simply add up the contributions of each variable.

Aside. 7.2 Comparing Coefficients

Coefficients and effect sizes have units. This imposes a difficulty in comparing the effect sizes of different variables. For instance, suppose you want to know whether sex or educ has a stronger effect size on wage. The effect size of sex will have units of dollars per hour, while the effect size of educ has units of dollars per hour per year. To compare the two coefficients 0.742 and 2.27 is meaningless — apples and oranges, as they say.

In order for the comparison to be meaningful, you have to put the effect sizes on a common footing. One approach that might work here is to find the number of years of education that produces a similar size effect of education on wages as is seen with sex**M**. The answer turns out to be about 3 years. (To see this, note that the wage gain associated with sex**M**, 2.27 dollars per hour to the wage gain associated with three years of education, $3 \times 0.742 = 2.21$ dollars per hour.) Thus, according to the model of these data, being a male is equivalent in wage gains to an increase of 3 years in education.

But this does not mean that an explanatory variable can be considered in isolation from other explanatory variables. There is something else going on that makes it important to consider the explanatory variables not one at a time but simultaneously, at the same time.

In many situations, the explanatory variables are themselves related to one another. As a result, variables can to some extent stand for one another. An effect attributed to one variable might equally well be assigned to some other variable.

Due to the relationships between explanatory variables, you need to untangle them from one another. The way this is done is to use the variables together in a model, rather than in isolation. The way the tangling shows up is in the way the coefficient on a variable will change when another variable is added to the model or taken away from the model. That is, model coefficients on a variable tend to depend on the context set by other variables in the model.

To illustrate, consider this criticism of spending on public education in the United States from a respected political essayist:

> *The 10 states with the lowest per pupil spending included four — North Dakota, South Dakota, Tennessee, Utah — among the 10 states with the top SAT scores. Only one of the 10 states with the highest per pupil expenditures — Wisconsin — was among the 10 states with the highest SAT scores. New Jersey has the highest per pupil expenditures, an astonishing $10,561, which teachers' unions elsewhere try to use as a negotiating benchmark. New Jersey's rank regarding SAT scores? Thirty-ninth... The fact that the quality of schools... [fails to correlate] with education appropriations will have no effect on the teacher unions' insistence that money is the crucial variable. — George F. Will, The Washington Post, Sept. 12, 1993, C7. Quoted in [13].*

The response variable here is the score on a standardized test taken by many students finishing high school: the SAT. The explanatory variable — there is only one — is the level of school spending. But even though the essayist implies that spending is *not* the "crucial variable," he doesn't include any other variable in the analysis. In part, this is because the method of analysis — pointing to individual cases to illustrate a trend — doesn't allow the simultaneous consideration of multiple explanatory variables. (Another flaw with the informal method of comparing cases is that it fails to quantify the strength of the effect: Just how much negative influence does spending have on performance? Or is the claim that there is no connection between spending and performance?)

DATA FILE
sat.csv

You can confirm the claims in the essay by modeling. The SAT dataset contains state-by-state information from the mid-1990s on *per capita* yearly school expenditures in thousands of dollars, average statewide SAT scores, average teachers' salaries, and other variables.[13]

The analysis in the essay corresponds to a simple model: sat $\sim$ 1 + expend. Fitting the model to the state-by-state data gives a model formula,

$$\underset{\text{Values}}{\text{Model}} \quad \text{sat} = 1089 - 20.9 \text{ expend}$$

The formula is consistent with the claim made in the essay; the coefficient on expend is negative. According to the model, an increase in expenditures by \$1000 per capita is associated with a 21 point decrease in the SAT score. That's not very good news for people who think society should be spending more on schools: the schools that spend the least per capita have the highest average SAT scores. (A 21 point decrease in the SAT doesn't mean much for an individual student, but as an average over tens of thousands of students, it's a pretty big deal.)

Perhaps expenditures is the wrong thing to look at — you might be studying administrative inefficiency or even corruption. Better to look at teachers' salaries. Here's the model sat $\sim$ 1 + salary, where salary is the average annual salary of public school teachers in \$1000s:

$$\underset{\text{Values}}{\text{Model}} \quad \text{sat} = 1159 - 5.54 \text{ salary}$$

The essay's claim is still supported. Higher salaries are associated with lower average SAT scores! But maybe states with high salaries manage to pay well because they overcrowd classrooms. So, look at the average student/teacher ratio in each state: sat $\sim$ 1 + ratio

$$\underset{\text{Values}}{\text{Model}} \quad \text{sat} = 921 + 2.68 \text{ ratio}$$

Finally, a positive coefficient! That means ... larger classes are associated with higher SAT scores.

All this goes against the conventional wisdom that holds that higher spending, higher salaries, and smaller classes will be associated with better performance.

At this point, many advocates for more spending, higher salaries, and smaller classes will explain that you can't measure the quality of an education with a standardized test, that the relationship between a student and a teacher is too complicated to be quantified, that students should be educated as complete human beings and not as test-taking machines, and so on. Perhaps.

Whatever the criticisms of standardized tests, the tests have the great benefit of allowing comparisons across different conditions: different states, different curricula, etc. If there is a problem with the tests, it isn't standardization itself but the material that is on the test. Absent a criticism of that material, rejections of standardized testing ought to be treated with considerable skepticism.

But there is something wrong with using the SAT as a test, even if the content of the test is good. What's wrong is that the test isn't required for all students. Depending on the state, a larger or smaller fraction of students will take the SAT. In states where very few students take the SAT, those students who do are the ones bound for out-of-state colleges, in other words, the high performers.

What's more, the states which spend the least on education tend to have the fewest students who take the SAT. That is, the fraction of students taking the SAT is entangled with expenditures and other explanatory variables.

To untangle the variables, they have to be included simultaneously in a model. That is, in addition to expend or salary or ratio, the model needs to take into account the fraction of students who take the SAT (variable frac).

Here are three models that attempt to untangle the influences of frac and the spending-related variables:

$$\text{Model Values} \quad \texttt{sat} = 994 + 12.29 \texttt{ expend} - 2.85 \texttt{ frac}$$

$$\text{Model Values} \quad \texttt{sat} = 988 + 2.18 \texttt{ salary} - 2.78 \texttt{ frac}$$

$$\text{Model Values} \quad \texttt{sat} = 1119 - 3.73 \texttt{ ratio} - 2.55 \texttt{ frac}$$

In all three models, including frac has completely altered the relationship between performance and the principal explanatory variable of interest, be it expend, salary, or ratio. Not only is the coefficient different, it is different in sign.

Chapter 10 discusses why adding frac to the model can be interpreted as an attempt to examine the other variables while holding frac constant, as if you compared only states with similar values of frac.

The situation seen here, where adding a new explanatory variable (e.g., `frac`) changes the sign of the coefficient on another variable (e.g., `expend`, `salary`, `ratio`) is called **Simpson's paradox**.

Simpson's Paradox is an extreme version of a common situation: that the coefficient on an explanatory variable can depend on what other explanatory variables have been included in the model. In other words, the role of an explanatory variable can depend, sometimes strongly, on the context set by other explanatory variables. You can't look at explanatory variables in isolation; you have to interpret them in context.

But which is the right model? What's the right context? Do `expend`, `salary`, and `ratio` have a positive role in school performance as the second set of models indicate, or should you believe the first set of models? This is an important question and one that comes up often in statistical modeling. At one level, the answer is that you need to be aware that context matters. At another level, you should always check to see if your conclusions would be altered by including or excluding some other explanatory variable. At a still higher level, the choice of which variables to include or exclude needs to be related to the modeler's ideas about what causes what.

Aside. 7.3 Interaction terms and partial derivatives

The mathematically oriented reader may recall that one way to describe the effect of one variable on another is a partial derivative: the derivative of the response variable with respect to the explanatory variable. The interaction — how one explanatory variable modulates the effect of another on the response variable — corresponds to a mixed second-order partial derivative. Writing the response as z and the explanatory variables as x and y, the interaction corresponds to $\frac{\partial^2 z}{\partial x \partial y}$ which is exactly equal to $\frac{\partial^2 z}{\partial y \partial x}$. That is, the way that x modulates the effect of y on z is the same thing as the way that y modulates the effect of x on z.

7.9   Why Linear Models?

Many people are uncomfortable with using linear models to describe potentially complicated relationships. The process seems a bit unnatural: specify the model terms, fit the model to the data, get the coefficients. How do you know that a model fit in this way will give a realistic match to the data? Coefficients seem an overly abstract way to describe a relationship. Modeling without graphing seems like dancing in the dark; it's nice to be able to see your partner.

Return to the example of world record swim times plotted in Figure 6.5 on page 113. There's a clear curvature to the relationship between record `time` and `year`. Without graphing the data, how would you have known whether to put in a transformation term? How would you know that you should use `sex` as an explanatory variable? But when you do graph the data, you can see easily that

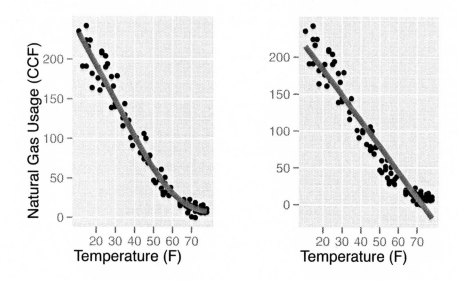

Figure 7.1: Two models of natural gas usage versus outdoor temperature.

something is wrong with a straight-line model like time ~ 1 + year.

However, the advantages of graphing are obvious only in retrospect, once you have found a suitable graph that is informative. Why graph world record time against year? Why not graph it versus body weight of the swimmer or the latitude of the pool in which the record was broken?

Researchers decide to collect some variables and not others based on their knowledge and understanding of the system under study. People know, for example, that world records can only get better over the years. This may seem utterly obvious but it is nonetheless a bit of expert knowledge. It is expert knowledge that makes year an obvious explanatory variable. In general, expert knowledge comes from experience and education rather than data. It's common knowledge, for example, that in many sports, separate world records are kept for men and women. This feature of the system, obvious to experts, makes sex a sensible choice as an explanatory variable.

When people use a graph to look at how well a model fits data, they tend to look for a satisfyingly snug replication of the details. In Chapter 6 a model was shown of the relationship between monthly natural gas usage in a home and the average outdoor temperature during the month. Figure 7.1 shows that model along with a straight-line model. Which do you prefer? Look at the model in the left panel. That's a nice looking model! The somewhat irregular curve seems like a natural shape, not a rigid and artificial straight line like the model in the right panel.

Yet how much better is the curved model than the straight-line model? The straight-line model captures an important part of the relationship between natural gas usage and outdoor temperature: that colder temperatures lead to more usage. The overall slopes of the two models are very similar. The biggest discrepancy comes at warm temperatures, above 65°F. But people who know about home heating can tell you that above 65°F, homes don't need to be heated. At those temperatures gas usage is due only to cooking and water heating: a very different mechanism. To study heating, you should use only data for fairly low temperatures, say below 65°F. To study two different mechanisms — heating at low temperatures and no heating at higher temperatures — you should perhaps construct two different models, perhaps by including an interaction between temperature as a quantitative variable and a categorical variable that indicates whether the temperature is above 65°.

Humans are powerful pattern recognition machines. People can easily pick out faces in a crowd, but they can also pick out faces in a cloud or on the moon. The downside to using human criteria to judge how well a model fits data is the risk that you will see patterns that aren't warranted by the data.

To avoid this problem, you can use formal measures of how well a model fits the data, measures based on the size of residuals and that take into account chance variations in shape. Much of the rest of the book is devoted to such measures.

With the formal measures of fit, a modeler has available a strategy for finding effective models. First, fit a model that matches, perhaps roughly, what you know about the system. The straight-line model in the right panel of Figure 7.1 is a good example of this. Check how good the fit is. Then, try refining the model, adding detail by including curvy transformation terms. Check the fit again and see if the improvement in the fit goes beyond what would be expected from chance.

A reasonable strategy is to start with model designs that include only main terms for your explanatory variables (and, of course, the intercept term, which is to be included in almost every model). Then add in some interaction terms, see if they improve the fit. Finally, you can try transformation terms to capture more detail.

Most of the time you will find that the crucial decision is which explanatory variables to include. Since it's difficult to graph relationships with multiple explanatory variables, the benefits of making a snug fit to a single variable are illusory.

Often the relationship between an explanatory variable and a response is rather loose. People, as good as they are at recognizing patterns, aren't effective at combining lots of cases to draw conclusions of overall patterns. People can have trouble seeing for forest for the trees. Figure 7.2 shows Galton's height data: child's height plotted against mother's height. It's hard to see anything more than a vague relationship in the cloud of data, but it turns out that there is sufficient data here to justify a claim of a pretty precise relationship. Use your human skills to decide which of the two models in Figure 7.2 is better. Pretty

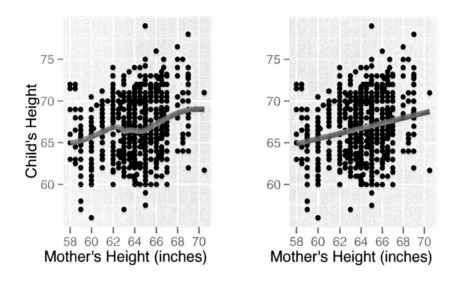

Figure 7.2: Two models of child's height as an adult versus mother's height.

hard to decide, isn't it! Decisions like this are where the formal methods of linear models pay off. Start with the straight-line terms then see if elaboration is warranted.

There are, however, some situations when you can anticipate that straight-line model terms will not do the job. For example, consider temperature versus month in a strongly seasonal climate: temperature goes up and then down as the seasons progress. Or consider the relationship between college grades and participation in extra-curricular activities such as school sports, performances, the newspaper, etc. There's reason to believe that some participation in extra-curricular activities is associated with higher grades. This might be because students who are doing well have the confidence to spend time on extra-curriculars. But there's also reason to think that very heavy participation takes away from the time students need to study. So the overall relationship between grades and participation might be Λ-shaped. Relationships that have a V- or Λ-shape won't be effectively captured by straight-line models; transformation terms and interaction terms will be required.

7.10 Computational Technique

The lm operator finds model coefficients. To illustrate, here's a pair of statements that read in a data frame and fit a model to it:

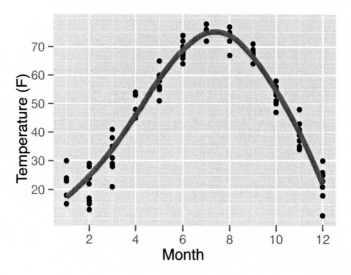

Figure 7.3: Temperature usage versus Month has a relationship that can't be captured by a straight-line model.

```
> swim = fetchData("swim100m.csv")
> mod = lm(time ~ year + sex, data=swim)
```

DATA FILE
swim100m.csv

The first argument to `lm` is a model design, the second is the data frame.

The object created by `lm` — here given the name `mod` — contains a variety of information about the model. To access the coefficients themselves, use the `coef` operator applied to the model:

```
> coef(mod)

(Intercept)        year         sexM
    555.717      -0.251       -9.798
```

As shorthand to display the coefficients, just type the name of the object that is storing the model:

```
> mod

...
(Intercept)        year         sexM
    555.717      -0.251       -9.798
```

A more detailed report can be gotten with the **summary** operator. This gives additional statistical information that will be used in later chapters:

```
> summary(mod)
```

	Estimate	Std. Error	t value	Pr(>|t|)
(Intercept)	555.7168	33.7999	16.44	0.0000
year	-0.2515	0.0173	-14.52	0.0000
sexM	-9.7980	1.0129	-9.67	0.0000

From time to time in the exercises, you will be asked to calculate model values "by hand." This is accomplished by multiplying the coefficients by the appropriate values and adding them up. For example, the model value for a male swimmer in 2010 would be:

```
> 555.7 - 0.2515*2010 - 9.798

[1] 40.4
```

Notice that the "value" used to multiply the intercept is always 1, and the "value" used for a categorical level is either 0 or 1 depending on whether there is a match with the level. In this example, since the swimmer in question was male, the value of sex**M** is 1. If the swimmer had been female, the value for sex**M** would have been 0.

When a model includes interaction terms, the interaction coefficients need to be multiplied by all the values involved in the interaction. For example, here is a model with an interaction between year and sex:

```
> mod2 = lm(time ~ year*sex, data=swim)
> coef(mod2)

(Intercept)        year        sexM   year:sexM
    697.301      -0.324    -302.464       0.150

> 697.3 - 0.3240*2010 - 302.5 + 0.1499*2010

[1] 44.9
```

The **year:sexM** coefficient is being multiplied by the year (2010) and the value of sex**M**, which is 1 for this male swimmer.

Other Useful Operators

cross() will combine two categorical variables into a single variable. For example, in the Current Population Survey data, the variable sex has levels F and M, while the variable race has levels W and NW. Crossing the two variables combines them; the new variable has four levels: F.NW, M.NW, F.W, M.W:

```
> cps = fetchData("cps.csv")
> with( data=cps, cross(sex, race) )

 [1] M:W  M:W  F:W  F:W  M:W  F:W  F:W  M:W  M:W  F:W  M:W  M:W  M:W  M:W
[15] M:W  M:W  M:W  M:NW M:NW M:W  F:NW M:NW F:W  F:W  M:NW F:W  F:W  M:W
Levels: F:NW F:W M:NW M:W
... for 534 cases altogether ...
```

When you use `cross()` with a modeling function, you won't need the
`with()`.

```
> mean( wage ~ cross(sex,race), data=cps)
 F:NW   F:W   M:NW   M:W
 7.49  7.93  8.46 10.23
> lm( wage ~ cross(sex,race) - 1, data=cps)

...
cross(sex, race)F:NW   cross(sex, race)F:W   cross(sex, race)M:NW
                7.49                   7.93                   8.46
 cross(sex, race)M:W
               10.23
> lm( wage ~ cross(sex,race), data=cps)

...

          (Intercept)   cross(sex, race)F:W   cross(sex, race)M:NW
                7.494                 0.434                  0.969
 cross(sex, race)M:W
                2.740
```

`as.factor()` will convert a quantitative variable to a categorical variable. This
is useful when a quantity like `month` has been coded as a number, say 1 for
January and 2 for February, etc. but you do not want models to treat it as
such.

To illustrate, consider two different models of the usage temperature versus
month:

DATA FILE
utilities.csv

```
> utils = fetchData("utilities.csv")
> mod1 = lm(temp ~ month, data=utils)
> mod2 = lm(temp ~ as.factor(month), data=utils)
```

Here are the graphs of those models:

```
> xyplot(temp + fitted(mod1) ~ month, data=utils)
```

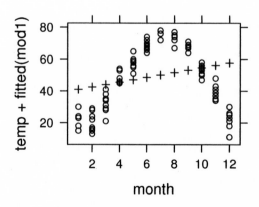

```
> xyplot( temp + fitted(mod2) ~ month, data=utils )
```

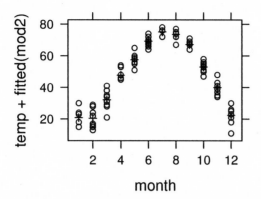

In the first model, month is treated quantitatively, so the model term `month` produces a straight-line relationship that does not correspond well to the data.

In the second model, month is treated categorically, allowing a more complicated model relationship.

Reading Questions

- What is the role of the response variable in a model formula?
- What is the purpose of constructing indicator variables from categorical variables?
- How can model coefficients be used describe relationships? What are the relationships between?
- What is Simpson's paradox?
- Given an example of how the meaning of a coefficient of a particular term can depend on what other model terms are included in the model?

For exercises, see **www.mosaic-web.org/StatisticalModeling/Exercises**.

Fitting Models to Data

8

With four parameters, I can fit an elephant; with five I can make it wiggle its trunk. — John von Neumann (1903-1957), mathematician and computer architect

The purpose of models is not to fit the data but to sharpen the questions. — Samuel Karlin (1924-2007), mathematician

The selection of variables and terms is part of the modeler's art. It is a creative process informed by your goals, your understanding of how the system you are studying works, and the data you can collect. Later chapters will deal with how to evaluate the success of the models you create as well as general principles for designing effective models that capture the salient aspects of your system.

This chapter is about a technical matter: **fitting**, how to find the coefficients that best match the model you choose to the data you have collected.

Fitting a model — once you have specified the design — is an entirely automatic process that requires no human decision making. It's ideally suited to computers and, in practice, you will always use the computer to find the best fit. Nevertheless, it's important to understand the way in which the computer finds the coefficients. Much of the logic of interpreting models is based on how firmly the coefficients are tied to the data, to what extent the data dictate precise values of the coefficients. The fitting process reveals this. In addition, depending on your data and your model design, you may introduce ambiguities into your model that make the model less reliable than it could be. These ambiguities, which stem from **redundancy** and "**multicollinearity**", are revealed by the fitting process.

8.1   The Least Squares Criterion

Fitting a model is somewhat like buying clothes. You choose the kind of clothing that you want: the cut, style, and color. There are usually several or many different items of this kind, and you have to pick the one that matches your body appropriately. In this analogy, the style of clothing is the model design — you choose this. Your body shape is like the data — you're pretty much stuck with what you've got.

There is a system of sizes of clothing: the waist, hip, and bust sizes, inseam, sleeve length, neck circumference, foot length, etc. By analogy, these are the model coefficients. When you are in the fitting room of a store, you try on different items of clothing with a range of values of the coefficients. Perhaps you bring in pants with waist sizes 31 through 33 and leg sizes 29 and 30. For each of the pairs of pants that you try on, you get a sense of the overall fit, although this judgment can be subjective. By trying on all the possible sizes, you can find the item that gives the best overall match to your body shape.

Similarly, in fitting a model, the computer tries different values for the model coefficients. Unlike clothing, however, there is a very simple, entirely objective criterion for judging the overall fit called the **least squares** criterion. To illustrate, consider the following very simple data set of age and height in children:

age (years)	height (cm)
5	80
7	100
10	110

As the model design, take `height ~ 1 + age`. To highlight the link between the model formula and the data, here's a way to write the model formula that includes not just the names of the variables, but the actual column of data for each variable. Each of these columns is called a **vector**. Note that the intercept vector is just a column of 1s.

$$\underset{\substack{\text{Model} \\ \text{Values}}}{\text{height}} = c_1 \overset{\text{intercept}}{\begin{bmatrix} 1 \\ 1 \\ 1 \end{bmatrix}} + c_2 \overset{\text{age}}{\begin{bmatrix} 5 \\ 7 \\ 10 \end{bmatrix}} .$$

The goal of fitting the model is to find the best numerical values for the two coefficients c_1 and c_2.

To start, guess something, say, $c_1 = 5$ and $c_2 = 10$. Just a starting guess. Plugging in these guesses to the model formula gives a model value of height for each case.

$$\underset{\substack{\text{Model} \\ \text{Values}}}{\text{height}} = 5 \overset{\text{intercept}}{\begin{bmatrix} 1 \\ 1 \\ 1 \end{bmatrix}} + 10 \overset{\text{age}}{\begin{bmatrix} 5 \\ 7 \\ 10 \end{bmatrix}} = \overset{\text{Model height}}{\begin{bmatrix} 55 \\ 75 \\ 105 \end{bmatrix}} .$$

Arithmetic with vectors is done in the ordinary way. Coefficients multiply each element of the vector, so that $10 \begin{bmatrix} 5 \\ 7 \\ 10 \end{bmatrix}$ gives $\begin{bmatrix} 50 \\ 70 \\ 100 \end{bmatrix}$. To add or subtract two vectors means to add or subtract the corresponding elements: $\begin{bmatrix} 5 \\ 5 \\ 5 \end{bmatrix} + \begin{bmatrix} 50 \\ 70 \\ 100 \end{bmatrix}$ gives $\begin{bmatrix} 55 \\ 75 \\ 105 \end{bmatrix}$.

The residuals tell you how the response values (that is, the actual heights) differ from the model value of height. For this model, the residuals are

$$
\underset{\text{height}}{\begin{bmatrix} 80 \\ 100 \\ 110 \end{bmatrix}} - \underset{\text{Model height}}{\begin{bmatrix} 55 \\ 77 \\ 105 \end{bmatrix}} = \underset{\text{residuals}}{\begin{bmatrix} 25 \\ 23 \\ 5 \end{bmatrix}} .
$$

The smaller the residuals, the better the model values match the actual response values.

The residual vector above is for the starting guess $c_1 = 5$ and $c_2 = 10$. Try another guess of the coefficients, say $c_1 = 40$ and $c_2 = 8$. Plugging in this new guess ...

$$
\underset{\text{Model Values}}{} \text{height} = 40 \underset{\text{intercept}}{\begin{bmatrix} 1 \\ 1 \\ 1 \end{bmatrix}} + 8 \underset{\text{age}}{\begin{bmatrix} 5 \\ 7 \\ 10 \end{bmatrix}} = \underset{\text{Model height}}{\begin{bmatrix} 80 \\ 96 \\ 120 \end{bmatrix}}
$$

The residuals from the new coefficients are

$$
\underset{\text{height}}{\begin{bmatrix} 80 \\ 100 \\ 110 \end{bmatrix}} - \underset{\text{Model height}}{\begin{bmatrix} 80 \\ 96 \\ 120 \end{bmatrix}} = \underset{\text{residuals}}{\begin{bmatrix} 0 \\ 4 \\ -10 \end{bmatrix}}
$$

The central question of fitting is this: Which of the two model formulas is better?

Look at the first case — the first row of the data and therefore the first row of each vector. This first case is a five-year old who is 80 cm tall. Plugging in the value 80 cm to the model formula gives a model height of 55 cm from the starting-guess model. For the second-guess model, the model height is 80 cm — exactly right.

The residuals carry the information about how close the model values are to the actual value. For the first-guess model, the residual is -25 cm, whereas for the second-guess model the residual is zero. Obviously, the second-guess model is closer for this one case.

As it happens, the second-guess model is closer for the second case as well — the 7-year old who is 100 cm tall. The residual for this child is 23 cm for the starting-guess model and only 4 cm for the second-guess model. But for the third case — the 10-year old who is 110 cm tall — the residual from the first-guess model is better; it's 5 cm, compared to a residual of -10 cm from the second-guess model.

It is not uncommon in comparing two formulas to find, as in this model, one formula is better for some cases and the other formula is better for other cases. This is not so different from clothing, where one item may be too snug in the waist but just right in the leg, and another item may be perfect in the waist but too long in the leg.

What's needed is a way to judge the *overall* fit. In modeling, the overall fit of a model formula is measured by a single number: the sum of squares of the residuals. For the first formula, this is $25^2 + 23^2 + 5^2 = 1179$. For the second formula, the sum of squares of the residuals is $0^2 + 4^2 + (-10)^2 = 116$. By this measure, the second formula gives a much better fit.

To find the **best** fit, keep trying different formulas until one is found that gives the least sum of square residuals: in short, the **least squares**. The process isn't nearly so laborious as it might seem. There are systematic ways to find the coefficients that give the least sum of square residuals, just as there are systematic ways to find clothing that fits without trying on every item in the store. The details of these systematic methods are not important here.

Using the least squares criterion, a computer will quickly find the best coefficients for the height vs age model to be $c_1 = 54.211$ and $c_2 = 5.789$. Plugging in these coefficients to the model formula produces fitted model values of $\begin{bmatrix} 83.158 \\ 94.737 \\ 112.105 \end{bmatrix}$, residuals of $\begin{bmatrix} -3.158 \\ 5.263 \\ -2.105 \end{bmatrix}$, and therefore a sum of square residuals of 42.105, clearly much better than either previous two model formulas.

How do you know that the coefficients that the computer gives are indeed the best? You can try varying them in any way whatsoever. Whatever change you make, you will discover that the sum of square residuals is never going to be less than it was for the coefficients that the computer provided.

Because of the squaring, negative residuals contribute to the sum of square residuals in the same way as positive residuals; it's the *size* and not the sign of the residual that matters when calculating whether a residual is big or small. Consequently, the smallest possible sum of square residuals is zero. This can occur only when the model formula gives the response values exactly, that is, when the fitted model values are an exact match with the response values. Because models typically do not capture all of the variation in the response variable, usually you do not see a sum of square residuals that is exactly zero. When you do get residuals that are all zeros, however, don't start the celebration too early. This may be a signal that there is something wrong, that your model is too detailed.

It's important to keep in mind that the coefficients found using the least squares criterion are the best possible but only in a fairly narrow sense. They are the best *given* the design of the model and *given* the data used for fitting. If the data change (for example, you collect new cases), or if you change the model design, the best coefficients will likely change as well. It makes sense to compare the sum of square residuals for two model formulas only when the two formulas have the same design and are fitted with the same data. So don't try to use the sum of square residuals to decide which of two different designs are better. Tools to do that will be introduced in later chapters.

Aside. 8.1 Why Square Residuals?

Why the sum of square residuals? Why not some other criterion? The answers are in part mathematical, in part statistical, and in part historical.

In the late 18th century, three different criteria were competing, each of which made sense:

1. The least squares criterion, which seeks to minimize the sum of square residuals.

2. The least absolute value criterion. That is, rather than the sum of square residuals, one looks at the sum of absolute values of the residuals.

3. Make the absolute value of the residual as small as possible for the single worst case.

All of these criteria make sense in the following ways. Each tries to make the residuals small, that is, to make the fitted model values match closely to the response values. Each treats a positive residual in the same way as a negative residual; a mismatch is a mismatch regardless of whether the fitted values are too high or too low. The first and second criteria each combine all of the cases in determining the best fit.

The third criterion is hardly ever used because it allows one or two cases to dominate the fitting process — only the two most extreme residuals count in evaluating the model. Think of the third criterion as a dead end in the historical evolution of statistical practice.

Computationally, the least squares criterion leads to simpler procedures than the least absolute value criterion. In the 18th century, when computing was done by hand, this was a very important issue. It's no longer so, and there can be good statistical reasons to favor a least absolute value criterion when it is thought that the data may contain outliers.

The least squares criterion is best justified when variables have a bell-shaped distribution. Insofar as this is the situation — and it often is — the least squares criterion is arguably better than least absolute value.

Another key advantage of the least squares criterion is in interpretation, as you'll see in Section 8.2.

8.2 Partitioning Variation

A model is intended to explain the variation in the response variable using the variation in the explanatory variables. It's helpful in quantifying the success of this to be able to measure how much variation there is in the response variable, how much has been explained, and how much remains unexplained. This is a **partitioning** of variation into parts.

Section 4.2 introduced the idea of partitioning variation in the context of simple group-wise models. There, it was shown that the variance — the square of the standard deviation — is a useful way to quantify variation because it has the property of exactly dividing total variation into parts: the variation of model values and the variation of the residuals.

The variance has this same useful partitioning property with least-squares models. Chapter 9 describes how the variance is used to construct a simple measure, called R^2, of the quality of fit of a model.

Aside. 8.2 Partitioning and the Sum of Squares

Another partitioning statistic is the **sum of squares**. The sum of squares is deceptively simple. To find the sum of squares of the response variable, just square the value for each case and add them up. Similarly, you can find the sum of squares of the fitted model values and the sum of squares of the residuals. The partitioning property is that the sum of squares of the response variable exactly equals the sum of squares of the fitted model values plus the sum of squares of the residuals.

8.3   The Geometry of Least Squares Fitting

The fitting process involves vectors. Earlier, vectors were presented as a column of numbers. Another way to regard vectors is as an "arrow": a direction and a length. For instance, the vector $\left[\begin{smallmatrix} 3 \\ 4 \end{smallmatrix}\right]$, when plotted in the usual Cartesian coordinate plane, points to the north-northeast and has square-length $3^2 + 4^2 = 5^2$.

Consider a very simple model, A ∼ B. Each of the vectors involved, A and B, has a length and a direction, something like this:

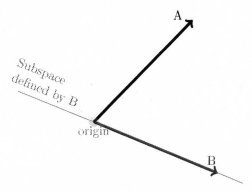

The process of least-squares fitting amounts to finding the point on the "subspace defined by B" that is as close as possible to A. You can do this by eye, if you like. Move your finger along the line that is the subspace defined by B to the point on that line that is as close as you can get to the tip of vector A. This is marked as the "Closest Pt." in the figure below.

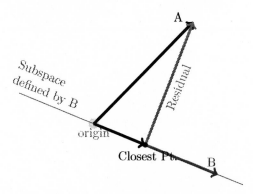

Of course, the closest point is not exactly the same as A. The vector that connects them is the **residual vector**.

Notice that choosing the fitted value as the closest point to A on the subspace defined by B means that the residual vector will be **perpendicular** to B. In statistics, the term that's used for "perpendicular" is **orthogonal**.

One consequence of the orthogonality is that the three vectors involved — A, B, and the residual — form a right triangle. This is why the Pythagorean theorem applies and why it's square quantities — the variance and the sum of squares — that have the partitioning property.

8.4   Redundancy

Data sets often contain variables that are closely related. For instance, consider the following data collected in 2009 on prices of used cars (the Ford Taurus model), the year the car was built, and the number of miles the car has been driven.

DATA FILE
used-fords.
csv

Price	Year	Mileage
14997	2008	22613
8995	2007	53771
7990	2006	36050
18990	2008	25896

... and so on.

Although the year and mileage variables are different, they are related: older cars typically have higher mileage than newer cars. A group of students thought to see how price depends on year and mileage. After collecting a sample of 635 cars advertised on the Internet, they fit a model price ~ mileage + year. The coefficients came out to be:

price ~ mileage + year

Term	Coefficient	Units
Intercept	-1136311.500	dollars
mileage	-0.069	dollars/mile
year	573.500	dollars/year

The coefficient on mileage is straightforward enough; according to the model the price of these cars typically decreases by 6.9 cents per mile. But the intercept seems strange: very big and negative. Of course this is because the intercept tells the model value at zero mileage in the year zero! They checked the plausibility of the model by plugging in values for a 2006 car with 50,000 miles: $-1136312 - 0.069 \times 50000 + 2006 \times 573.50$ giving $10679.50 — a reasonable sounding price for such a car.

The students thought that the coefficients would make more sense if they were presented in terms of the age of the car rather than the model year. Since their data was from 2009, they calculated the age by taking $2009 - year$. Then they fit the model price ~ mileage + age. Of course, there is no new information in the age variable that isn't already in the year variable. Even so, the information is provided in a new way and so the coefficients in the new model are somewhat different.

price ~ mileage + age

Term	Coefficient	Units
Intercept	15850.000	dollars
mileage	-0.069	dollars/mile
age	-573.500	dollars/year

From the table, you can see that the mileage coefficient is unchanged, but now the intercept term looks much more like a real price: the price of a hypothetical brand new car with zero miles. The age coefficient makes sense; typically the cars decrease in price by $573.50 per year of age. Again, the students calculated the model for a 2006 car (thus age 3 years in 2009) with 50,000 miles: $10679.50, the same as before.

At first, the students were surprised by the differences between the two sets of coefficients. Then they realized that the two different model formulas give exactly the same model value for every car. This makes sense. The two models are based on exactly the same information. The only difference is that in one model the age is given by the model year of the car, in the other by the age itself.

The students decided to experiment. "What happens if we include both age and year in the model?" The started with the model price ~ mileage + year + age. They got these coefficients:

price ~ mileage + year + age		
Term	Coefficient	Units
Intercept	-1136311.500	dollars
mileage	-0.069	dollars/mile
year	573.500	dollars/year
age	NA	dollars/year

The model is effectively disregarding the age variable, reporting the coefficient as "NA", not available.

The dual identity of age and year is **redundancy**. (The mathematical term is **"linear dependence."**) It arises whenever an explanatory model vector can be modeled exactly in terms of the other explanatory vectors. Here, age can be computed by 2009 times the intercept plus -1 times the year.

The problem with redundancy is that it creates ambiguity. Which of the four sets of coefficients in the table above is the right one? Whenever there is redundancy, there is more than one set of coefficients that gives the best fit of the model to the data.

In order to avoid this ambiguity, modeling software is written to spot any redundancy and drop the redundant model vectors from the model. One possibility would be to report a coefficient of zero for the redundant vector. But this could be misleading. For instance, the user might interpret the zero coefficient on Set 1 above as meaning that year isn't associated with price. But that would be wrong; year is a very important determinant of price, it's just that all the relationship is represented by the coefficient on age in Set 1. Rather than report a coefficient of zero, it's helpful when software reports the redundancy by displaying a NA. This makes it clear that it is redundancy that is the issue and not that a coefficient is genuinely zero.

When model vectors are redundant, modeling software can spot the redundancy and do the right thing. But sometimes, the redundancy is only approximate, a situation called **multi-collinearity**. In such cases it's important for you to be aware of the potential for problems; they will not be clearly marked by NA as happens with exact redundancy.

Example 8.1: Almost redundant

DATA FILE
cps.csv

In collecting the Current Population Survey wage data, interviewers asked people their age and the number of years of education they had. From this, they computed the number of years of experience. They presumed that kids spend six years before starting school. So a 40-year old with 12 years of education would have 22 years of experience: $6 + 12 + 22 = 40$. This creates redundancy of experience with age and education. Ordinarily, the computer could identify such a situation. However, there is a mistake in the CPS data. Case 350 is an 18-year old woman with 16 years of education. This seems hard to believe since very few people start their education at age 2. Presumably, either the age or education were mis-recorded. But either way, this small mistake in one case means that the redundancy among experience, age, and education is not exact. It also means that standard software doesn't spot the problem when all three of these variables are included in a model. As a result, coefficients on these variables are highly unreliable.

With such multi-collinearity, as opposed to exact redundancy, there is a unique least-squares fit of the model to the data. However, this uniqueness is hardly a blessing. What breaks the tie to produce a unique best fitting set of coefficients are the small deviations from exact redundancy. These are often just a matter of random noise, arithmetic round-off, or mistakes as with case 350 in the Current Population Survey data. As a result, the choice of the winning set of coefficients is to some extent arbitrary and potentially misleading.

The costs of multi-collinearity can be measured when fitting a model. (See Section 12.5.) When the costs of multi-collinearity are too high, the modeler often chooses to take terms out of the model.

Aside. 8.3 Redundancy: (Almost) Anything Goes

Even with the duplicate information in year and age, there is no mathematical reason why the computer could not have given coefficients for all four model terms in the model price ~ mileage + year + age. For example, any of the following sets of coefficients would give exactly the same model values for *any* inputs of year and mileage, with age being appropriately calculated from year.

Term	Set 1	Set 2	Set 3	Set 4
Intercept	15850.000	-185050.000	-734511.500	-1136311.500
mileage	-0.069	-0.069	-0.069	0.069
year	0.000	100.000	373.500	573.500
age	-573.500	-473.500	-200.000	0.000

The overall pattern is that the coefficient on age minus the coefficient on year has to be -573.5. This works because age and year are basically the same thing since age $= 2009 -$ year.

8.5 Computational Technique

Using the lm software is largely a matter of familiarity with the model design language described in Chapter 6. Computing the fitted model values and the residuals is done with the **fitted** and **resid**. These operators take a model as an input. To illustrate:

```
> swim = fetchData("swim100m.csv")
> mod1 = lm(time ~ year + sex, data=swim)
> coef(mod1)
```

```
(Intercept)        year        sexM
    555.717      -0.251      -9.798
```

Once you have constucted the model, you can use `fitted` and `resid`:

```
> fitted(mod1)

   1    2    3    4    5    6    7    8    9   10   11   12
66.9 66.1 65.6 65.1 63.6 63.1 62.6 62.1 59.6 59.3 59.1 57.1
... for 62 cases altogether ...
```

8.5.1 Sums of Squares

Computations can be performed on the fitted model values and the residuals, just like any other quantity:

```
> mean(fitted(mod1))

[1] 59.9

> var(resid(mod1))

[1] 15.3

> sd(resid(mod1))

[1] 3.92

> summary(resid(mod1))

   Min. 1st Qu.  Median    Mean 3rd Qu.    Max.
  -4.70   -2.70   -0.60    0.00    1.28   19.10
```

Sums of squares are very important in statistics. Here's how to calculate them for the response values, the fitted model values, and the residuals:

```
> sum(swim$time^2)

[1] 228635

> sum(fitted(mod1)^2)

[1] 227699

> sum(resid(mod1)^2)

[1] 936
```

The partitioning of variation by models is seen by the way the sum of squares of the fitted and the residuals add up to the sum of squares of the response:

```
> 227699 + 935.8

[1] 228635
```

Don't forget the squaring stage of the operation! The sum of the residuals (without squaring) is very different from the sum of squares of the residuals:

```
> sum(resid(mod1))

[1] 1.85e-14
```

```
> sum(resid(mod1)^2)
```

```
[1] 936
```

Take care in reading numbers formatted like `1.849e-14`. The notation stands for 1.849×10^{-14}. That number, 0.00000000000001849, is effectively zero compared to the residuals themselves!

8.5.2 Redundancy

The `lm` operator will automatically detect redundancy and deal with it by leaving the redundant terms out of the model.

To see how redundancy is handled, here is an example with a constructed redundant variable in the swimming dataset. The following statement adds a new variable to the dataframe counting how many years after the end of World War II each record was established:

```
> swim = transform(swim, afterwar = year-1945)
```

Here is a model that doesn't involve redundancy

```
> mod1 = lm( time ~ year + sex, data=swim)
> coef(mod1)
(Intercept)        year        sexM
    555.717      -0.251      -9.798
```

When the redundant variable is added in, `lm` successfully detects the redundancy and handles it. This is indicated by a coefficient of NA on the redundant variable.

```
> mod2 = lm( time ~ year + sex + afterwar, data=swim)
> coef(mod2)
(Intercept)        year        sexM    afterwar
    555.717      -0.251      -9.798          NA
```

In the absence of redundancy, the model coefficients don't depend on the order in which the model terms are specified. But this is not the case when there is redundancy, since any redundancy is blamed on the later variables. For instance, here `afterwar` has been put first in the explanatory terms, so `lm` identifies `year` as the redundant variable:

```
> mod3 = lm( time ~ afterwar + year + sex, data=swim)
> coef(mod3)
(Intercept)    afterwar        year        sexM
     66.620      -0.251          NA      -9.798
```

Even though the coefficients are different, the fitted model values and the residuals are exactly the same (to within computer round-off) regardless of the order of the model terms.

```
> fitted(mod2)

   1    2    3    4    5    6    7    8    9   10   11   12
66.9 66.1 65.6 65.1 63.6 63.1 62.6 62.1 59.6 59.3 59.1 57.1
... for 62 cases altogether ...

> fitted(mod3)

   1    2    3    4    5    6    7    8    9   10   11   12
66.9 66.1 65.6 65.1 63.6 63.1 62.6 62.1 59.6 59.3 59.1 57.1
... for 62 cases altogether ...
```

Note that whenever you use a categorical variable and an intercept term in a model, there is a redundancy. This is not shown explicitly. For example, here is a model with no intercept term, and both levels of the categorical variable sex show up with coefficients:

```
> lm(time ~ sex - 1, data=swim)
...
sexF  sexM
65.2  54.7
```

If the intercept term is included (as it is by default unless -1 is used in the model formula), one of the levels is simply dropped in the report:

```
> lm(time ~ sex, data=swim)
...
(Intercept)        sexM
      65.2       -10.5
```

Remember that this coefficient report implicitly involves a redundancy. If the software had been designed differently, the report might look like this:

```
(Intercept)     sexF      sexM
      65.2       NA      -10.5
```

Reading Questions

- What is a residual? Why does it make sense to make them small when fitting a model?
- What is "least squares?"
- What does it mean to "partition variability" using a model?
- How can a model term be redundant? Why are redundant terms a problem?

For exercises, see www.mosaic-web.org/StatisticalModeling/Exercises.

9

Correlation and Partitioning of Variation

The invalid assumption that correlation implies cause is probably among the two or three most serious and common errors of human reasoning. — Stephen Jay Gould (1941-2002), paleontologist and historian of science

"Co-relation or correlation of structure" is a phrase much used ... but I am not aware of any previous attempt to define it clearly, to trace its mode of action in detail, or to show how to measure its degree.' — Francis Galton (1822-1911), statistician

Chapters 4 and 8 introduced the idea of partitioning the variance of the response variable into two parts: the variance of the fitted model values and the variance of the residuals. This partitioning is at the heart of a statistical model; the more of the variation that's accounted for by the model, the less is left in the residuals.

The partition property of the variance offers a simple way to summarize a model: the proportion of the total variation in the response variable that is accounted for by the model. This description is called the R^2 ("**R-Squared**") of the model. It is a ratio:

$$R^2 = \frac{\text{variance of fitted model values}}{\text{variance of response values}}.$$

Another name for R^2 is the **coefficient of determination**, but this is not a coefficient in the same sense used to refer to a multiplier in a model formula.

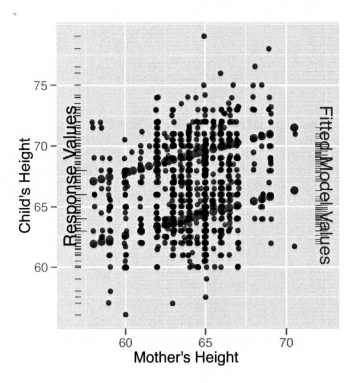

Figure 9.1: The small dots show child's height versus mother's height from Galton's data. The bigger symbols show the fitted model values from the linear model height $\sim 1 +$ mother $+$ sex that includes both mother's height and child's sex as explanatory variables.

9.1   Properties of R^2

R^2 has a nice property that makes it easy to interpret: its value is always between zero and one. When $R^2 = 0$, the model accounts for none of the variance of the response values: the model is useless. When $R^2 = 1$, the model captures all of the variance of the response values: the model values are exactly on target. Typically, R^2 falls somewhere between zero and one, meaning that the model accounts for some, but not all, of the variance in the response values.

DATA FILE
galton.csv

The history of R^2 can be traced to a paper[14] presented to the Royal Society in 1888 by Francis Galton. It is fitting to illustrate R^2 with some of Galton's data: measurements of the heights of parents and their children.

Figure 9.1 shows a scatter plot of the children's height versus mother's height. Also plotted are the fitted model values for the model height $\sim$ mother $+$ sex. The model values show up as two parallel lines, one for males and one for females.

The slope of the lines shows how the child's height typically varies with the mother's height.

Two rug plots have been added to the scatter plot in order to show the distribution of the response values (child's height) and the fitted model values (the output of the model). The rug plots are positioned vertically because each of them relates to the response variable height, which is plotted on the vertical axis.

The spread of values in each rug plot gives a visual indication of the variation. It's evident that the variation in the response variable is larger than the variation in the fitted model values. The variance quantifies this. For height, the variance is 12.84 square-inches. (Recall that the units of the variance are always the square of the units of the variable.) The fitted model values have a variance of 7.21 square-inches. The model captures a little more than half of the variance; the R^2 statistic is

$$R^2 = \frac{7.21}{12.84} = 0.56$$

One nice feature of R^2 is that the hard-to-interpret units of variance disappear; my any standard, square-inches is a strange way to describe height! Since R^2 is the ratio of two variances, the units cancel out. R^2 is unitless.

Example 9.1: Quantifying the capture of variation   Back in Chapter 6, a model of natural gas usage and a model of wages were presented. It was claimed that the natural gas model captured more of the variation in natural gas usage than the wage model captured in the hourly wages of workers. At one level, such a claim is absurd. How can you compare natural gas usage to hourly wages? If nothing else, they have completely different units.

R^2 is what enables this to be done. For any model, R^2 describes the fraction of the variance in the response variable that is accounted for by the model. Here are the R^2 for the two models:

- wage ∼ sex*married: $R^2 = 0.07$

- ccf ∼ temp: $R^2 = 0.91$

Sex and marital status explain only a small fraction of the variation in wages. Temperature explains the large majority of the variation in natural gas usage (ccf).

9.2   Simple Correlation

The idea Galton introduced in 1888 is that the relationship between two variables — "co-relation" as he phrased it — can be described with a single number. This is now called the **correlation coefficient**, written r and often simply called "r".

The correlation coefficient is still very widely used. Part of the reason for this is that the single number describes an important mathematical aspect of the relationship between two variables: the extent to which they are aligned or **collinear**.

The correlation coefficient r is the square root of R^2 for the simple straight-line model: response $\sim$ explanatory variable. As with all square roots, there is a choice of negative or positive. The sign of the r is chosen to indicate the slope of the model line.

It may seem very limiting, in retrospect, to define correlation in terms of such a simple model. But Galton was motivated by a wonderful symmetry involved in the correlation coefficient: the R^2 from the straight-line model of A versus B is the same as that from the straight-line model of B versus A. In this sense, the correlation coefficient describes the relationship between the two variables and not merely the dependence of one variable on another. Of course, a more modern perspective on relationships accepts that additional variables can be involved as well as interaction and transformation terms.

Example 9.2: Relationships without Correlation   Consider how the temperature varies over the course of the year. In most places, temperature changes predictably from month to month: a very strong relationship. Figure 9.2 shows data for several years of the average temperature in St. Paul, Minnesota (in the north-central US). Temperature is low in the winter months (January, February, December, months 1, 2, and 12) and high in the summer months (June, July, August, months 6, 7, and 8).

DATA FILE
utilities.csv

The Figure also shows a very simple straight-line model: temperature $\sim$ month. This model doesn't capture very well the relationship between the two variables. Still, like any model, it has an R^2. Since the response values have a variance of 409.3 deg.F^2 and the fitted model values have a variance of 25.6 deg.F^2 the R^2 value works out to be $R^2 = \frac{25.6}{409.3} = 0.0624$.

As a way to describe the overall relationship between variables, r is limited. Although r is often described as measuring the relationship between two variables, it's more accurate to say that r quantifies a particular model rather than "the relationship" between two variables.

But not all relationships are linear. The simple correlation coefficient r does not reflect any nonlinear relationship in the data.

If you want to describe a relationship, you need to choose a model appropriately.

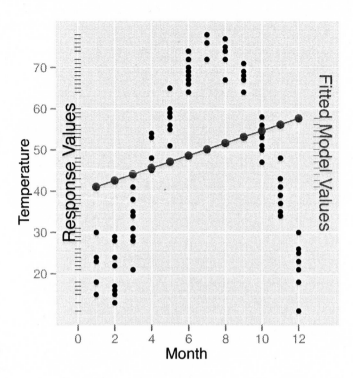

Figure 9.2:   Temperature versus month in St. Paul, Minnesota, from the utilities dataset and a linear model of the data. The variance of the fitted model values is much smaller than the variance of the response values, producing a low $R^2 = 0.0624$.

For the temperature versus month data, the straight line model isn't appropriate. A nonlinear model, as in Figure 9.3, does a much better job. The R^2 of this model is 0.946. This value confirms the very strong relationship between month and temperature.

Example 9.3: R versus R^2 The correlation coefficient r is often reported in squared form r^2. However, the coefficient of determination is R^2. You will occasionally see reports of the square root of the coefficient of determination: $R = \sqrt{R^2}$. Perhaps this is because it seems unnatural to report squares, just as the variance seem less natural than standard deviation. It's hard to claim that R^2 is right and R is wrong, but do make sure that you know what you are reading about. What's wrong is to read an R value and interpret it as R^2.

To illustrate, consider the relationship between standardized college admissions tests and performance in college. A widely used college admissions test in the

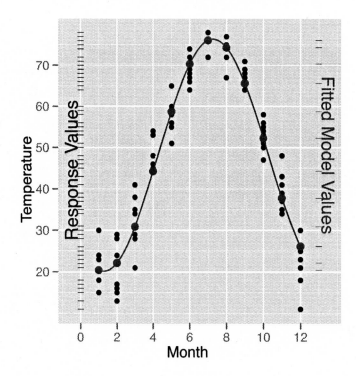

Figure 9.3: Temperature versus month fitted to a nonlinear model. $R^2 = 0.946$. The variance of the fitted model values is almost as large as the variance of the response values.

US is the SAT, administered by the College Board. The first-year grade-point average is also widely used to reflect a student's performance in college. The College Board publishes its studies that relate students' SAT scores to their first-year GPA.[15] The reports present results in terms of R — the square-root of R^2. A typical value is about $R = 0.40$.

Translating this to R^2 gives $0.40^2 = 0.16$. Seen as R^2, the connection between SAT scores and first-year GPA does not seem nearly as strong! Of course, $R = 0.40$ and $R^2 = 0.16$ are exactly the same thing. Just make sure that when you are reading about a study, you know which one you're dealing with.

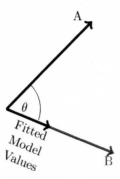

Figure 9.4: The correlation coefficient between A and B compares the length of the fitted model values vector to the length of the vector A. Trigonometrically, this ratio is $\cos(\theta)$.

Whether an R^2 of 0.16 is "large" depends on your purpose. It's low enough to indicate that SAT provides little ability to predict GPA for an individual student. But 0.16 is high enough — as you'll see in Chapter 14 — to establish that there is indeed a link between SAT score and college performance when averaged over lots of students. Consequently, there can be some legitimate disagreement about how to interpret the R^2. In reporting on the 2008 College Board report, the New York *Times* headlined, "Study Finds Little Benefit in New SAT" (June 18, 2008) while the College Board press release on the previous day announced, "SAT Studies Show Test's Strength in Predicting College Success." Regretably, neither the news reports nor the press release stated the R^2.

9.3   The Geometry of Correlation

The correlation coefficient r was introduced in 1888. It was an early step in the development of modeling theory, but predates the ideas of model vectors. It turns out that r has a very simple interpretation using model vectors: correlation is an angle between vectors.

Recall that for quantitative variables, the variable itself is a vector. (In contrast, categorical variables are transformed into a set of indicator vectors, one for each level of the categorical variable.) The correlation coefficient r is the cosine of the angle between the two quantitative variable vectors, after the mean of each variable has been subtracted.

This means that a perfect correlation, $r = 1$ corresponds to exact alignment of

Figure 9.5: The correlation coefficient corresponds to the angle between vectors.

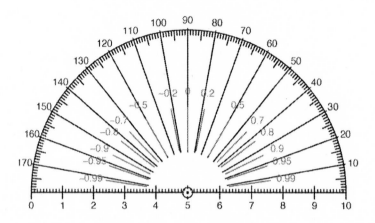

Figure 9.6:   Measure correlation with a protractor! Each value of the correlation coefficient r corresponds to an angle between vectors. This protractor is marked both in degrees and in the corresponding values of r. Notice that moderate values of r correspond to angles that are close to $90°$.

A and B: the angle $\theta = 0$. No correlation at all, $r = 0$ corresponds to A and B being at right angles: $\theta = 90°$. A negative correlation, $r < 0$, corresponds to A and B pointing in opposite directions. Figure 9.5 shows some examples.

Vectors that are perpendicular are said to be **orthogonal**.

9.4   Nested Models

Models are often built up in stages; start with an existing model and then add a new model term. This process is important in deciding whether the new term contributes to the explanation of the reponse variable. If the new, extended model is substantially better than that old one, there's reason to think that the new term is contributing.

You can use R^2 to measure how much better the new model is than the old model. But be careful. It turns out that whenever you add a new term to a model, R^2 can increase. It's never the case that the new term will cause R^2 to go down.

Even a random variable, one that's utterly unrelated to the response variable, can cause an increase in R^2 when it's added to a model.

This raises an important question: When is an increase in R^2 big enough to justify concluding that the added explanatory term is genuinely contributing to the model? Answering this question will require concepts that will be introduced in later chapters.

An important idea is that of **nested models**. Consider two models: a "small" one and a "large" one that includes all of the explanatory terms in the small one. The small model is said to be nested in the large model.

To illustrate, consider a series of models of the Galton height data. Each model will take child's height as the response variable, but the different models will include different variables and model terms constructed from these variables.

DATA FILE
galton.csv

Model A   height ~ 1

Model B   height ~ 1 + mother

Model C   height ~ 1 + mother + sex

Model D   height ~ 1 + mother + sex + mother:sex

Model B includes all of the explanatory terms that are in Model A. So, Model A is nested in Model B. Similarly, A and B are both nested in Model C. Model D is even more comprehensive; A, B, and C are all nested in D.

When one model is nested inside another, the variance of the fitted model values from the smaller model will be less than the variance of the fitted model values from the larger model. The same applies to R^2, since R^2 is proportional to the variance of the fitted model values.

In the four nested models listed above, for example, the increase in fitted variance and R^2 is this:

Model	A	B	C	D
Variance of model values	0.00	0.52	7.21	7.22
R^2		0.00	0.0407	0.5618	0.5621

Notice that the variance of the fitted model values for Model A is exactly zero. This is because Model A has only the interept term 1 as an explanatory term. This simple model treats all cases as the same and so there is no variation at all in the fitted model values: the variance and R^2 are zero.

Example 9.4: R^2 Out of the Headlines

Consider this headline from the *BBC News*: "Finger length 'key to aggression.'" The length of a man's fingers can reveal how physically aggressive he is. Or, from *Time* magazine, this summary of the same story: "The shorter a man's index finger is relative to his ring finger, the more aggressive he is likely to be (this doesn't apply to women)."

These news reports were based on a study examining the relationship between finger-length ratios and aggressiveness.[16] It has been noticed for years that men tend to have shorter index fingers compared to ring fingers, while women tend the opposite way. The study authors hypothesized that a more "masculine finger ratio" might be associated with other masculine traits, such as aggressiveness. The association was found and reported in the study: $R^2 = 0.04$. The underlying data are shown in this figure from the original report:

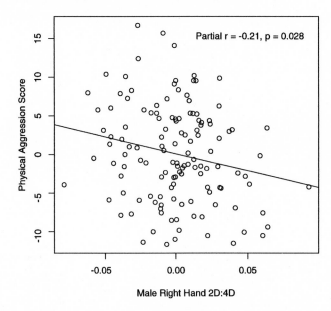

As always, R^2 gives the fraction of the variance in the response variable that is accounted for by the model. This means that of all the variation in aggressiveness among the men involved in the study, 4% was accounted for, leaving 96% unexplained by the models. This suggests that finger length is no big deal.

Headline words like "key" and "reveal" are vague but certainly suggest a strong relationship. The news media got it wrong.

9.5   The Geometry of R^2

Recall from Section 9.3 that the correlation r corresponds to the cosine of the angle between two vectors.

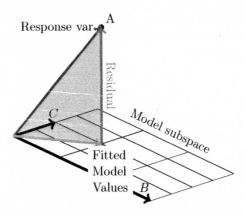

Figure 9.7: Projecting A onto the subspace defined by a set of two model vectors, B and C. The model triangle is shaded.

R^2 for models has a similar interpretation. Consider the model A $\sim$ B+C. Since there are two explanatory vectors involved, there is an ambiguity: which is the angle to consider: the angle A to B or the angle A to C?

Figure 9.7 shows the situation. Since there are two explanatory vectors, the response is projected down onto the space that holds both of them, the **model subspace**. There is still a vector of fitted model values and a residual vector. The three vectors taken together — response variable, fitted model values, and residual — form a right triangle. The angle between the response variable and the fitted model values is the one of interest. R is the cosine of that angle.

Because the vectors B and C could be oriented in any direction relative to one another, there's no sense in worrying about whether the angle is acute (less than $90°$) or obtuse. For this reason, R^2 is used — there's no meaning in saying that R is negative.

9.6 Computational Technique

The coefficient of determination, R^2, compares the variation in the response variable to the variation in the fitted model value. It can be calculated as a ratio of variances:

DATA FILE
swim100m.csv

```
> swim = fetchData("swim100m.csv")
> mod = lm(time ~ year + sex, data=swim)
> with(swim, var(fitted(mod)) / var(time))

[1] 0.844
```

The **regression report** is a standard way of summarizing models. Such a report is produced by most statistical software packages and used in many fields. The first part of the table contains the coefficients — labeled "Estimate" — along with other information that will be introduced starting in Chapter 12. The R^2 statistic is a standard part of the report; look at the second line from the bottom.

```
> summary(mod)
...
            Estimate Std. Error t value Pr(>|t|)
(Intercept) 555.7168   33.7999   16.44  < 2e-16 ***
year         -0.2515    0.0173  -14.52  < 2e-16 ***
sexM         -9.7980    1.0129   -9.67  8.8e-14 ***
---
Signif. codes:  0 '***' 0.001 '**' 0.01 '*' 0.05 '.' 0.1 ' ' 1

Residual standard error: 3.98 on 59 degrees of freedom
Multiple R-squared: 0.844,        Adjusted R-squared: 0.839
F-statistic:  160 on 2 and 59 DF,  p-value: <2e-16
```

Occasionally, you may be interested in the correlation coefficient r between two quantities. You can, of course, compute r by fitting a model, finding R^2, and taking a square root.

```
> mod2 = lm(time ~ year, data=swim)
> summary(mod2)
```

The summary report (not shown here — you can do the calculation yourself!) gives $R^2 = 0.5965$. This corresponds to r of

```
> sqrt(0.5965)
[1] 0.772
```

The cor() function computes this directly:

```
> with(swim, cor(time, year))
[1] -0.772
```

Note that the negative sign on r indicates that record swim time decreases as year increases. This information about the direction of change is contained in the sign of the coefficient from the model. The magnitude of the coefficient tells how fast the time is changing (with units of seconds per year). The correlation coefficient (like R^2) is without units.

Keep in mind that the correlation coefficient r summarizes only the simple linear model A $\sim$ B where B is quantitative. But the coefficient of determination, R^2, summarizes any model; it is much more useful. If you want to see the direction of change, look at the sign of the coefficient.

Reading Questions

- How does R^2 summarize the extent to which a model has captured variability?

- What does it mean for one model to be nested in another?
- How does the correlation coefficient differ from R^2?

For exercises, see www.mosaic-web.org/StatisticalModeling/Exercises.

10

Total and Partial Relationships

I do not feel obliged to believe that the same God who has endowed us with sense, reason, and intellect has intended us to forgo their use.
—Galileo Galilei (1564-1642), Italian physicist

One of the most important ideas in science is **experiment**. In a simple, ideal form of an experiment, you cause one explanatory factor to vary, hold all the other conditions constant, and observe the response. A famous story of such an experiment involves Galileo Galilei (1564-1642) dropping balls of different masses but equal diameter from the Leaning Tower of Pisa.[1] Would a heavy ball fall faster than a light ball, as theorized by Aristotle 2000 years previously? The quantity that Galileo varied was the weight of the ball, the quantity he observed was how fast the balls fell, the conditions he held constant were the height of the fall and the diameter of the balls. The experimental method of dropping balls side by side also holds constant the atmospheric conditions: temperature, humidity, wind, air density, etc.

Of course, Galileo had no control over the atmospheric conditions. By carrying out the experiment in a short period, while atmospheric conditions were steady, he effectively held them constant.

Today, Galileo's experiment seems obvious. But not at the time. In the history of science, Galileo's work was a landmark: he put *observation* at the fore, rather than the beliefs passed down from authority. Aristotle's ancient theory, still considered authoritative in Galileo's time, was that heavier objects fall faster.

The ideal of "holding all other conditions constant" is not always so simple as with dropping balls from a tower in steady weather. Consider an experiment to test

---

[1]The picturesque story of balls dropped from the Tower of Pisa may not be true. Galileo did record experiments done by rolling balls down ramps.

the effect of a blood-pressure drug. Take two groups of people, give the people in one group the drug and give nothing to the other group. Observe how blood pressure changes in the two groups. The factor being caused to vary is whether or not a person gets the drug. But what is being held constant? Presumably the researcher took care to make the two groups as similar as possible: similar medical conditions and histories, similar weights, similar ages. But "similar" is not "constant."

For non-experimentalists — people who study data collected through observation, without doing an experiment — a central question is whether there is a way to mimic "holding all other conditions constant." For example, suppose you observe the academic performance of students, some taught in large classes and some in small classes, some taught by well-paid teachers and some taught by poorly-paid teachers, some coming from families with positive parental involvement and some not, and so on. Is there a way to analyze data so that you can separate the influences of these different factors, examining one factor while, through analysis if not through experiment, holding the others constant?

In this chapter you'll see how models can be used to examine data as if some variables were being held constant. Perhaps the most important message of the chapter is that there is no point hiding your head in the sand; simply ignoring a variable is not at all the same thing as holding that variable constant. By including multiple variables in a model you make it possible to interpret that model in terms of holding the variables constant. But there is no methodological magic at work here. The results of modeling can be misleading if the model does not reflect the reality of what is happening in the system under study. Understanding how and when models can be used effectively, and when they can be misleading, will be a major theme of the remainder of the book.

10.1 Total and Partial Relationships

The common phrase "all other things being equal" is an important qualifier in describing relationships. To illustrate: A simple claim in economics is that a high price for a commodity reduces the demand. For example increasing the price of heating fuel will reduce demand as people turn down thermostats in order to save money. But the claim can be considered obvious only with the qualifier *all other things being equal*. For instance, the fuel price might have increased because winter weather has increased the demand for heating compared to summer. Thus, higher prices may be associated with higher demand. Unless you hold other variables constant — e.g., weather conditions — increased price may not in fact be associated with lower demand.

In fields such as economics, the Latin equivalent of "all other things being equal" is sometimes used: **ceteris paribus**. So, the economics claim would be, "higher prices are associated with lower demand, *ceteris paribus*."

Although the phrase "all other things being equal" has a logical simplicity, it's impractical to implement "all." Instead of the blanket "all other things," it's helpful to be able to consider just "some other things" to be held constant, being explicit about what those things are. Other phrases along these lines are "taking into account ..." and "controlling for ...." Such phrases apply when you want to examine the relationship between two variables, but there are additional variables that may be coming into play. The additional variables are called **covariates** or **confounders**.

A covariate is just an ordinary variable. The use of the word "covariate" rather than "variable" highlights the interest in holding this variable constant, to indicate that it's not a variable of primary interest.

Example 10.1: Covariates and Death   This news report appeared in 2007

> **Heart Surgery Drug Carries High Risk, Study Says.** A drug widely used to prevent excessive bleeding during heart surgery appears to raise the risk of dying in the five years afterward by nearly 50 percent, an international study found.
>
> The researchers said replacing the drug — aprotinin, sold by Bayer under the brand name Trasylol — with other, cheaper drugs for a year would prevent 10,000 deaths worldwide over the next five years.
>
> Bayer said in a statement that the findings are unreliable because Trasylol tends to be used in more complex operations, and the researchers' statistical analysis did not fully account for the complexity of the surgery cases.
>
> The study followed 3,876 patients who had heart bypass surgery at 62 medical centers in 16 nations. Researchers compared patients who received aprotinin to patients who got other drugs or no antibleeding drugs. Over five years, 20.8 percent of the aprotinin patients died, versus 12.7 percent of the patients who received no antibleeding drug. [This is a 64% increase in the death rate.]
>
> When researchers adjusted for other factors, they found that patients who got Trasylol ran a 48 percent higher risk of dying in the five years afterward.
>
> The other drugs, both cheaper generics, did not raise the risk of death significantly.
>
> The study was not a randomized trial, meaning that it did not randomly assign patients to get aprotinin or not. In their analysis, the researchers took into account how sick patients were before surgery, but they acknowledged that some factors they did not account for may have contributed to the extra deaths. - Carla K. Johnson, Associated Press, 7 Feb. 2007

The report involves several variables. Of primary interest is the relationship between (1) the risk of dying after surgery and (2) the drug used to prevent excessive bleeding during surgery. Also potentially important are (3) the complexity of the surgical operation and (4) how sick the patients were before surgery. Bayer disputes the published results of the relationship between (1) and (2) holding (4) constant, saying that it's also important to hold variable (3) constant.

In the aprotinin drug example, the total relationship involves a death rate of 20.8 percent of patients who got aprotinin, versus 12.7 percent for others. This implies an increase in the death rate by a factor of 1.64. When the researchers looked at a partial relationship (holding constant the patient sickness before the operation), the death rate was seen to increase by less: a factor of 1.48.

In evaluating the drug, it's best to examine its effects holding other factors constant. So, even though the data directly show a 64% increase in the death rate, 48% is a more meaningful number since it adjusts for covariates such as patient sickness. The difference between the two estimates reflect that sicker patients tended to be given aprotinin. As the last paragraph of the story indicates, however, the researchers did not take into account all covariates. Consequently, it's hard to know whether the 48% number is a reliable guide for decision making.

The term **partial relationship** describes a relationship with one or more covariates being held constant. A useful thing to know in economics might be the partial relationship between fuel price and demand with weather conditions being held constant. Similarly, it's a partial relationship when the article refers to the effect of the drug on patient outcome in those patients with a similar complexity of operation.

In contrast to a partial relationship where certain variables are being held constant, there is also a **total relationship**: how an explanatory variable is related to a response variable *letting those other explanatory variables change as they will.* (The corresponding Latin phrase is **mutatis mutandis**.)

Here's an everyday illustration of the difference between partial and total relationships. I was once involved in a budget committee that recommended employee health benefits for the college at which I work. At the time, college employees who belonged to the college's insurance plan received a generous subsidy for their health insurance costs. Employees who did not belong to the plan received no subsidy but were instead given a moderate monthly cash payment. After the stock-market crashed in year 2000, the college needed to cut budgets. As part of this, it was proposed to eliminate the cash payment to the employees who did not belong to the insurance plan. This proposal was supported by a claim that this would save money without reducing health benefits. I argued that this claim was about a partial relationship: how expenditures would change assuming that the number of people belonging to the insurance plan remained constant. I thought that this partial relationship was irrelevant; the loss of the cash payment would cause some employees, who currently received health benefits through their spouse's health plan, to switch to the college's health plan. Thus, the total relationship between the cash payment and expenditures might be the opposite of the partial relationship: the savings from the moderate cash payment would trigger a much larger expenditure by the college.

Perhaps it seems obvious that one should be concerned with the "big picture," the total relationship between variables. If eliminating the cash payment increases expenditures overall, it makes no sense to focus exclusively on the narrow savings from the suspending the payment itself. On the other hand, in the aprotinin drug example, for understanding the impact of the drug itself it seems important to take into account how sick the various patients were and how complex the surgical operations. There's no point ascribing damage to aprotinin that might instead be the result of complicated operations or the patient's condition.

Whether you wish to study a partial or a total relationship is largely up to you and the context of your work. But certainly you need to know which relationship you are studying.

Example 10.2: Used Car Prices   Figure 10.1 shows a scatter plot of the price of used Honda Accords versus the number of miles each car has been driven. The graph shows a pretty compelling relationship: the more miles that a car goes, the lower the price. This can be summarized by a simple linear model: `price ~ mileage`. Fitting such a model gives this model formula

$$\underset{\text{Values}}{\overset{\text{Model}}{}} \text{price} = 20770 - 0.10\,\text{mileage}.$$

> **DATA FILE**
> used-hondas.
> csv

Keeping in mind the units of the variables, the price of these Honda Accords typically falls by about 10 cents per mile driven. Think of that as the cost of the wear and tear of driving: depreciation.

As the cars are being driven, other things are happening to them. They are wearing out, they are being involved in minor accidents, and they are getting older. The relationship shown in Figure 10.1 takes none of these into account. As mileage changes, the other variables such as age are changing as they will: a total relationship.

In contrast to the total relationship, the *partial* relationship between price and mileage holding age constant tells you something different than the total relationship. The partial relationship would be relevant, for instance, if you were interested in the cost of driving a car. This cost includes gasoline, insurance, repairs, and depreciation of the car's value. The car will age whether or not you drive it; the extra depreciation due to driving it will be indicated by the partial relationship between price and mileage holding age constant.

The most intuitive way to hold age constant is to look at the relationship between price and mileage for a subset of the cars; include only those cars of a given age. This is shown in Figure 10.2. The cars have been divided into age groups (less than 2 years old, between 3 and 4 years old, etc.) and the data for each group has been plotted separately together with the best fitting linear model for the

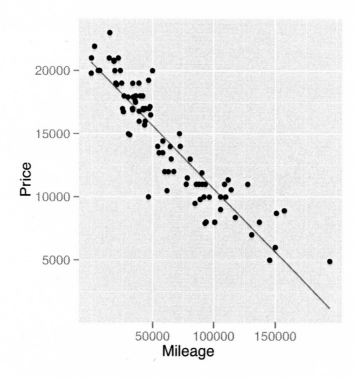

Figure 10.1: The price of used cars falls with increasing miles driven. The gray diagonal line shows the best fitting linear model. Price falls by about $10,000 for 100,000 miles, or 10 cents per mile driven.

cars in that group. From the figure it's easy to see that the slope of the fitted models for each group is shallower than the slope fitted to all the cars combined. Instead of the price falling by about 10 cents per mile as it does for all the cars combined, within the 4-8 year old group the price decrease is only about 7 cents per mile, and only 3 cents per mile for cars older than 8 years.

By looking at the different age groups individually, you are holding age approximately constant in your model. The relationship you find in this way between price and mileage is a partial relationship. Of course, there are other variables that you didn't hold constant. So, to be precise, you should describe the relationship you found as a partial relationship *with respect to age*.

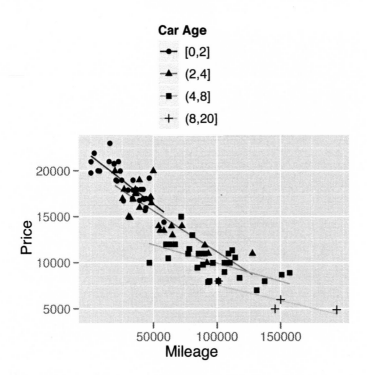

Figure 10.2: The relationship between price and mileage for cars in different age groups, indicating the partial relationship between price and mileage holding age constant. (The dotted diagonal line shows the total relationship between price and age, from Figure 10.1.)

10.1.1   Models and Partial Relationships

Models make it easy to estimate the partial relationship between a response variable and an explanatory variable, holding one or more covariates constant.

The first step is to fit a model using both the explanatory variable and the covariates that you want to hold constant. For example, to find the partial relationship between car price and miles driven, holding age constant, fit the model price $\sim$ mileage+age. For the car-price data from Figure 10.1, this gives the model formula

$$\underset{\text{Values}}{\overset{\text{Model}}{}} \text{price} = 21330 - 0.077\,\text{mileage} - 538\,\text{age}$$

The second step is to interpret this model as a partial relationship between price and mileage holding age constant. A simple way to do this is to plug in some particular value for age, say 1 year. With this value plugged in, the formula for price as a function of mileage becomes

$$\underset{\text{Values}}{\text{Model}} \quad \text{price} = 21330 - 0.077\,\text{mileage} - 538 \times 1 = 20792 - 0.077\,\text{mileage}$$

The partial relationship is that price goes down by 0.077 dollars per mile, holding age constant.

Note the use of the phrase "estimate the partial relationship" in the first paragraph of this section. The model you fit creates a representation of the system you are studying that incorporates both the variable of interest and the covariates in explaining the response values. In this mathematical representation, it's easy to hold the covariates constant. If you don't include the covariate in the model, you can't hold it constant and so you can't estimate the partial relationship between the response and the variable of interest while holding the covariate constant. But even when you do include the covariates in your model, there is a legitimate question of whether your model is a faithful reflection of reality; holding a covariate constant in a model is not the same thing as holding it constant in the real world. These issues, which revolve around the idea of the causal relationship between the covariate and the response, are discussed in Chapter 18.

Aside. 10.1 Partial change and partial derivatives

If you are familiar with calculus and **partial derivatives**, you may notice that this rate is the partial derivative of price with respect to mileage. Using partial derivatives allows one to interpret more complicated models relatively easily. For example, Figure 10.2 shows pretty clearly that the price vs mileage lines have different slopes for different age group. To capture this in your model, you might choose to include an interaction term between mileage and age. This gives a model with four terms:

$$\underset{\text{Values}}{\text{Model}} \quad \text{price} = 22140 - 0.094\,\text{mileage} - 750\,\text{age} + 0.0034\,\text{mileage} \times \text{age}$$

For this model, the partial relationship between price and mileage is not just the coefficient on mileage. Instead it is the partial derivative of price with respect to mileage, or:

$$\frac{\partial \text{price}}{\partial \text{mileage}} = -0.094 + 0.0034 \times \text{age}$$

Keeping in mind the units of the variables, this means that for a new car (age = 0), the price declines by 0.094 — 9.4 cents per mile. But for a 10-year old car, the decline is less rapid: $-0.094 + 10 \times 0.0034 = -0.060$ — only six cents a mile.

10.1.2 Adjustment

The table shows data on professional and sales employees of a large mid-western US trucking company: the annual earnings in 2007, sex, age, job title, how many

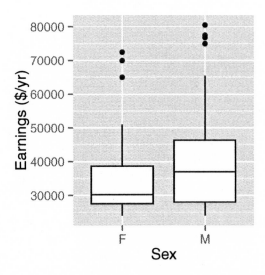

Figure 10.3: The distribution of annual earnings broken down by sex for professional and sales employees of a trucking company.

DATA FILE
truckingjobs.
csv

years of employment with the company. Data such as these are sometimes used to establish whether or not employers discriminate on the basis of sex.

sex	earnings	age	title	hiredyears
M	35000	25	PROGRAMMER	0
F	36800	62	CLAIMS ADJUSTER	5
F	25000	34	RECRUITER	1
M	45000	44	CLAIMS ADJUSTER	0
M	40000	30	PROGRAMMER	5

... and so on for 129 cases altogether.

A boxplot reveals a clear pattern: men are being paid more than women. (See Figure 10.3.) Fitting the model earnings ~ sex indicates the average difference in earnings between men and women:

$$\text{earnings} = 35501 + 4735\,\text{sex}\mathbf{M}.$$

Since earnings are in dollars per year, Men are being paid, on average, \$4735 more per year than women. This difference reflects the *total* relationship between earnings and sex, letting other variables change as they will.

Notice from the boxplot that even within the male or female groups, there is considerable variability in annual earnings from person to person. Evidently, there is something other than sex that influences the wages.

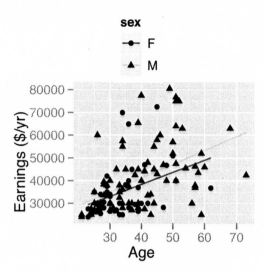

Figure 10.4: Annual earnings versus age. The lines show fitted models separately for men (top) and women (bottom).

An important question is whether you should be interested in the total relationship between earnings and sex, or the partial relationship, holding other variables constant. This is a difficult issue. Clearly there are some legitimate reasons to pay people differently, for example different levels of skill or experience or different job descriptions, but it's always possible that these legitimate factors are being used to mask discrimination.

For the moment, take as a covariate something that can stand in as a proxy for experience: the employee's age. Unlike job title, age is hardly something that can be manipulated to hide discrimination. Figure 10.4 shows the employees' earnings plotted against age. Also shown are the fitted model values of wages against age, fitted separately for men and women. It's evident that for both men and women, earnings tend to increase with age. The model design imposes a straight line structure on the fitted model values. The formulas for the two lines are:

For Women   Model Values   Earnings =   17178 + 530   age
For Men: Model Values   Earnings =   16735 + 609   age

From the graph, you can see the partial relationship between earnings and sex, holding age constant. Pick an age, say 30 years. At 30 years, according to the model, the difference in annual earnings is $1931, with men making more. At 40 years of age, the difference between the sexes is even more ($2722), at 20 years of age, the difference is less ($1140). All of these partial differences (holding age constant) are substantially less than the difference when age is not taken into account ($4735).

One way to summarize the differences in earnings between men and women is to answer this question: How would the earnings of the men have been different if the men were women? Of course you can't know all the changes that might occur if the men were somehow magically transformed, but you can use the model to calculate the change assuming that all other variables except sex are held constant. This process is called **adjustment**.

To find the men's wages adjusted as if they were women, take the age data for the men and plug them into the model formula for women. The difference between the earnings of men and women, adjusting for age, is $2125. This is much smaller than the difference, $4735, when earnings are not adjusted for age. Differences in age between the men and women in the data set appear to account for more than half of the overall earnings difference between men and women.

Of course, before you draw any conclusions, you need to know how precise these coefficients are. For instance, it's a different story if the sex difference is $2125±10 or if it is $2125±5000. In the latter case, it would be sensible to conclude only that the data leave the matter of wage difference undecided. Later chapters in this book describe how to characterize the precision of an estimate.

Another key matter is that of causation. $2125 indicates a difference, but doesn't say completely where the difference comes from. By adjusting for age, the model disposes of the possibility that the earnings difference reflects differences in the typical ages of male and female workers. It remains to be found out whether the earnings difference might be due to different skill sets, discrimination, or other factors.

10.1.3   Simpson's Paradox

Sometimes the total relationship is the opposite of the partial relationship. This is **Simpson's paradox**.

One of the most famous examples involves graduate admissions at the University of California in Berkeley. It was observed that graduate admission rates were lower for women than for men overall. This reflects the total relationship between admissions and sex. But, on a department-by-department basis, admissions rates for women were consistently as high or higher than for men. The partial relationship, taking into account the differences between departments, was utterly different from the total relationship.

Example 10.3: Cancer Rates Increasing?   Consider another example of partial versus total relationships. In 1962, naturalist author Rachel Carson published

Silent Spring,[17] a powerful indictment of the widespread use of pesticides such as DDT. Carson pointed out the links between DDT and dropping populations of birds such as the bald eagle. She also speculated that pesticides were the cause of a recent increase in the number of human cancer cases. The book's publication was instrumental in the eventual banning of DDT.

The increase in deaths from cancer over time is a total relationship between cancer deaths and time. It's relevant to consider a partial relationship between the number of cancer deaths and time, holding the population constant. This partial relationship can be indicated by a death *rate*: say, the number of cancer deaths per 100,000 people. It seems obvious that the covariate of population size ought to be held constant. But there are still other covariates to be held constant. The decades before *Silent Spring* had seen a strong decrease in deaths at young ages from other non-cancer diseases which now were under greater control. It had also seen a strong increase in smoking. When adjusting for these covariates, the death rate from cancer was actually falling, not increasing as Carson claimed.[18]

10.2 Explicitly Holding Covariates Constant

The distinction between explanatory variables and covariates is in the modeler's mind. When it comes to fitting a model, both sorts of variables are considered on an equal basis when calculating the residuals and choosing the best fitting model to produce a model function. The way that you choose to interpret and analyze the model function is what determines whether you are examining partial change or total change.

The intuitive way to hold a covariate constant is to do just that. Experimentalists arrange their experimental conditions so that the covariates are the same. Think of Galileo using balls of the same diameter and varying only the mass. In a clinical trial of a new drug, perhaps you would test the drug only on women so that you don't have to worry about the covariate sex.

When you are not doing an experiment but rather working with observational data, you can hold a covariate constant by throwing out data. Do you want to see the partial relationship between `price` and `mileage` while holding `age` constant? Then restrict your analysis to cars that are all the same age, say 3 years old. Want to know the relationship between breath-holding time and body size holding `sex` constant? Then study the relationship in just women or in just men.

Dividing data up into groups of similar cases, as in Chapter 4, is an intuitive way to study partial relationships. It can be effective, but it is not a very efficient way to use data.

The problem with dividing up data into groups is that the individual groups may not have many cases. For example, for the used cars shown in Figure 10.2 there are only a dozen or so cases in each of the groups. To get even this number of cases, the groups had to cover more than one year of age. For instance, the group labeled "age < 8" includes cars that are 5, 6, 7, and 8 years old. It would have been nice to be able to consider six-year old cars separately from seven-year old cars, but this would have left me with very few cases in either the six- or seven-year old group.

At the same time, it seems reasonable to think that 5- and 7-year old cars have something to say about 6-year old cars; you would expect the relationship between price and mileage to shift gradually with age. For instance, the relationship for 6-year old cars should be intermediate to the relationships for 5- and for 7-year old cars.

Modeling provides a powerful and efficient way to study partial relationships that does not require studying separate subsets of data. Just include multiple explanatory variables in the model. Whenever you fit a model with multiple explanatory variables, the model gives you information about the partial relationship between the response and each explanatory variable *with respect to each of the other explanatory variables.*

Example 10.4: SAT Scores and School Spending   Chapter 7 (page 141) showed some models relating school expenditures to SAT scores. The model sat $\sim$ 1 + expend produced a negative coefficient on expend, suggesting that higher expenditures are associated with lower test scores. Including another variable, the fraction of students who take the SAT (variable frac) reversed this relationship.

DATA FILE
sat.csv

The model sat $\sim$ 1 + expend + frac attempts to capture how SAT scores depend both on expend and frac. In interpreting the model, you can look at how the SAT scores would change with expend while holding frac constant. That is, from the model formula, you can study the partial relationship between SAT and expend while holding frac constant.

The example also looked at a couple of other fiscally related variables: student-teacher ratio and teachers' salary. The total relationship between each of the fiscal variables and SAT was negative — for instance, higher salaries were associated with lower SAT scores. But the partial relationship, holding frac constant, was the opposite: Simpson's Paradox.

For a moment, take at face value the idea that higher teacher salaries and smaller class sizes are associated with better SAT scores as indicated by the following models:

$$\text{\tiny Model Values} \quad \text{sat} = 988 + 2.18 \text{ salary} - 2.78 \text{ frac}$$

$$\text{\tiny Model Values} \quad \text{sat} = 1119 - 3.73 \text{ ratio} - 2.55 \text{ frac}$$

In thinking about the impact of an intervention — changing teachers' salaries or changing the student-teacher ratio — it's important to think about what other things will be changing during the intervention. For example, one of the ways to make student-teacher ratios smaller is to hire more teachers. This is easier if salaries are held low. Similarly, salaries can be raised if fewer teachers are hired: increasing class size is one way to do this. So, salaries and student-teacher ratio are in conflict with each other.

If you want to anticipate what might be the effect of a change in teacher salary while holding student-teacher ratio constant, then you should include ratio in the model along with salary (and frac, whose dominating influence remains confounded with the other variables if it is left out of the model):

$$\underset{\text{Values}}{\text{Model}} \quad \text{sat} = 1058 + 2.55 \text{ salary} - 4.64 \text{ ratio} - 2.91 \text{ frac}$$

Comparing this model to the previous ones gives some indication of the trade-off between salaries and student-teacher ratios. When **ratio** is included along with salary, the salary coefficient is somewhat bigger: 2.55 versus 2.18. This suggests that if salary is increased while holding constant the student-teacher ratio, salary has a stronger relationship with SAT scores than if salary is increased while allowing student-teacher ratio to vary in the way it usually does, accordingly.

Of course, you still need to have some way to determine whether the precision in the estimate of the coefficients is adequate to judge whether the detected difference in the salary coefficient is real — 2.18 in one model and 2.55 in the other. Such issues are introduced in Chapter 12.

10.3   Adjustment and Truth

It's tempting to think that including covariates in a model is a way to reach the truth: a model that describes how the real world works, a model that can correctly anticipate the consequences of interventions such as medical treatments or changes in policy, etc. This overstates the power of models.

A model design — the response variable and explanatory terms — is a statement of a hypothesis about how the world works. If this hypothesis happens to be right, then under ideal conditions the coefficients from the fitted model will approximate how the real world works. But if the hypothesis is wrong, for example if an

Aside. 10.2 Divide and Be Conquered!

Efficiency starts to be a major issue when there are many covariates. Consider a study of the partial relationship between lung capacity and smoking, holding constant all these covariates: sex, body size, smoking status, age, physical fitness. There are two sexes and perhaps three or more levels of body size (e.g., small, medium, large). You might divide age into five different groups (e.g., pre-teens, teens, young adults, middle aged, elderly) and physical fitness into three levels (e.g., never exercise, sometimes, often). Taking the variables altogether, there are now $2 \times 3 \times 5 \times 3 = 90$ groups. It's very inefficient to treat these 90 groups completely separately, as if none of the groups had anything to say about the others. A model of the form `lung capacity ~ body size + sex + smoking status + age + fitness` can not only do the job more efficiently, but avoids the need to divide quantitative variables such as `body size` or `age` into categories.

To illustrate, consider this news report:

> Higher vitamin D intake has been associated with a significantly reduced risk of pancreatic cancer, according to a study released last week.
>
> Researchers combined data from two prospective studies that included 46,771 men ages 40 to 75 and 75,427 women ages 38 to 65. They identified 365 cases of pancreatic cancer over 16 years.
>
> Before their cancer was detected, subjects filled out dietary questionnaires, including information on vitamin supplements, and researchers calculated vitamin D intake. After statistically adjusting for [that is, holding constant] age, smoking, level of physical activity, intake of calcium and retinol and other factors, the association between vitamin D intake and reduced risk of pancreated cancer was still significant.
>
> Compared with people who consumed less than 150 units of vitamin D a day, those who consumed more than 600 units reduced their risk by 41 percent. - New York Times, 19 Sept. 2006, p. D6.

There are more than 125,000 cases in this study, but only 365 of them developed pancreatic cancer. If those 365 cases had been scattered around dozens or hundreds of groups and analyzed separately, there would be so little data in each group that no pattern would be discernible.

important covariate has been left out, then the coefficients may not correctly describe how the world works.

In certain situations — the idealized **experiment** — researchers can create a world in which their modeling hypothesis is correct. In such situations there can be good reason to take the model results as indicating how the world works. For this reason, the results from studies based on experiments are generally taken as more reliable than results from non-experimental studies. But even when an experiment has been done, the situation may not be ideal; experimental subjects don't always do what the experimenter tells them to and uncontrolled influences can sometimes remain at play.

It's appropriate to show some humility about models and recognize that they can be no better than the assumptions that go into them. Useful object lessons are given by the episodes where conclusions from modeling (with careful adjustment for covariates) can be compared to experimental results. Some examples (from [19]):

- Does it help to use telephone canvassing to get out the vote? Models suggest it does, but experiments indicate otherwise.

- Is a diet rich in vitamins, fruits, vegetables and low in fat protective against cancer, heart disease or cognitive decline? Models suggest yes, but experiments generally do not.

The divergence between models and experiment suggests that an important covariate has been left out of the models.

10.4   The Geometry of Covariates and Adjustment

Figure 9.7 showed how the least-squares process for fitting a model like A ~ B+C projects a response variable A onto a model subspace B + C. Now consider the picture in that model subspace, after the projection has been done, as in Figure 10.5.

No residual vector appears in the picture because the perspective is looking straight down the vector, with the B+C model subspace drawn exactly on the plane of the page. (Recall that the residual vector is always perpendicular to the model subspace.)

In order to find the coefficients on B and C, you look for the number of steps you need to take in each direction, starting at the origin, to reach point A. In the picture, that's about 2 B steps forward and 3 C steps *backward*, so the model formula will be A = 2B − 3C.

Now imaging that you had fit the model A ~ B without including the covariate C. In fitting this model, you would find the point on the B subspace that is as

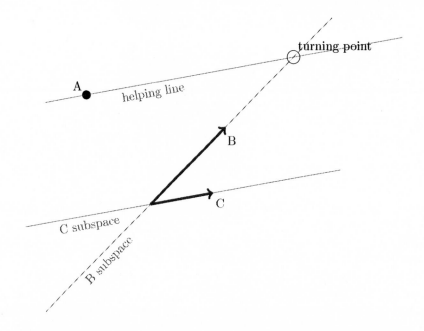

Figure 10.5: Finding coefficients with two explanatory vectors.

close as possible to A. That point is just about at the origin: 0 steps along B. So, including variable C as a covariate changes the model relationship between A and B.

Such changes in coefficients are inevitable whenever you add a new covariate to the model, unless the covariate happens to be exactly perpendicular — orthogonal — to the model vectors. The alignment of model vectors and covariates is called **collinearity** and will play a very important role in Chapter 12 in shaping not just the coefficients themselves but also the precision with coefficients can be estimated.

10.5 Computational Technique

10.5.1 Adjustment

There are two basic approaches to adjusting for covariates. Conceptually, the simplest one is to hold the covariates constant at some level when collecting data or by extracting a subset of data which holds those covariates constant. The other approach is to include the covariates in your models.

For example, suppose you want to study the differences in the wages of male and females. The very simple model wage ∼ sex might give some insight, but it

---

Aside. 10.3 Interaction terms and partial derivatives

Earlier, the idea of measuring effect size using a partial derivative was introduced. Partial derivatives also provide a way to think about interaction terms.

To measure the effect size of an explanatory variable, consider the partial derivative of the response variable with respect to the explanatory. Writing the response as z and the explanatory variables as x and y, the effect size of x corresponds to $\frac{\partial z}{\partial x}$.

An interaction — how one explanatory variable modulates the effect of another on the response variable — corresponds to a mixed second-order partial derivative. For instance, the size of an interaction between x and y on response z corresponds to $\frac{\partial^2 z}{\partial x \partial y}$.

A theorem in calculus shows that mixed partials have the same value regardless of the order in which the derivatives are taken. In other words, $\frac{\partial^2 z}{\partial x \partial y} = \frac{\partial^2 z}{\partial y \partial x}$. This is the mathematical way of stating that the way x modulates the effect of y on z is the same thing as the way that y modulates the effect of x on z.

---

attributes to `sex` effects that might actually be due to level of education, age, or the sector of the economy in which the person works. Here's the result from the simple model:

> DATA FILE
> cps.csv

```
> cps = fetchData("cps.csv")
> mod0 = lm( wage ~ sex, data=cps)
> summary(mod0)

. . .

            Estimate Std. Error t value Pr(>|t|)
(Intercept)   7.879      0.322    24.50  < 2e-16 ***
sexM          2.116      0.437     4.84  1.7e-06 ***
---
Signif. codes:  0 '***' 0.001 '**' 0.01 '*' 0.05 '.' 0.1 ' ' 1

Residual standard error: 5.03 on 532 degrees of freedom
Multiple R-squared: 0.0422,        Adjusted R-squared: 0.0404
F-statistic: 23.4 on 1 and 532 DF,  p-value: 1.7e-06
```

The coefficients indicate that a typical male makes \$2.12 more per hour than a typical female. (Notice that $R^2 = 0.0422$ is very small: `sex` explains hardly any of the person-to-person variability in wage.)

By including the variables `age`, `educ`, and `sector` in the model, you can adjust for these variables:

```
> mod1 = lm( wage ~ age + sex + educ + sector, data=cps)
> summary(mod1)

. . .

            Estimate Std. Error t value Pr(>|t|)
(Intercept)  -4.6941     1.5378   -3.05  0.00238 **
age           0.1022     0.0166    6.17  1.4e-09 ***
sexM          1.9417     0.4228    4.59  5.5e-06 ***
educ          0.6156     0.0944    6.52  1.6e-10 ***
```

```
sectorconst      1.4355      1.1312      1.27  0.20500
sectormanag      3.2711      0.7668      4.27  2.4e-05 ***
sectormanuf      0.8063      0.7311      1.10  0.27064
sectorother      0.7584      0.7592      1.00  0.31829
sectorprof       2.2478      0.6698      3.36  0.00085 ***
sectorsales     -0.7671      0.8420     -0.91  0.36273
sectorservice   -0.5687      0.6660     -0.85  0.39356
---
Signif. codes:  0 '***' 0.001 '**' 0.01 '*' 0.05 '.' 0.1 ' ' 1

Residual standard error: 4.33 on 523 degrees of freedom
Multiple R-squared: 0.302,        Adjusted R-squared: 0.289
F-statistic: 22.6 on 10 and 523 DF,  p-value: <2e-16
```

The adjusted difference between the sexes is \$1.94 per hour. (The $R^2 = 0.30$ from this model is considerably larger than for mod0, but still a lot of the person-to-person variation in wages has not be captured.)

It would be wrong to claim that simply including a covariate in a model guarantees that an appropriate adjustment has been made. The effectiveness of the adjustment depends on whether the model design is appropriate, for instance whether appropriate interaction terms have been included. However, it's certainly the case that if you **don't** include the covariate in the model, you have **not** adjusted for it.

The other approach is to subsample the data so that the levels of the covariates are approximately constant. For example, here is a subset that considers workers between the ages of 30 and 35 with between 10 to 12 years of education and working in the sales sector of the economy:

```
> small = subset(cps, age <=35 & age >= 30 &
                 educ>=10 & educ <=12 &
                 sector=="sales" )
```

The choice of these particular levels of age, educ, and sector is arbitrary, but you need to choose some level if you want to hold the covariates appproximately constant.

The subset of the data can be used to fit a simple model:

```
> mod4 = lm( wage ~ sex, data=small)
> summary(mod4)

...
            Estimate Std. Error t value Pr(>|t|)
(Intercept)    4.500      0.500     9.0     0.07 .
sexM           4.500      0.866     5.2     0.12
---
Signif. codes:  0 '***' 0.001 '**' 0.01 '*' 0.05 '.' 0.1 ' ' 1

Residual standard error: 0.707 on 1 degrees of freedom
Multiple R-squared: 0.964,        Adjusted R-squared: 0.929
```

```
F-statistic:   27 on 1 and 1 DF,  p-value: 0.121
```

At first glance, there might seem to be nothing wrong with this approach and, indeed, for very large data sets it can be effective. In this case, however, there are only 3 cases that satisfy the various criteria: two women and one man.

```
> tally( ~ sex, data=small )
    F    M Total
    2    1    3
```

So, the \$4.50 difference between the sexes and wages depends entirely on the data from a single male! (Chapter 12 describes how to assess the precision of model coefficients. This one works out to be 4.50 ± 11.00 — not at all precise.)

Reading Questions

- What is a covariate? Why use a special word for it when it is just a variable?
- What is the difference between a *partial* change and a *total* change?
- In the experimental method, how are covariates dealt with?
- What is the modeling approach to dealing with covariates?
- What is Simpson's paradox?

For exercises, see www.mosaic-web.org/StatisticalModeling/Exercises.

11

Modeling Randomness

The race is not to the swift, nor the battle to the strong, neither yet bread to the wise, nor yet riches to men of understanding, nor yet favor to men of skill; but time and chance happeneth to them all. — Ecclesiastes

Until now, emphasis has been on the deterministic description of variation: how explanatory variables can account for the variation in the response. Little attention has been paid to the residual other than to minimize it in the fitting process.

It's time now to take the residual more seriously. It has its own story to tell. By listening carefully, the modeler gains insight into even the deterministic part of the model. Keep in mind the definition of statistics offered in Chapter 1:

> Statistics is the explanation of variability **in the context of what remains unexplained.**

The next two chapters develop concepts and techniques for dealing with "what remains unexplained." In later chapters these concepts will be used when interpreting the deterministic part of models.

11.1 Describing Pure Randomness

Consider an **event** whose **outcome** is completely random, for instance, the flip of a coin. How to describe such an event? Even though the outcome is random, there is still structure to it. With a coin, for instance, the outcome must be "heads" or "tails" — it can't be "rain." So, at least part of the description should say what are the possible outcomes: H or T for a coin flip. This is called the **outcome set**. (The outcome set is conventionally called the **sample space** of the event. This terminology can be confusing since it has little to do with the sort of sampling encountered in the collection of data nor with the sorts of spaces that vectors live in.)

For a coin flip, one imagines that the two outcomes are equally likely. This is usually specified as a **probability**, a number between zero and one. Zero means "impossible." One means "certain."

A **probability model** assigns a probability to each member of the outcome set. For a coin flip, the accepted probability model is 0.5 for H and 0.5 for T — each outcome is equally likely.

What makes a coin flip purely random is *not* that the probability model assigns equal probabilities to each outcome. If coins worked differently, an appropriate probability model might be 0.6 for H and 0.4 for T. The reason the flip is purely random is that the probability model contains all the information; there are no explanatory variables that account for the outcomes in any way.

Example 11.1: Rolling a Die   The outcome set is the possibilities 1, 2, 3, 4, 5, and 6. The accepted probability model is to assign probability $\frac{1}{6}$ to each of the outcomes. They are all equally likely.

Now suppose that the die is "loaded." This is done by drilling into the dots to place weights in them. In such a situation, the heavier sides are more likely to face down. Since 6 is the heaviest side, the most likely outcome would be a 1. (Opposite sides of a die are arranged to add to seven, so 1 is opposite 6, 2 opposite 5, and 3 opposite 4.) Similarly, 5 is considerably heavier than 2, so a 2 is more likely than a 5. An appropriate probability model is this:

Outcome	1	2	3	4	5	6
Probability	0.28	0.22	0.18	0.16	0.10	0.06

One view of probabilities is that they describe how often outcomes occur. For example, if you conduct 100 trials of a coin flip, you should expect to get something like 50 heads. According to the **frequentist** view of probability, you should base a probability model of a coin on the relative proportion of times that heads or tails comes up in a very large number of trials.

Another view of probabilities is that they encode the modeler's assumptions and beliefs. This view gives everyone a license to talk about things in terms of probabilities, even those things for which there is only one possible trial, for instance current events in the world. To a **subjectivist**, it can be meaningful to think about current international events and conclude, "there's a one-quarter chance that this dispute will turn into a war." Or, "the probability that there will be an economic recession next year is only 5 percent."

Example 11.2: The Chance of Rain.   Tomorrow's weather forecast calls for a 10% chance of rain. Even though this forecast doesn't tell you what the outcome will be, it's useful; it contains information. For instance, you might use the forecast in making a decision not to cancel your picnic plans.

But what sort of probability is this 10%? The *frequentist* interpretation is that it refers to seeing how many days it rains out of a large number of trials of identical days. Can you create identical days? There's only one trial — and that's tomorrow. The *subjectivist* interpretation is that 10% is the forecaster's way of giving you some information, based on his or her expertise, the data available, etc.

Saying that a probability is subjective does not mean that anything goes. Some probability models of an event are better than others. There is a reason why you look to the weather forecast on the news rather than gazing at your tea leaves. There are in fact rules for doing calculations with probabilities: a "probability calculus." Subjective probabilities are useful for encoding beliefs, but the probability calculus should be used to work through the consequences of these beliefs. The **Bayesian** philosophy of probability emphasizes the methods of probability calculus that are useful for exploring the consequences of beliefs.

Example 11.3: Flipping two coins.   You flip two coins and count how many heads you get. The outcome space is 0 heads, 1 head, and 2 heads. What should the probability model be? Here are two possible models:

<table>
<tr><td colspan="4" align="center">Model 1</td></tr>
<tr><td># of Heads</td><td>0</td><td>1</td><td>2</td></tr>
<tr><td>Probability</td><td>$\frac{1}{3}$</td><td>$\frac{1}{3}$</td><td>$\frac{1}{3}$</td></tr>
</table>

<table>
<tr><td colspan="4" align="center">Model 2</td></tr>
<tr><td># of Heads</td><td>0</td><td>1</td><td>2</td></tr>
<tr><td>Probability</td><td>$\frac{1}{4}$</td><td>$\frac{1}{2}$</td><td>$\frac{1}{4}$</td></tr>
</table>

If you are unfamiliar with probability calculations, you might decide to adopt Model 1. However heartfelt your opinion, though, Model 1 is not as good as Model 2. Why? Given the assumptions that a head and a tail are equally likely outcomes of a single coin flip, and that there is no connection between successive coin flips — that they are **independent** of each other — the probability calculus leads to the $\frac{1}{4}, \frac{1}{2}, \frac{1}{4}$ probability model.

How can you assess whether a probability model is a good one, or which of two probability models are better? One way is to compare observations to the predictions made by the model. To illustrate, suppose you actually perform 100 trials of the coin flips in example above and you record your observations. Each of the models also gives a prediction of the expected number of outcomes of each type:

	# of Heads		
	0	1	2
Observed	28	45	27
Model 1	33.3	33.3	33.3
Model 2	25	50	25

The discrepancy between the model predictions and the observed counts tells something about how good the model is. A strict analogy to linear modeling would suggest looking at the residual: the difference between the model values and the observed values. For example, you might look at the familiar sum of squares of the residuals. For Model 2 this is $(28-25)^2 + (45-50)^2 + (27-25)^2$. More than 100-years ago, it was worked out that for probability models this is not the most informative way to calculate the size of the residuals. It's better to adjust each of the terms by the model value, that is, to calculate $\frac{(28-25)^2}{25} + \frac{(45-50)^2}{50} + \frac{(27-25)^2}{25}$. The details of the measure are not important right now, just that there is a way to quantify how well a probability model matches the observations.

11.2   Settings for Probability Models

A statistical model describes one or more variables and their relationships. In contrast, a probability model describes the outcomes of a random event, sometimes called a **random variable**. The **setting** of a random variable refers to how the event is configured. Some examples of settings:

- The number of radio-active particles given off by a substance in a minute.

- A particular student's score on a standardized test consisting of 100 questions.

- The number of blood cells observed in a small area of a microscope slide.

- The number of people from a random sample of 1000 voters who support the incumbent candidate.

In constructing a probability model, the modeler picks a form for the model that is appropriate for the setting. By using expert knowledge (e.g., how radioactivity works) and the probability calculus, probability models can be derived for each of these settings.

It turns out that there is a reasonably small set of standard probability models that apply to a wide range of settings. You don't always need to derive probability models, you can use the ones that have already been derived. This simplifies things dramatically, since you can accomplish a lot merely by learning which of the models to apply in any given setting.

Each of the models has one or more **parameters** that can be used to adjust the models to the particular details of a setting. In this sense, the parameters are akin to the model coefficients that are set when fitting models to data.

11.3   Models of Counts

11.3.1   The Binomial Model

Setting.   The standard example of a **binomial** model is a series of coin flips. A coin is flipped n times and the outcome of the event is a count: how many heads. The outcome space is the set of counts $0, 1, \ldots, n$.

To put this in more general terms, the setting for the binomial model is an event that consists of n trials. Each of those trials is itself a purely random event where the outcome set has two possible values. For a coin flip, these would be heads or tails. For a medical diagnosis, the outcomes might be "cancer" or "not cancer." For a political poll, the outcomes might be "support" or "don't support." All of the individual trials are identical and independent of the others.

The name binomial — "bi" as in two, "nom" as in name — reflects these two possible outcomes. Generically, they can be called "success" and "failure." The outcome of the overall event is a count of the number of successes out of the n trials.

Parameters.   The binomial model has two parameters: the number of trials n and the probability p of success in each trial.

Example 11.4: Multiple Coin Flips   Flip 10 coins and count the number of heads. The number of trials is 10 and the probability of "success" is 0.5. Here is the probability model:

Outcome	0	1	2	3	4	5
Probability	0.001	0.010	0.044	0.117	0.205	0.246
Outcome		6	7	8	9	10
Probability		0.205	0.117	0.044	0.01	0.001

Examples of Binomial Models

Example 11.5: Houses for Sale   Count the number of houses on your street with a for-sale sign. Here n is the number of houses on your street. p is the probability that any randomly selected house is for sale. Unlike a coin flip, you likely don't know p from first principles. Still, the count is appropriately modeled by the binomial model. But until you know p, or assume a value for it, you can't calculate the probabilities.

11.3.2   The Poisson Model

Setting.   Like the binomial, the **Poisson** model also involves a count. It applies when the things you are counting happen at a typical rate. For example, suppose you are counting cars on a busy street on which the city government claims the typical traffic level is 1000 cars per hour. You count cars for 15 minutes to check whether the city's claimed rate is right. According to the rate, you expect to see 250 cars in the 15 minutes. But the actual number that pass by is random and will likely be somewhat different from 250. The Poisson model assigns a probability to each possible count.

Parameters.   The **Poisson** model has only one parameter: the average rate at which the events occur.

Example 11.6: The Rate of Highway Accidents   In your state last year there were 300 fatal highway accidents: a rate of 300 per year. If this rate continued, how many accidents will there be today?

Since you are interested in a period of one day, divide the annual rate by 365 to give a rate of $300/365 = 0.8219$ accidents per day. According to the Poisson model, the probabilities are:

Outcome	0	1	2	3	4	5	$\cdots$
Probability	0.440	0.361	0.148	0.041	0.008	0.001	$\cdots$

People often confuse the binomial setting with the Poisson setting. Notice that in a Poisson setting, there is not a fixed number of trials, just a typical rate at which events occur. The count of events has no firm upper limit. In contrast, in a binomial setting, the count can never be higher than the number of trials, n.

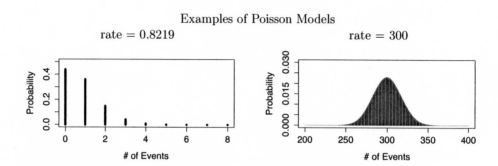

11.4   Common Probability Calculations

A probability model assigns a probability to each member of the outcome set. Usually, though, you are not interested in these probabilities directly. Instead, you want other information that is based on the probabilities:

Percentiles. Students who take standardized tests know that the test score can be converted to a percentile: the fraction of test takers who got that score or less. Similarly, each possible outcome of a random variable falls at a certain percentile. It often makes sense to refer to the outcomes by their percentiles rather than the value itself. For example, the 90th percentile is the value of the outcome such that 90 percent of the time a random outcome will be at that value or smaller.

Percentiles are used, for instance, in finding what range of outcomes is likely, as in calculating a coverage interval for the outcome.

Example 11.7: A Political Poll   You conduct 500 interviews with likely voters about their support for the incumbent candidate. You believe that 55% of voters support the incumbent. What is the likely range in the results of your survey?

This is a binomial setting, with parameters $n = 500$ and $p = 0.55$. It's reasonable to interpret "likely range" to be a 95% coverage interval. The boundaries of this interval are the 2.5- and 97.5-percentiles, or, 253 and 297 respectively.

Quantiles or **Inverse percentiles.** Here, instead of asking what is the outcome at a given percentile, you invert the question and ask what is the percentile at a given outcome. This sort of question is often asked to calculate the probability that an outcome exceeds some limit.

> **Example 11.8: A Normal Year?**   Last year there were 300 highway accidents in your state. This year saw an increase to 321. Is this a likely outcome if the underlying rate hadn't changed from 300?
>
> This is a Poisson setting, with the rate parameter at 300 per year. According to the Poisson model, the probability of seeing 321 or more is 0.119: not so small.

Calculation of percentiles and inverse percentiles is almost always done with software. The "computational technique" section gives specific instructions for doing this.

11.5   Continuous Probability Models

The binomial and Poisson models apply to settings where the outcome is a count. There are other settings where the outcome is a number that is not necessarily a counting number.

11.5.1   The Uniform Model

Setting.   A random number is generated that is equally likely to be anywhere in some range. An example is a spinner that is equally likely to come to rest at any orientation between 0 and 360 degrees.

Parameters. Two parameters: the upper and the lower end of the range.

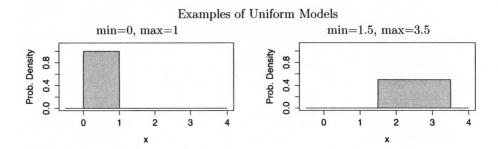

Examples of Uniform Models

Example 11.9: Equally Likely   A uniform random number is generated in the range 0 to 1. What is the probability that it will be smaller than 0.05? Answer: 0.05. (Simple as it seems, this particular example will be relevant in studying p-values in a later chapter.)

11.5.2   The Normal Model

Setting. The normal model turns out to be a good approximation for many purposes, thus the name "normal." When the outcome is the result of adding up **lots** of independent numbers, the normal model often applies well. In statistical modeling, model coefficients are calculated with dot products, involving lots of addition. Thus, model coefficients are often well described by a normal model.

The normal model is so important that Section 11.6 is devoted to it exclusively.

Parameters. Two. The **mean** which describes the most likely outcome, and the **standard deviation** which describes the typical spread around the mean.

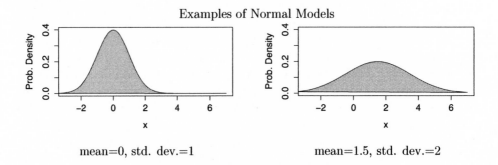

Examples of Normal Models

mean=0, std. dev.=1   mean=1.5, std. dev.=2

Example 11.10: IQ Test Scores   Scores on a standardized IQ test are arranged to have a mean of 100 points and a standard deviation of 15 points. What's a typical score from such a test? Answer: According to the normal model, the 95% coverage interval is 70.6 to 129.4 points.

11.5.3   The Log-normal Model

Setting.   The normal distribution is widely used as a general approximation in a large number of settings. However, the normal distribution is symmetrical and fails to give a good approximation when a distribution is strongly skewed. The log-normal distribution is often used when the skew is important. Mathematically, the log-normal model is appropriate when taking the logarithm of the outcome would produce a bell-shaped distribution.

Parameters.   In the normal distribution, the two parameters are the mean and standard deviation. Similarly, in the log-normal distribution, the two parameters are the mean and standard deviation of the log of the values.

Example 11.11: High Income   In most societies, incomes have a skew distribution; very high incomes are more common than you might expect. In the United States, for instance, data on middle-income families in 2005 suggests a mean of about $50,000 per year and a standard deviation of about $20,000 per year (taking "middle-income" to mean the central 90% of families). If incomes were distributed in a bell-shaped, normal manner, this would imply that the 99th percentile of income would be $100,000 per year. But this understates matters. Rather than being normal, the distribution of incomes is better approximated with a log-normal distribution.[20] Using a log-normal distribution with parameters set to match the observations for middle-income familes gives a 99th percentile of $143,000.

Examples of Log-normal Models

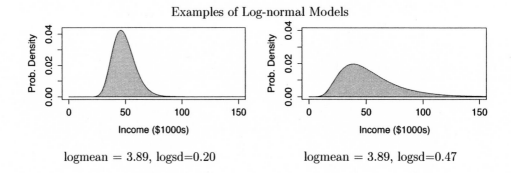

logmean = 3.89, logsd=0.20   logmean = 3.89, logsd=0.47

11.5.4   The Exponential Model

Setting.   The exponential model is closely related to the Poisson. Both models describing a setting where events are happening at random but at a certain rate. The Poisson describes *how many* events happen in a given period. In contrast, the exponential model describes the *spacing* between events.

Parameters.   Just like the Poisson, the exponential model has one parameter, the rate.

Example 11.12: Times between Earthquakes   In the last 202 years, there have been six large earthquakes in the Himalaya mountains. The last one was in 2005. This suggests a typical rate of $\frac{6}{202} = 0.03$ earthquakes per year — about one every 33 years. If earthquakes happen at random at this rate, what is the probability that there will be another large earthquake within 10 years of the last, that is, by 2015? According to the exponential model, this is 0.259. That's a surprisingly large probability if you expected that earthquakes won't happen again until a suitable interval passes. There can also be surprisingly large gaps between earthquakes. For instance, the probability that another large earthquake won't occur until 2105 is 0.05 according to the exponential model.

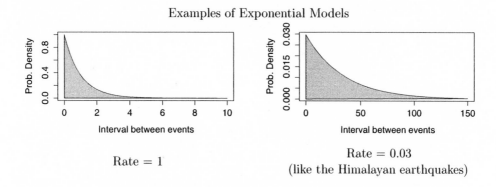

Examples of Exponential Models

Rate = 1

Rate = 0.03
(like the Himalayan earthquakes)

11.6 The Normal Distribution

Many quantities have a bell-shaped distribution so the normal model makes a good approximation in many settings. The parameters of the normal model are the mean and standard deviation. It is important to realize that a mean and standard deviation can be calculated for other models as well.

To see this, imagine a large number of trials generated according to a probability model. For the models discussed in this chapter, the outcomes are always numbers. So it makes sense to take the mean or the standard deviation of the trial outcomes.

When applied to probability models, the mean describes the center or typical value of the random outcome, just as the mean of a variable describes the center of the distribution of that variable. The standard deviation describes how the outcomes are spread around the center.

The calculation of percentiles, coverage intervals, and inverse percentiles is so common, that a shorthand way of doing it has been developed for normal models. At the heart of this method is the **z-score**.

The z-score is a way of referring a particular value of interest to a probability model or a distribution of values. The z-score measures how far a value is from the center of the distribution. The units of the measurement are in terms of the standard deviation of the distribution. That is, if the value is x in a distribution with mean m and standard deviation s, the z-score is:

$$z = \frac{x - m}{s}.$$

Example 11.13: IQ Percentiles from Scores.   In a standard IQ test, scores are arranged to have a mean of 100 and a standard deviation of 15. A person gets an 80 on the exam. What is their z-score? Answer: $z = \frac{80-100}{15} = -1.33$.

In some calculations, you know the z-score and need to figure out the corresponding value. This can be done by solving the z-score equation for x, or

$$x = m + sz.$$

Example 11.14: IQ Scores from Percentiles.   In the IQ test, what is the value that has a z-score of 2? Answer: $x = 100 + 15 \times 2 = 130$.

Here are the rules for calculating percentiles and inverse percentiles from a normal model:

95% Coverage Interval This is the interval bounded by the two values with $z = -2$ and 2.

Percentiles The percentile of a value is indicated by its z-score.

z-score	-3	-2	-1	0	1	2	3
Percentile	0.1	2.3	15.9	50	84.1	97.7	99.9

Values with z-scores greater than 3 or smaller than -3 are very uncommon, at least according to the normal model.

Example 11.15: Bad Luck at Roulette?   You have been playing a roulette game all night, betting on red, your lucky color. Altogether you have played $n = 100$ games and you know the probability of a random roll coming up red is $16/34$. You've won only 42 games — you're losing serious money. Are you unlucky? Has red abandoned you?

If you have a calculator, you can find out approximately how unlucky you are. The setting is binomial, with $n = 100$ trials and $p = 16/34$. The mean and standard deviation of a binomial random variable are np and $\sqrt{np(1-p)}$ respectively; these formulas are ones that all skilled gamblers ought to know. The z-score of your performance is:

$$z = \frac{42 - 100\frac{16}{34}}{\sqrt{100\frac{16}{34}(1 - \frac{16}{34})}} = \frac{42 - 47.06}{5} = -1$$

The score of $z = -1$ translates to the 16th percentile — your performance isn't good, but it's not too surprising either.

When you get back to your hotel room, you can use your computer to do the exact calculation based on the binomial model. The probability of winning 42 games or fewer is 0.181.

11.7   Computational Technique

One of the most surprising outcomes of the revolution in computing technology has been the discovery of diverse uses for randomness in the analysis of data and in science generally. Most young people have little trouble with the idea of a computer generating random data; they see it in computer games and simulations. Older people, raised with the idea that computers do mathematical operations and that such operations are completely deterministic, sometimes find computer-generated randomness suspect. Indeed, conventional algebraic notation ($+$, $-$, $\sqrt{}$, cos, and so on) has no notation for "generate at random."

One of the simplest operators for generating random events is `resample`. This takes two arguments: the first is a set of items to choose from at random, the second is how many events to generate. Each item is equally likely to be choosen. For example, here is a simulation of a coin flip:

```
> coin = c("H","T")
> resample(coin, 5)

[1] "H" "T" "T" "H" "H"

> resample(coin, 5)

[1] "T" "H" "T" "T" "H"
```

The first command creates an object holding the possible outcome of each event, called `coin`. The next command generated five events, each event being a random choice of the outcomes in `coin`.

Another example is rolling dice. First, construct a set of the possible outcomes: the numbers 1, 2, 3, 4, 5, 6.

```
> die = seq(1,6)
> die

[1] 1 2 3 4 5 6
```

Then generate random events. Here is a roll of two dice.

```
> resample(die,2)

[1] 1 1
```

The `resample()` function is also useful for selecting cases at random from a data frame. This use will be the basis for statistical methods introduced in later chapters.

11.7.1   Random Draws from Probability Models

Although `resample()` is useful for random sampling, it can work only with finite sets of possible outcomes such as H/T or 1/2/3/4/5/6 or the cases in a data frame. By default in `resample()`, the underlying probability model is **equiprobability**

— each possible outcome is equally likely. You can specify another probability model by using the **prob=** argument to resample(). For instance, to flip coins that are very likely to come up heads:

```
> resample( coin, 10, prob=c(.9,.1))

 [1] "H" "H" "T" "T" "H" "H" "H" "H" "H" "H"
```

R provides other operators that allow draws to be made from outcome sets that are infinite.

For example, the rnorm() function makes random draws from a normal probability distribution. The required argument tells how many draws to make. Optional, named arguments let you specify the mean and standard deviation of the particular normal distribution that you want. To illustrate, here is a set of 15 random numbers from a normal distribution with mean 1000 and standard deviation 75:

```
> samps = rnorm(15, mean=1000, sd=75)
> samps

 [1]   903 1072 1071   885 1094 1116 1010 1001 1096 1210   888
[12] 1060   989   971   861
```

In this example, the output was assigned to an object **samps** to facilitate some additional computations to the values. For instance, here is the mean and standard deviation of the sample:

```
> mean(samps)

[1] 1015

> sd(samps)

[1] 101
```

Don't be surprised that the mean and standard deviation of the sample don't match exactly the parameters that were set with the arguments **mean=1000,sd= 75**. The sample was drawn at random and so the sample statistics are going to vary from one sample to the next. Part of the statistical methodology to be studied in later chapters has to do with determining how close the statistics calculated from a sample are likely to be to the parameters of the underlying population.

Often you will generate very large samples. In these situations you usually don't want to display all the samples, just do calculations with them. The practical limits of "large" depend on the computer you are using and how much time you are willing to spend on a calculation. For an operator like **rnorm** and the others to be introduced in this chapter, it's feasible to generate samples of size 10,000 or 100,000 on an ordinary laptop computer.

```
> samps = rnorm(100000, mean=1000, sd=75)
> mean( samps )

[1] 1000
```

```
> sd( samps )
[1] 75
```

Notice that the sample mean and standard deviation are quite close to the population parameters in this large sample. (Remember not to put commas in as punctuation in large numbers: it's 100000 not 100,000.)

The simulations that you will do in later chapters will be much more elaborate than the simple draws here. Even with today's computers, you will want to use only a few hundred trials.

11.7.2 Standard Probability Models

R provides a large set of operators like `rnorm` for different probability models. All of these operators work in the same way:

- Each has a required first argument that gives the number of draws to make.

- Each has an optional set of parameters that specify the particular probability distribution you want.

All the operators start with the letter `r` — standing for "random" — followed by the name of the probability model:

Family	R name	Parameters	
Normal	`rnorm`	`mean,sd`	continuous
Uniform	`runif`	`min,max`	continuous
Binomial	`rbinom`	`size,prob`	discrete
Poisson	`rpois`	Average rate (written `lambda`)	discrete
Exponential	`rexp`	Same rate as in poisson but the parameter is called `rate`.	continuous
Lognormal	`rlnorm`	Mean and sd of the natural logarithm. `meanlog, sdlog`	continuous
χ^2	`rchisq`	Degrees of freedom (`df`)	continuous
t	`rt`	Degrees of freedom (`df`)	continuous
F	`rf`	Degrees of freedom in the numerator and in the denominator (`df1, df2`)	continuous

To use these operators, you first must choose a particular probability model based on the setting that applies in your situation. This setting will usually indicate what the population parameters should be. Some examples:

- You are in charge of a hiring committee that is going to interview three candidates selected from a population of job applicants that is 63% female. How many of the interviewees will be female? Modeling this as random selection from the applicant pool, a binomial model is appropriate. The `size` of each trial is 3, the probability of being female is 63%:

```
> samps = rbinom(40, size=3, prob=0.63)
> samps
 [1] 1 2 1 3 1 2 2 2 1 2 2 3 3 2 3 2 1 1 1 1 2 3 2 1 2 2 2 3 2
[29] 2 3 3 2 1 2 1 3 2 1 2 0
```

There are 40 trials here, since the first argument was set to 40. Remember, each of the trials is a simulation of one hiring event. In the first simulated event, two of the interviewees were female; in the third only one was female. Typically, you will be summarizing all the simulations, for example to see how likely each possible outcome is.

```
> tally(samps)
    0    1    2    3 Total
    1   12   18    9   40
```

- You want to simulate the number of customers who come into a store over the course of an hour. The average rate is 15 per hour. To simulate a situation where customers arrive randomly, the poisson model is appropriate:

```
> rpois(25, lambda=15)
 [1] 10 11 11 14 16 18 13 11 17 13 16 16 19 14 10 18 18 13
[19] 18 16  9 11 17 18 20
```

- You want to generate a simulation of the interval between earthquakes as in Example 11.5.4. To simulate the random intervals with a typical rate of 0.03 earthquakes per year, you would use

```
> rexp( 15, rate=0.03 )
 [1] 26.945 18.264 36.254  8.998  8.556 56.742  0.804 14.045
 [9]  2.501 33.284 21.656 50.795 21.240  4.651  4.332
```

Notice the huge variation in the intervals, from less than half a year to almost 90 years between earthquakes.

11.7.3 Coverage Intervals

You will often need to compute coverage intervals in order to describe the range of likely outcomes from a random process. R provides a series of operators for this purpose; a separate operator for each named probability model. The operators all begin with q, standing for **quantiles**. In all cases, the first argument is the set of quantiles you want to calculate for the particular probability model. The optional named arguments are the parameters.

Remember that to find a 95% coverage interval you need the 0.025 and 0.975 quantiles. For a 99% interval, you need the 0.005 and 0.995 quantiles.

To illustrate, here are 95% coverage intervals for a few probability models.

- A normal distribution with mean 0 and standard deviation 1:

```
> qnorm( c(0.025, 0.975), mean=0, sd=1)
[1] -1.96  1.96

>
```

- The hiring committee situation modelled by a binomial distribution with **size=3** and **prob=0.63**:

```
> qbinom( c(0.025, 0.975), size=3, prob=0.63)
[1] 0 3
```

Perhaps you are surprised to see that the coverage interval includes all the possible outcomes. That's because the number of cases in each trial ($n = 3$) is quite small.

- The number of customers entering a store during an hour as modelled by a poisson distribution with an average rate of 15 per hour.

```
> qpois( c(0.025, 0.975), lambda=15)
[1]  8 23
```

- The interval between earthquakes modelled by an exponential distribution with a typical rate of 0.03 earthquakes per year:

```
> qexp( c(.025, .975), rate=0.03)
[1]    0.844 122.963
```

You can also use the **q** operators to find the value that would be at a particular percentile. For example, the exponential model with **rate=0.03** gives the 25th percentile of the interval between earthquakes as:

```
> qexp( .25, rate=0.03)
[1] 9.59
```

A quarter of the time, the interval between earthquakes will be 9.59 years or less.

It's entirely feasible to calculate percentiles and coverage intervals by combining the random-number generators with **quantile**. For example, here is the 95% coverage interval from a normal distribution with mean 0 and standard deviation 1:

```
> samps = rnorm(10000, mean=0, sd=1)
> qdata( c(.025, .975), samps )
 2.5% 97.5%
-1.97  1.98
```

The disadvantage of this approach is that it is a simulation and the results will vary randomly. By making the sample size large enough — here it is $n = 10000$ — you can reduce the random variation. Using the q operators uses mathematical analysis to give you what is effectively an infinite sample size. For this reason, it's advisable to use the q operators when you can. However, for many of the techniques to be introduced in later chapters you will have to generate a random sample and then apply `quantile` to approximate the coverage intervals.

11.7.4   Cumulative Probability

A cumulative probability computation applies to situations where you have a measured value and you want to know where that value ranks relative to the entire set of possible outcomes. You have already seen cumulative probabilities computed from samples; they also apply to probability models.The word "cumulative" is used because the probability reflects the chance of seeing a particular value *or smaller*.

It's easy to confuse cumulative probabilities with quantiles because they are so closely related. Mathematically, the cumulative probability operators are the inverse of the quantile operators. To help you remember which is which, it's helpful to distinguish them based on the type of argument that you give to the operator:

Cumulative Probability The input argument is a measured value, something that could be the output of a single draw from the probability distribution. The output is always a number between 0 and 1 — a probability.

Quantile The input is a cumulative probability, a number between 0 and 1. The output is on the scale of the measured variable.

Example: You have just gotten your score, 670, on a professional school admissions test. According to the information published by the testing company, the scores are normally distributed with a mean of 600 and a standard deviation of 100. So, your ranking on the test, as indicated by a cumulative probability, is:

```
> pnorm(670, mean=600, sd=100)
[1] 0.758
```

Your score is at about the 75th percentile.

Example: Unfortunately, the professional school that you want to go to accepts only students with scores in the top 15 percent. Your score, at 75.8%, isn't good enough. So, you will study some more and take practice tests until your score is good enough. How well will you need to score to reach the 85th percentile?

```
> qnorm(0.85, mean=600, sd=100)
[1] 704
```

Reading Questions

- What is a probability model?
- What are some of the different probability models and what different situations do they describe?
- What is a "parameter" in a probability model? Give some examples.

For exercises, see www.mosaic-web.org/StatisticalModeling/Exercises.

12

Confidence in Models

To know one's ignorance is the best part of knowledge. — Lao-Tsu
(6th century BC), Chinese philosopher

Doubt is not a pleasant condition, but certainty is an absurd one. —
Voltaire (1694-1778), French writer and philosopher

If you are a skilled modeler, you try to arrange things so that your model coefficients are random numbers.

That statement may sound silly, but before you jump to conclusions it's important to understand where the randomness comes from and why it's a good thing. Then you can use the tools in the previous two chapters to deal with the randomness and interpret it.

Recall the steps in building a statistical model:

1. Collect data. This is the hardest part, often involving great effort and expense.

2. Design your model, choosing the response variable, the explanatory variables, and the model terms. (It's sensible to have the design in mind *before* you collect your data, so you know what data are needed.)

3. Fit the model design to your data.

Step (3) is entirely deterministic. Given the model design and the data to which the model is to be fitted, fitting is an automatic process that will give the same results every time and on every computer. There is no randomness there. (There is some choice in choosing which to remove from a set of vectors containing redundancy, but that is a choice, not randomness. In any event, the fitted model values are not affected by this choice.)

Step (2) appears, at first glance, to leave space for chance. After all, when explanatory terms are collinear, as they often are, the fitted coefficients on any term can depend strongly on which other terms have been included in the model. The coefficients depend on the modeler's choices. But this means only that the coefficients reflect the beliefs of the modeler. If those beliefs aren't random, then the randomness of coefficients doesn't stem from the modeler.

It's step (1) that introduces the randomness. In collecting data, the sample cases are selected from a population. As described in Chapter 2, it's advantageous to make a random selection from the population; this helps to make the sample representative of the population.

Saying something is random means that it is uncertain, that if the process were repeated again the result might be different. When a sample is selected at random, the particular sample that is produced is just one of a set of possibilities. One can imagine other possibilities that might have come about from the luck of the draw.

Insofar as the sample is random, the coefficients that come from fitting the model design to the sample are also random. The randomness of model coefficients means that the coefficients that come from a model design fitted to any particular data set are not likely to be an exact match to what you would get if the model design were fitted to the *entire population*. After all, the randomly selected sample is unlikely to be an exact match to the entire population.

It's helpful to know how close the results from the sample are to what would have been obtained if the sample had been the entire population. Ultimately, the only way to know this for sure is to create a sample that is the entire population. Usually this is impractical and often it is impossible.

As described in Chapter 5, there is an approach that will give insight, even if it does not give certainty. To start, imagine that the sample were actually a census: a sample that contains the entire population. Repeating the study with a new sample would give exactly the same result because the new sample would be the same as the old one; it's the same population.

When the sample is not the entire population, repeating the study won't give the same result every time because the sample will include different members of the population. If the results vary wildly from one repeat to another, you have reason to think that the results are not a reliable indication of the population. If the results vary only a small amount from one repeat to another, then there's reason to think that you have closely approximated the results that you would have gotten if the sample had been the entire population. The repeatability of the process indicates how well the modeler knows the coefficients, or, in a word, the **precision** of the coefficients.

Knowing the precision of coefficients is key in drawing conclusions from them. Consider Galton's problem in studying whether height is a heritable trait. Had Galton known about modeling, he might have constructed a model like height $\sim 1 +$ mother $+$ father $+$ sex. A relationship between the mother's height and her child's height should show up in the coefficient on mother. If there is a relationship, that coefficient should be non-zero.

Fitting the model to Galton's data, the coefficient is 0.32. Is this non-zero? Yes, for this particular set of data. But how might it have been different if Galton repeated his sampling, selecting a new set of cases from the population? How precise is the coefficient? Until this is known, it's mere bravado to say that a result of 0.32 means anything.

This chapter introduces methods that can be used to estimate the precision of coefficients from data. A standard format for presenting this estimation is the **confidence interval**. For instance, from Galton's data, the estimated coefficient on mother is 0.32 ± 0.06, giving confidence that a different sample would also show a non-zero coefficient.

It's important to contrast precision with **accuracy**. Precision is about repeatability. Accuracy is about how the result matches the real world. Ultimately, accuracy is what the modeler wants. A major reason to introduce modeling techniques beyond the simple group-wise models of Chapter 5 is to enable you to account for the multiple factors that shape outcomes. But the results of a model always depend on the choices the modeler makes, e.g., which explanatory variables to include, how to choose a sample, etc. The results can be accurate only if the modeler makes good choices. Knowing whether this is the case depends on knowing how the world really works, and this is what you are seeking to find out in the first place. Accuracy is elusive knowledge. Precision will have to suffice.

12.1   The Sampling Distribution & Model Coefficients

The same principles of sampling and re-sampling distributions introduced in Chapter 5 can be used to find confidence intervals on model coefficients.

DATA FILE
ten-mile-
race.csv

To illustrate, consider the ten-mile race dataset. This is a census containing the running times for all 8636 registered participants in the Cherry Blossom Ten Mile race held in Washington, D.C. in April 2005.

The variable net records the start-line to finish-line time of each runner. There are also variables age and sex. Any model would do to illustrate the sampling distribution. Try

```
net ~ 1 + age + sex
```

Just for reference, here are the coefficients when the model is fit to the entire population:

	Intercept	age	sex**M**
Population	5540	16.9	-727

The coefficients indicate that runners who are one year older tend to take about 17 seconds longer to run the 10 miles.

Of course, if you knew the coefficients that fit the whole population, you would hardly need to collect a sample! But the purpose here is to demonstrate the effects of a random sampling process. The table below gives the coefficients from several sampling draws; each sample has $n = 100$ cases randomly selected from the population. That is, each sample simulates the situation where someone has randomly selected $n = 100$ cases.

	Intercept	age	sex**M**
Sample 1	5570	12.6	-867
Sample 2	4630	31.2	-430
Sample 3	5980	2.1	-765
Sample 4	5850	5.0	-772
Sample 5	5420	16.5	-1010
Sample 6	5950	3.1	-583
Sample 7	4770	33.7	-779
Sample 8	5420	11.9	-551

Judging from these few samples, there is a lot of variability in the coefficients. For example, the age coefficient ranges from 2.1 to 33.7 in just these few samples. Figure 12.1 shows the distribution of coefficients for the age and sex coefficients for 1000 repeats of the sampling process. Each of the samples has 100 cases randomly selected from the population. These distributions, which reflect the randomness of the sampling process, are called **sampling distributions**. It's very common for sampling distributions to be bell-shaped and to be centered on the population value.

The width of the sampling distribution shows the reliability or repeatability of the coefficients. There are two common ways to summarize the width: the standard deviation and the 95% coverage interval.

An important item to add to your vocabularly is the "standard error."

> Sampling distributions, like other distributions, have standard deviations. The term **standard error** is used to refer to the standard deviation of a sampling distribution.

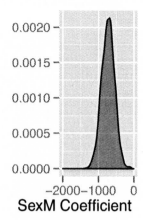

Figure 12.1: Sampling distributions for the age and sex coefficients for a sample size of $n = 100$. The bell-shaped distributions are centered on the population value.

For the age coefficient, the standard error is about 9.5 seconds per year (keeping in mind the units of the data), and the standard error in sex**M** is about 192 seconds. These standard errors were calculated by drawing 10,000 repeats of samples of size $n = 100$, and fitting the model to each of the 10000 samples. This is easy to do on the computer, but practically impossible in actual field work.

Every model coefficient has its own standard error which indicates the precision of the coefficient. The size of the standard error depends on several things:

- The quality of the data. The precision with which individual measurements of variables is made, or errors in those measurements, translates through to the standard errors on the model coefficients.

- The quality of the model. The size of standard errors is proportional to the size of the residuals, so a model that produces small residuals tends to have small standard errors. However, collinearity or multi-collinearity among the explanatory variables tends to inflate standard errors.

- The sample size n. Standard errors tend to get tighter the more data is used to fit the model. A simple relationship holds very widely; it's worth remembering this rule:

  The standard error typically gets smaller as the sample size n increases, but slowly; it's proportional to $1/\sqrt{n}$. This means, for instance, that to make the standard error 10 times smaller, you need a dataset that is 100 times larger.

12.2   Standard Errors and the Regression Report

Finding the standard error of a model coefficient would be straightforward if one could follow the procedure above: repeatedly draw new samples from the population, fit the model to each new sample, and collect the resulting coefficients from each sample to produce the sampling distribution. This process is impractical, however, because of the expense of collecting new samples.

Fortunately, there can be enough information in the original sample to make a reasonable guess about the sampling distribution. How to make this guess is the subject of Section 5.2. For now, it suffices to say that the guess is based on an approximation to the sampling distribution called the **resampling distribution**.

A conventional report from software, often called a **regression report**, provides an estimate of the standard error. Here is the regression report from the model net $\sim 1 +$ age $+$ sex fitted to a sample of size $n = 100$ from the running data:

	Estimate	Std. Error	t value	$\Pr(>|t|)$
Intercept	5110	340.0	14.89	0.0001
age	29	9.1	3.21	0.0018
sexM	-860	188.0	-4.57	0.0001

The coefficient itself is in the column labelled "Estimate." The next column, labelled "Std. Error," gives the standard error of each coefficient. You can ignore the last two columns of the regression report for now. They present the information from the first two columns in a different format.

12.3   Confidence Intervals

The regression report gives the standard error explicitly, but it's common in many fields to report the precision of a coefficient in another way, as a **confidence interval**. This was introduced in Chapter 5 in the context of group-wise models, but it applies to other sorts of models as well.

A confidence interval is a little report about a coefficient like this one about the age coefficient in the regression table above: "29 ± 18 with 95% confidence." The confidence interval involves three components:

Point Estimate The center of the confidence interval: 29 here. Read this directly from the regression report.

Margin of Error The half-width of the confidence interval: 18 here. This is two times the standard error of 9.1 shown in the regression report.

Confidence Level The percentage of the coverage interval. This is typically 95%. Since people get tired of saying the same thing over and over again, they often omit the "with 95% confidence" part of the report. This can be dangerous, since sometimes people use confidence levels other than 95%.

The purpose of multiplying the standard error by two is to make the confidence interval approximate a 95% coverage interval of the resampling distribution.

DATA FILE
truckingjobs.
csv

Example 12.1: Wage discrimination in trucking?   Section 10.1.2 (page 185) looked at data from a trucking company to see how earnings differ between men and women. It's time to revisit that example, using confidence intervals to get an idea of whether the data clearly point to the existence of a wage difference.

The model earnings ~ sex ascribed all differences between men and women to their sex itself. Here is the regression report:

	Estimate	Std. Error	t value	Pr(>|t|)
Intercept	35501	2163	16.41	0.0001
sexM	4735	2605	1.82	0.0714

The estimated difference in earnings between men and women is $4700 ±5200 — not at all precise.

Another model can be used to take into account the worker's experience, using age as a proxy:

	Estimate	Std. Error	t value	Pr(>|t|)
Intercept	14970	3912	3.83	0.0002
sexM	2354	2338	1.01	0.3200
age	594	99	6.02	0.0001

Earnings go up by $600 ±200 for each additional year of age. The model suggests that part of the difference between the earnings of men and women at this trucking company is due to their age: women tend to be younger than men. The confidence interval on the earnings difference is very broad — $2350 ±4700 — so broad that the sample doesn't provide much evidence for any difference at all.

One issue is whether the age dependence of earnings is just a mask for discrimination. To check out this possibility, fit another model that looks at the age dependence separately for men and women:

	Estimate	Std. Error	t value	Pr(>|t|)
Intercept	17178	8026	2.14	0.0343
sexM	-443	9174	-0.05	0.9615
age	530	225	2.35	0.0203
sexM:age	79	251	0.32	0.7530

The coefficient on the interaction term between age and sex is 79 ± 502 — no reason at all to think that it's different from zero. So, evidently, both women and men show the same increase in earnings with age.

Notice that in this last model the coefficient on sex itself has reversed sign from the previous models: Simpson's paradox. But note also that the confidence interval is very broad: $-\$443 \pm 18348$. Since the confidence interval includes zero, there is not good evidence to conclude that the coefficient is distinguishable from zero.

The broad confidence interval stems from the multi-collinearity between age and sex and their interaction term. As discussed in Section 12.5, sometimes it is necessary to leave out model terms in order to get reliable results.

Example 12.2: SAT Scores and Spending, revisited   Example 10.2 used data from 50 US states to try to see how teacher salaries and student-teacher ratios are related to test scores.The model used was sat ~ salary+ratio + frac, where frac is a covariate — what fraction of students in each state took the SAT. To interpret the results properly, it's important to know the confidence interval of the coefficients:

DATA FILE
sat.csv

	Estimate	Std. Error	t value	Pr(>|t|)
Intercept	1057.9	44.3	23.86	0.0000
salary	2.5	1.0	2.54	0.0145
ratio	-4.6	2.1	-2.19	0.0339
frac	-2.9	0.3	-12.76	0.0000

The confidence interval on salary is 2.5 ± 2.0, leaving little doubt that the data support the idea that higher salaries are associated with higher test scores. Higher student-faculty ratios seem to be associated with lower test scores. You can see this because the confidence interval on ratio, -4.6 ± 4.2, doesn't cover zero. The important role of the covariate frac is also confirmed by its tight confidence interval away from zero.

Collecting more data would allow more precise estimates to be made. For instance, collecting data over 4 years would reduce the standard errors in half, although what the estimates would be with the new data cannot be known until the analysis is done.

Aside. 12.1 Confidence intervals for very small samples.

When you have data with a very small n, say $n < 20$, a multiplier of 2 can be misleading. The reason has to do with how well a small sample can be assumed to represent the population. The correct multiplier depends on the difference between the sample size n and the number of model coefficients m:

$n - m$	1	2	3	5	10	15
Multiplier for 95% confidence level	12.7	4.3	3.2	2.6	2.2	2.1

For example, if you fit the running time versus age and sex model to 4 cases, the appropriate multiplier should be 12.7, not even close to 2.

12.4   Confidence in Predictions

When a model value is used for making a prediction, the coefficients themselves aren't of direct interest; it's the prediction that counts. Just as the precision of a coefficient can be established, each prediction has a precision that can be described using a confidence interval.

DATA FILE
galton.csv

To illustrate, consider making a prediction of a child's adult height when you know the heights of the mother and father and the child's sex. Using Galton's data from the 19th century, a simple and appropriate model is `height ~ sex + mother + father`.

	Estimate	Std. Error	t value	Pr($>$|t|)
Intercept	15.3448	2.7470	5.59	0.0000
sexM	5.2260	0.1440	36.29	0.0000
mother	0.3215	0.0313	10.28	0.0000
father	0.4060	0.0292	13.90	0.0000

Now consider a hypothetical man — call him Bill — whose mother is 67 inches tall and whose father is 69 inches tall. According to the model formula, Bill's predicted height is $15.3448 + 5.226 + 0.3215 \times 67 + 0.406 \times 69 = 70.13$ inches.

One way to calculate a confidence interval on a model value is similar to bootstrapping. Conduct many trials on resampled data. For each trial, fit the model and calculate the model value from the resulting coefficients. The spread of the various model values from the trials gives the standard error and confidence interval. For Bill, the 95% confidence interval on his model height works out to be 70.13 ± 0.27 inches: a precision of about a quarter of an inch. This high precision reflects the small standard errors of the coefficients which arise in turn from the large amount of data used to fit the model.

It is wrong to interpret this interval as saying something about the actual range of heights of men like Bill, that is, men whose mother is 67 inches and father 69 inches. The model-value confidence interval should not be interpreted as saying that 95 percent of such men will have heights in the interval 70.13 ± 0.27. Instead, this interval means that if you were to fit a model based on the entire population — not just the 898 cases in Galton's data — the model you would fit would likely produce a model value for Bill close to 70.13. In other words, the model-value confidence interval is not so much about the uncertainty in Bill's height as in what the model has to say about the average for men like Bill.

If you are interested in what the model has to say about the uncertainty the prediction of Bill's height, you need to ask a different question and compute a different confidence interval. The **prediction confidence interval** takes into account the spread of the cases around their model values: the residuals. For the model given above, the standard deviation of the residuals is 2.15 inches — a typical person varies from the model value by that amount.

The prediction confidence interval takes into account this case-by-case residual to give an indication of the range of heights into which the actual value is likely to fall. For men like Bill, the 95% prediction interval is 70.13 ± 4.24 inches. This is much larger than the interval on the model values, and reflects mainly the size of the residual of actual cases around their model values.

Example 12.3: Catastrophe in Grand Forks   In April 1997, there was massive flooding on the Red River in Minnesota and North Dakota, states in the northern US, due to record setting winter snows. The towns of Grand Forks and East Grand Forks were endangered and the story was in the news. I remember hearing a news report saying that the dikes in Grand Forks could protect against a flood level of 50 feet and that the National Weather Service predictions were for the river to reach a maximum of 47.5 to 49 feet. To the reporter and the city planners, this was good news. The city had never been better prepared and the preparations were paying off. To me, even knowing nothing about the area, the report was a sign of trouble. What kind of confidence interval was this 47.5 to 49? No confidence level was reported. Was it at a 50% level, was it at a 95% level? Was it a confidence interval on the model values alone or did it include the residuals from the model values? Did it take into account the extrapolation involved in handling record-setting conditions? Nothing in the news stories gave any insight into how precise previous predictions had been.

In the event, the floods reached 54.11 feet in Grand Forks, overtopping the dikes and innundating both towns. Damage was estimated to be more than \$1 billion, a huge amount given the small population of the area. In the aftermath of the flood, the mayor of East Grand Forks said, understandably, "They [the National Weather Service] missed it, and they not only missed it, they blew it big." The Grand Forks city engineer lamented, "with proper advance notice we could have protected the city to almost any elevation . . . if we had known, I'm sure that we could have protected a majority of the city."

But all the necessary information was available at the time. The forecast would have been accurate if a proper prediction confidence interval had been given. It turns out that the quoted 47.5 to 49 foot interval was not a confidence interval at all — it was the range of predictions from a model under two different scenarios, with and without ongoing precipitation.

Looking back on the history of predictions from the National Weather Service, the typical residual was about 11% of the prediction. Thus, a reasonable 95% confidence interval might have been ±22%, or, translated to feet, 48 ± 10 feet. Had this interval been presented, the towns might have been better prepared for the actual level of 54.11 feet, well within the confidence band.

Whether a 95% confidence level is appropriate for disaster planning is an open question and reflects the balance between the costs of preparation and the potential damage. If you plan using a 95% level, the upper boundary of the interval will be exceeded something like 2.5% of the time. This might be acceptable, or it might not be.

What shouldn't be controversial is that confidence intervals need to come with a clear statement of what they mean. For disaster planning, a model-value confidence interval is not so useful — it's about the quality of the model rather than the uncertainty in the actual outcome.

[Much of this example is drawn from the account by Roger Pielke [21].]

12.4.1   A Formula for the Standard Error

When you do lots of simulations, you start to see patterns. Sometimes these patterns are strong enough that you can anticipate the result of a simulation without doing it. For example, suppose you generate two random vectors A and B and calculate their correlation coefficient: the cosine of the angle between them. You will see some consistent patterns. The distribution of correlation coefficients will have zero mean and it will have standard deviation of $1/\sqrt{n}$.

Traditionally, statisticians have looked for such patterns in order save computational work. Why do a simulation, repeating something over and over again, if you can anticipate the result with a formula?

Such formulas exist for the standard error of a model coefficient. They are implemented in statistical software and used to generate the regression report. Here is a formula for computing the standard error of the coefficient on a model vector B in a model with more than one explanatory vector, e.g., $A \sim B + C + D$. You don't need to use this formula to calculate standard errors; the software will do that. The point of giving the formula is to show how the standard error depends on features of the model, so that you can strategize about how to design your models to give suitable standard errors.

$$\text{standard error of B coef.} = \| \text{ residuals } \| \frac{1}{\| B \|} \frac{1}{\sin(\theta)} \frac{1}{\sqrt{n}} \sqrt{\frac{n}{n-m}}.$$

There are five components to this formula, each of which says something about the standard error of a coefficient:

$\| \text{ residuals } \|$ The standard error is directly proportional to the size of the residuals.

$1/\| B \|$ The length of the model vector reflects the units of that variable or, for the indicator vector for a categorical variable, how many cases are at the corresponding level.

$1/\sin(\theta)$ This is the magnifying effect of collinearity. θ is the angle between explanatory vector B and all the other explanatory vectors. More precisely, it is the angle between B and the vector that would be found by fitting B to all the other explanatory vectors. When θ is $90°$, then $\sin(\theta) = 1$ and there is no collinearity and no magnification. When $\theta = 45°$, the magnification is only 1.4. But for strong collinearity, the magnification can be very large: when $\theta = 10°$, the magnification is 5.8. When $\theta = 1°$, magnification is 57. For $\theta = 0$, the alignment becomes a matter of redundancy, since B can be exactly modeled by the other explanatory variables. Magnification would be infinite, but statistical software will identify the redundancy and eliminate it.

$1/\sqrt{n}$ This reflects the amount of data. Larger samples give more precise estimates of coefficients, that is, a smaller standard error. Because of the square-root relationship, quadrupling the size of the sample will halve the size of the standard error. To improve the standard error by ten-fold requires a 100-fold increase in the size of the sample.

$\sqrt{n/(n-m)}$ The fitting process chooses coefficients that make the residuals as small as possible consistent with the data. This tends to underestimate the size of residuals — for any other estimate of the coefficients, even one well within the confidence interval, the residuals would be larger. This correction factor balances this bias out. n is, as always, the number of cases in the sample and m is the number of model vectors. So long as m is much less than n, which is typical of models, the bias correction factor is close to 1.

The formula suggests some ways to build models that will have coefficients with small standard errors.

- Use lots of data: large n.

- Include model terms that will account for lots of variation in the response and produce small residuals.

- But avoid collinearity.

The next section emphasizes the problems that can be introduced by collinearity.

12.5   Confidence and Collinearity

One of the key decisions that a modeler makes is whether to include an explanatory term; it might be a main term or it might be an interaction term or a transformation term.

The starting point for most people new to statistics might be summarized as follows:

Methodologically Ignorant Approach. Include just one explanatory variable.

Most people who work with data can understand tabulations of group means (in modeling language, $A \sim 1 + G$, where G is a categorical variable) or simple straight-line models ($A \sim 1 + B$, where B is a quantitative variable.)

At this point, the reader of this book should understand how to include in a model multiple explanatory variables and terms such as interactions. When people first learn this, they typically start putting in lots of terms:

Greedy Approach. Include everything, just in case.

The idea here is that you don't want to miss any detail; the fitting technology will untangle everything.

Perhaps the word "greedy" is already signalling the problem in a metaphorical way. The poet Horace (65BC-8BC) wrote, "He who is greedy is always in want." Or Seneca (1st century AD), "To greed, all nature is insufficient."

The flaw with the greedy approach to statistical modeling is not a moral fault. If adding a term improves your model, go for it! The problem is that, sometimes, adding a term can hurt the model by dramatically inflating standard errors.

DATA FILE
cps.csv

To illustrate, consider a set of models of wage from the Current Population Survey dataset.

A relatively simple model might take just the worker's education into account: wage ~ 1 + educ:

	Estimate	Std. Error	t value	Pr(>|t|)
Intercept	-0.746	1.045	-0.71	0.4758
educ	0.750	0.079	9.53	0.0000

The coefficient on educ says that a one-year increase in education is associated with a wage that is higher by 75 cents/hour. (Remember, these data are from the mid-1980s.) The standard error is 8 cents/hour per year of education, so the confidence interval is 75 ± 16 cents/hour per year of education.

A slightly more elaborate model includes age as a covariate. This might be important because education levels typically are lower in older workers, so a comparison of workers with the same level of education ought to hold age constant. A simple adjustment will take that into account. Here's the regression table on the model wage ~ 1 + educ + age:

	Estimate	Std. Error	t value	Pr(>|t|)
Intercept	-5.534	1.279	-4.33	0.0001
educ	0.821	0.077	10.66	0.0001
age	0.105	0.017	6.11	0.0001

In this new model, the coefficient on educ slightly from 75 to 82 cents/hour per year of education while leaving the standard error more or less the same.

Of course, wages also depend on experience. Every year of additional education tends to cut out a year of experience. Here is the regression report from the model wage ~ 1 + educ + age + exper:

	Estimate	Std. Error	t value	Pr(>|t|)
Intercept	-4.770	7.042	-0.68	0.4985
educ	0.948	1.155	0.82	0.4121
age	-0.022	1.155	-0.02	0.9845
exper	0.128	1.156	0.11	0.9122

Look at the regression table carefully. The standard errors have exploded! The confidence interval on educ is now 95 ± 231 cents/hour per year of education — a very imprecise estimate. Indeed, the confidence interval now includes zero, so the model is consistent with the skeptic's claim that education has no effect on wages, once you hold constant the level of experience and age of the worker.

A better interpretation is that greed has gotten the better of the modeler. The large standard errors in this model reflect a deficiency in the data: the multi-collinearity of `exper` with `age` and `educ` as described in Example 8.4.

A simple statement of the situation is this:

> Collinearity and multi-collinearity cause model coefficients to become less precise — they increase standard errors.

This doesn't mean that you should never include model terms that are collinear or multi-collinear. If the precision of your estimates is good enough, even with the collinear terms, then there is no problem. You, the modeler, can judge if the precision is adequate for your purposes.

The estimate 95 ± 231 cents/hour is probably not precise enough for any reasonable purpose. Including the `exper` term in the model has made the entire model useless, not just the `exper` term, but the other terms as well! That's what happens when you are greedy.

The good news is that you don't need to be afraid of trying a model term. Use the standard errors to judge when your model is acceptable and when you need to think about dropping terms due to collinearity.

Aside. 12.2 Redundancy and Multi-collinearity

Redundancy can be seen as an extreme case of multi-collinearity. So extreme that it renders the coefficients completely meaningless. That's why statistical software is written to delete redundant vectors. With multi-collinearity, things are more of a judgment call. The judgment needs to reside in you, the modeler.

12.6   Confidence and Bias

The margin of error tells you about the **precision** of a coefficient: how much variation is to be anticipated due to the random nature of sampling. It does not, unfortunately, tell you about the **accuracy** of the coefficient; how close it is to the "true" or "population" value.

A coefficient makes sense only within the context of a model. Suppose you fit a model $A \sim B + C$. Then you think better of things and look at the model $A \sim B + C + D$. Unless variable D happens to be orthogonal to B and C, the coefficients on B and C are going to change from the first model to the second.

If you take the point of view that the second model is "correct," then the coefficients you get from the first model are wrong. That is, the omission of D in the first model has **biased** the estimates of B and C.

On the other hand, if you think that the model A ~ B + C reflects the "truth," then the coefficients on B and C from A ~ B + C + D are biased.

The margin of error from any model tells you nothing about the potential bias. How could it? In order to measure the bias you would have to know the "correct" or "true" model.

The issue of bias often comes down to which is the correct set of model terms to include. This is not a statistical issue — it depends on how well your model corresponds to reality. Since people disagree about reality, perhaps it would be best to think about bias with respect to a given theory of how the world works. A model that produces unbiased coefficients according to your theory of reality might give biased coefficients with respect to someone else's theory.

Avoiding bias is a difficult matter and it's hard to know when you have succeeded. A very powerful but challenging strategy is to intervene to make your system simpler, so that every modeler's theories can agree. See Chapter 18.

12.7 Computational Technique

Regression reports are generated using software you have already encountered: lm to fit a model and **summary** to construct the report from the fitted model. To illustrate:

DATA FILE
swim100m.csv

```
> swim = fetchData("swim100m.csv")
> mod = lm(time ~ year + sex, data=swim)
> summary(mod)

...

            Estimate Std. Error t value Pr(>|t|)
(Intercept) 555.7168    33.7999   16.44  < 2e-16 ***
year         -0.2515     0.0173  -14.52  < 2e-16 ***
sexM         -9.7980     1.0129   -9.67  8.8e-14 ***
---
Signif. codes:  0 '***' 0.001 '**' 0.01 '*' 0.05 '.' 0.1 ' ' 1

Residual standard error: 3.98 on 59 degrees of freedom
Multiple R-squared: 0.844,        Adjusted R-squared: 0.839
F-statistic:  160 on 2 and 59 DF,  p-value: <2e-16
```

12.7.1 Confidence Intervals from Standard Errors

Given the coefficient estimate and the standard error from the regression report, the confidence interval is easily generated. For a 95% confidence interval, you just multiply the standard error by 2 to get the margin of error. For example, in the above, the margin of error on sexM is $2 \times 1.013 = 2.03$, or, in computer notation:

```
> 2 * 1.0129
[1] 2.03
```

If you want the two endpoints of the confidence interval, rather than just the margin of error, do these simple calculations: (1) subtract the margin of error from the estimate; (2) add the margin of error to the estimate. So,

```
> -9.798 - 2*1.0129
[1] -11.8
> -9.798 + 2*1.0129
[1] -7.77
```

The key thing is to remember the multiplier that is applied to the standard error. A multiplier of approximately 2 is for a 95% confidence level.

The confint() function provides a convenient way to calculate confidence intervals directly. It calculates the exact multiplier (which depends somewhat on the sample size) and applies it to the standard error to produce the confidence intervals.

```
> mod = lm(time ~ year + sex, data=swim)
> confint(mod)
                2.5 %  97.5 %
(Intercept) 488.083 623.350
year         -0.286  -0.217
sexM        -11.825  -7.771
```

It would be convenient if the regression report included confidence intervals rather than the standard error. Part of the reason it doesn't is historical: the desire to connect to the traditional by-hand calculations.

12.7.2 Bootstrapping Confidence Intervals

Confidence intervals on model coefficients can be computed using the same boot-strapping technique introduced in Chapter 5.

Start with your fitted model. To illustrate, here is a model of swimming time over the years, taking into account sex:

```
> swim = fetchData("swim100m.csv")
> lm(time ~ year + sex, data=swim)
...
(Intercept)        year        sexM
    555.717      -0.251      -9.798
```

These coefficients reflect one hypothetical draw from the population-based sampling distribution. It's impossible to get another draw from the "population" here: the actual records are all you've got.

But to approximate sampling variation, you can treat the sample as your population and re-sample:

```
> lm(time ~ year + sex, data=resample(swim))
...
(Intercept)          year          sexM
    620.387        -0.284       -10.031
```

Constructing many such re-sampling trials and collect the results

```
> s = do(500) * lm(time ~ year + sex, data=resample(swim))

> s

  Intercept    year    sexM sigma r-squared
1       508  -0.227   -9.04  2.61     0.910
2       508  -0.227   -9.12  2.57     0.924
3       526  -0.237   -8.80  3.03     0.879
4       552  -0.249  -11.28  4.68     0.822
5       528  -0.238   -8.86  3.80     0.823
... for 500 cases altogether ...
```

To find the standard error of the coefficients, just take the standard deviation across the re-sampling trials:

```
> sd(s)

Intercept      year      sexM     sigma r-squared
  44.2582    0.0224    0.9448    0.8354    0.0356
```

Multiplying the standard error by 2 gives the approximate 95% margin of error. Alternatively, you can use the `confint()` function to calculate this for you:

```
> confint(s, method="stderr")
       name    lower    upper
1 Intercept  467.419  641.330
2      year   -0.295   -0.207
3      sexM  -11.594   -7.881
4     sigma    2.096    5.378
5 r-squared    0.788    0.928
```

12.7.3 Prediction Confidence Intervals

When a model is used to make a prediction, it's helpful to be able to describe how precise the prediction is. For instance, suppose you want to use the `kidsfeet.csv` data set to make a prediction of the foot width of a girl whose foot length is 25 cm.

DATA FILE
kidsfeet.csv

First, fit your model:

```
> feet = fetchData("kidsfeet.csv")
> names(feet)
```

```
[1] "name"       "birthmonth" "birthyear"  "length"    "width"
[6] "sex"        "biggerfoot" "domhand"
> with(data=feet,levels(sex))
[1] "B" "G"
> mod = lm(width ~ length + sex, data=feet)
```

The object created by lm() contains a lot of information about the model and the data used for fitting the model. For the purposes of using the model to make a prediction, you want a function that takes the values for the explanatory variables as inputs and returns the corresponding model value as the output. To turn the model into a function, use makeFun(). You can call the resulting function anything you want. Here, it's called f:

```
> f = makeFun(mod)
```

Now you can use f() to convert inputs into outputs. Take care to use the right coding for categorical variables.

```
> f( length=25, sex="G" )
   1
8.93
```

In order to generate a confidence interval, the prediction function f() needs to be told what type of interval is wanted. There are two types of prediction confidence intervals:

Interval on the model value which reflects the sampling distributions of the coefficients themselves. To calculate this, use the interval="confidence" named argument:

```
> f( length=25, sex="G", interval="confidence")
     fit  lwr  upr
1 8.93 8.74 9.13
```

The components named lwr and upr are the lower and upper limits of the confidence interval, respectively.

Interval on the prediction which includes the variation due to the uncertainty in the coefficients as well as the size of a typical residual. To find this interval, use the interval="prediction" named argument:

```
> f( length=25, sex="G", interval="prediction" )
     fit  lwr  upr
1 8.93 8.13 9.74
```

The prediction interval is larger than the model-value confidence interval because the residual always gives additional uncertainty around the model value.

Reading Questions

- What is the difference between a "standard error" and a "confidence interval?"

- Why are confidence intervals generally constructed at a 95% level? What does the level mean?

- What is a sampling distribution?

- What is resampling? What is it used for?

- How does a confidence interval describe what might be called the reliability of a measurement?

- Does collinearity between explanatory vectors tend to make confidence intervals smaller or larger?

For exercises, see www.mosaic-web.org/StatisticalModeling/Exercises.

13

The Logic of Hypothesis Testing

Extraordinary claims demand extraordinary evidence. — Carl Sagan (1934-1996), astronomer

The test of a first-rate intelligence is the ability to hold two opposing ideas in mind at the same time and still retain the ability to function. — F. Scott Fitzgerald (1896-1940), novelist

A **hypothesis test** is a standard format for assessing statistical evidence. It is ubiquitous in scientific literature, most often appearing in the form of statements of **statistical significance** and notations like "$p < 0.01$" that pepper scientific journals.

Hypothesis testing involves a substantial technical vocabulary: null hypotheses, alternative hypotheses, test statistics, significance, power, p-values, and so on. The last section of this chapter lists the terms and gives definitions.

The technical aspects of hypothesis testing arise because it is a highly formal and quite artificial way of reasoning. This isn't a criticism. Hypothesis testing is this way because the "natural" forms of reasoning are inappropriate. To illustrate why, consider an example.

The stock market's ups and downs are reported each working day. Some people make money by investing in the market, some people lose. Is there reason to believe that there is a trend in the market that goes beyond the random-seeming daily ups and downs?

Figure 13.1 shows the closing price of the Dow Jones Industrial Average stock index for a period of about 10 years up until just before the 2008 recession, a

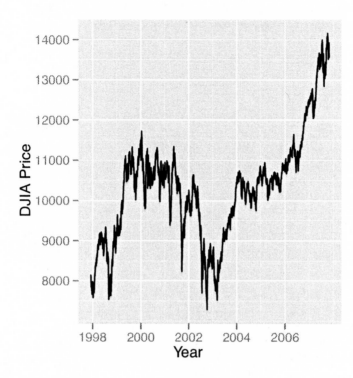

Figure 13.1: The closing price of the DJIA each day over 2500 trading days — a roughly 10 year period from the close on Dec. 5, 1997 to the close on Nov. 14, 2007. See Section 13.8 for an update on stock prices.

period when stocks were considered a good investment. It's evident that the price is going up and down in an irregular way, like a random walk. But it's also true that the price at the end of the period is much higher than the price at the start of the period.

Is there a trend or is this just a random walk? It's undeniable that there are fluctuations that look something like a random walk, but is there a trend buried under the fluctuations?

As phrased, the question contrasts two different possible hypotheses. The first is that the market is a pure random walk. The second is that the market has a systematic trend in addition to the random walk.

The natural question to ask is this: Which hypothesis is right?

Each of the hypotheses is actually a model: a representation of the world for a particular purpose. But each of the models is an incomplete representation of the world, so each is wrong.

It's tempting to rephrase the question slightly to avoid the simplistic idea of right versus wrong models: Which hypothesis is a better approximation to the real world? That's a nice question, but how to answer it in practice? To say how each hypothesis differs from the real world, you need to know already what the real world is like: Is there a trend in stock prices or not? That approach won't take you anywhere.

Another idea: Which hypothesis gives a better match to the data? This seems a simple matter: fit each of the models to the data and see which one gives the better fit. But recall that even junk model terms can lead to smaller residuals. In the case of the stock market data, it happens that the model that includes a trend will almost always give smaller residuals than the pure random walk model, even if the data really do come from a pure random walk.

The logic of hypothesis testing avoids these problems. The basic idea is to avoid having to reason about the real world by setting up a hypothetical world that is completely understood. The observed patterns of the data are then compared to what would be generated in the hypothetical world. If they don't match, then there is reason to doubt that the data support the hypothesis.

13.1   An Example of a Hypothesis Test

To illustrate the basic structure of a hypothesis test, here is one using the stock-market data.

The **test statistic** is a number that is calculated from the data and summarizes the observed patterns of the data. A test statistic might be a model coefficient or an R^2 value or something else. For the stock market data, it's sensible to use as the test statistic the start-to-end dollar difference in prices over the 2500-day period. The observed value of this test statistic is \$5446 — the DJIA stocks went up by this amount over the 10-year period.

The start-to-end difference can be used to test the hypothesis that the stock market is a random walk. (The reason to choose the random walk hypothesis for testing instead of the trend hypothesis will be discussed later.)

In order to carry out the hypothesis test, you construct a conjectural or hypothetical world in which the hypothesis is true. You can do this by building a simulation of that world and generating data from the simulation. Traditionally, such simulations have been implemented using probability theory and algebra to carry out the calculations of what results are likely in the hypothetical world. It's also possible to use direct computer simulation of the hypothetical world.

The challenge is to create a hypothetical world that is relevant to the real world. It would not, for example, be relevant to hypothesize that stock prices never change, nor would it be relevant to imaging that they change by an unrealistic amount.

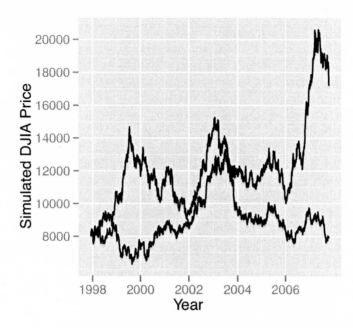

Figure 13.2: Two simulations of stock prices in a hypothetical world where the day-to-day change is equally likely to be up or down.

Later chapters will introduce a few techniques for doing this in statistical models. For this stock-price hypothesis, we'll imagine a hypothetical world in which prices change randomly up and down by the same daily amounts that they were seen to change in the real world.

Figure 13.2 shows a few examples of stock prices in the hypothetical world where prices are equally likely to go up or down each day by the same daily percentages seen in the actual data.

By generating many such simulations, and measuring from each individual simulation the start-to-end change in price, you get an indication of the range of likely outcomes in the hypothetical world. This is shown in Figure 13.3, which also shows the value observed in the real world — a price increase of $5446.

Since the observed start-to-end change in price is well within the possibilities generated by the simulation, it's tempting to say, "the observations support the hypothesis." For reasons discussed in the next section, however, the logically permitted conclusion is stiff and unnatural: *We fail to reject the hypothesis.*

Figure 13.3: The distribution of start-to-end differences in stock price in the hypothetical world where that day-to-day changes in price are equally likely to be up or down by the proportions observed in the real world. The value observed in the data, $5446, is marked with a vertical line.

13.2   Inductive and Deductive Reasoning

Hypothesis testing involves a combination of two different styles of reasoning: deduction and induction. In the deductive part, the hypothesis tester makes an assumption about how the world works and draws out, deductively, the consequences of this assumption: what the observed value of the test statistic should be if the hypothesis is true. For instance, the hypothesis that stock prices are a random walk was translated into a statement of the probability distribution of the start-to-end price difference.

In the inductive part of a hypothesis test, the tester compares the actual observations to the deduced consequences of the assumptions and decides whether the observations are consistent with them.

13.2.1   Deductive Reasoning

Deductive reasoning involves a series of rules that bring you from given assumptions to the consequences of those assumptions. For example, here is a form of deductive reasoning called a **syllogism**:

Assumption 1 No healthy food is fattening.

Assumption 2 All cakes are fattening.

Conclusion No cakes are healthy.

The actual assumptions involved here are questionable, but the pattern of logic is correct. If the assumptions were right, the conclusion would be right also.

Deductive reasoning is the dominant form in mathematics. It is at the core of mathematical proofs and lies behind the sorts of manipulations used in algebra. For example, the equation $3x + 2 = 8$ is a kind of assumption. Another assumption, known to be true for numbers, is that subtracting the same amount from both sides of an equation preserves the equality. So you can subtract 2 from both sides to get $3x = 6$. The deductive process continues — divide both sides by 3 — to get a new statement, $x = 2$, that is a logical consequence of the initial assumption. Of course, if the assumption $3x + 2 = 8$ was wrong, then the conclusion $x = 2$ would be wrong too.

The **contrapositive** is a way of recasting an assumption in a new form that will be true so long as the original assumption is true. For example, suppose the original assumption is, "My car is red." Another way to state this assumption is as a statement of implication, an if-then statement:

Assumption If it is my car, then it is red.

To form the contrapositive, you re-arrange the assumption to produce another statement:

Contrapositive If it is **not** red, then it is **not** my car.

Any assumption of the form "if [statement 1] then [statement 2]" has a contrapositive. In the example, statement 1 is "it is my car." Statement 2 is "it is red." The contrapositive looks like this:

Contrapositive If [negate statement 2] then [negate statement 1]

The contrapositive is, like algebraic manipulation, a re-rearrangement: reverse and negate. Reversing means switching the order of the two statements in the if-then structure. Negating a statement means saying the opposite. The negation of "it is red" is "it is not red." The negation of "it is my car" is "it is not my car." (It would be wrong to say that the negation of "it is my car" is "it is your car." Clearly it's true that if it is your car, then it is not my car. But there are many ways that the car can be not mine and yet not be yours. There are, after all, many other people in the world than you and me!)

Contrapositives often make intuitive sense to people. That is, people can see that a contrapostive statement is correct even if they don't know the name of the logical re-arrangement. For instance, here is a variety of ways of re-arranging the two clauses in the assumption, "If that is my car, then it is red." Some of the arrangements are logically correct, and some aren't.

Original Assumption: *If it is my car, then it is red.*

— Negate first statement: *If it is not my car, then it is red.*

   Wrong. Other people can have cars that are not red.

— Negate only second statement: *If it is my car, then it is not red.*

   Wrong. The statement contradicts the original assumption that my car is red.

— Negate both statements: *If it is not my car, then it is not red.*

   Wrong. Other people can have red cars.

— Reverse statements: *If it is red, then it is my car.*

   Wrong. Apples are red and they are not my car. Even if "it" is a car, not every red car is mine.

— Reverse and negate first: *If it is red, then it is not my car.*

   Wrong. My car is red.

— Reverse and negate second: *If it is not red, then it is my car.*

   Wrong. Oranges are not red, and they are not my car.

— Reverse and negate both — the contrapositive: *If it is not red, then it is not my car.*

   Correct.

13.2.2   Inductive Reasoning

In contrast to deductive reasoning, **inductive reasoning** involves generalizing or extrapolating from a set of observations to conclusions. An observation is not an assumption: it is something we see or otherwise perceive. For instance, you can go to Australia and see that kangaroos hop on two legs. Every kangaroo you see is hopping on two legs. You conclude, inductively, that all kangaroos hop on two legs.

Inductive conclusions are not necessarily correct. There might be one-legged kangaroos. That you haven't seen them doesn't mean they can't exist. Indeed, Europeans believed that all swans are white until explorers discovered that there are black swans in Australia.

Suppose you conduct an experiment involving 100 people with fever. You give each of them aspirin and observe that in all 100 the fever is reduced. Are you entitled to conclude that giving aspirin to a person with fever will reduce the fever? Not really. How do you know that there are no people who do not respond to aspirin and who just happened not be be included in your study group?

Perhaps you're tempted to hedge by weakening your conclusion: "Giving aspirin to a person with fever will reduce the fever most of the time." This seems reasonable, but it is still not necessarily true. Perhaps the people in you study had a special form of fever-producing illness and that most people with fever have a different form.

By the standards of deductive reasoning, inductive reasoning does not work. No reasonable person can argue about the deductive, contrapositive reasoning concerning the red car. But reasonable people can very well find fault with the conclusions drawn from the study of aspirin.

Here's the difficulty. If you stick to valid deductive reasoning, you will draw conclusions that are correct given that your assumptions are correct. But how can you know if your assumptions are correct? How can you make sure that your assumptions adequately reflect the real world? At a practical level, most knowledge of the world comes from observations and induction.

The philosopher David Hume noted the everyday inductive "fact" that food nourishes us, a conclusion drawn from everyday observations that people who eat are nourished and people who do not eat waste away. Being inductive, the conclusion is suspect. Still, it would be a foolish person who refuses to eat for want of a deductive proof of the benefits of food.

Inductive reasoning may not provide a proof, but it is nevertheless useful.

13.3   The Null Hypothesis

A key aspect of hypothesis testing is the choice of the hypothesis to test. The stock market example involved testing the random-walk hypothesis rather than the trend hypothesis. Why? After all, the hypothesis of a trend is more interesting than the random-walk hypothesis; it's more likely to be useful if true.

It might seem obvious that the hypothesis you should test is the hypothesis that you are most interested in. But this is wrong.

In a hypothesis test one *assumes* that the hypothesis to be tested is true and draws out the consequences of that assumption in a deductive process. This can be written as an if-then statement:

> If hypothesis H is true, then the test statistic S will be drawn from a probability distribution P.

For example, in the stock market test, the assumption that the day-to-day price change is random leads to the conclusion that the test statistic — the start-to-end price difference — will be a draw from the distribution shown in Figure 13.3.

The inductive part of the test involves comparing the observed value of the test statistic S to the distribution P. There are two possible outcomes of this comparison:

Agreement S is a plausible outcome from P.

Disagreement S is not a plausible outcome from P.

Suppose the outcome is agreement between S and P. What can be concluded? Not much. Recall the statement "If it is my car, then it is red." An observation of a red car does not legitimately lead to the conclusion that the car is mine. For an if-then statement to be applicable to observations, one needs to observe the if-part of the statement, not the then-part.

An outcome of disagreement gives a more interesting result, because the contrapositive gives logical traction to the observation; "If it is not red, then it is not my car." Seeing "not red" implies "not my car." Similarly, seeing that S is not a plausible outcome from P, tells you that H is not a plausible possibility. In such a situation, you can legitimately say, "I reject the hypothesis."

Ironically, in the case of observing agreement between S and P, the only permissible statement is, "I fail to reject the hypothesis." You certainly aren't entitled to say that the evidence causes you to accept the hypothesis.

This is an emotionally unsatisfying situation. If your observations are consistent with your hypothesis, you certainly want to accept the hypothesis. But that is not an acceptable conclusion when performing a formal hypothesis test. There are only two permissible conclusions from a formal hypothesis test:

- I reject the hypothesis.

- I fail to reject the hypothesis.

In choosing a hypothesis to test, you need to keep in mind two criteria.

Criterion 1 The only possible interesting outcome of a hypothesis test is "I reject the hypothesis." So make sure to pick a hypothesis that it will be interesting to reject.

The role of the hypothesis is to be refuted or nullified, so it is called the **null hypothesis**.

What sorts of statements are interesting to reject? Often these take the form of the **conventional wisdom** or of **no effect**.

For example, in comparing two fever-reducing drugs, an appropriate null hypothesis is that the two drugs have the same effect. If you reject the null, you can say that they don't have the same effect. But if you fail to reject the null, you're in much the same position as before you started the study.

Failing to reject the null may mean that the null is true, but it equally well may mean only that your work was not adequate: not enough data, not a clever enough experiment, etc. Rejecting the null can reasonably be taken to indicate that the null hypothesis is false, but failing to reject the null tells you very little.

Criterion 2 To perform the deductive stage of the test, you need to be able to calculate the range of likely outcomes of the test statistic. This means that the hypothesis needs to be specific.

The assumption that stock prices are a random walk has very definite consequences for how big a start-to-end change you can expect to see. On the other hand, the assumption "there is a trend" leaves open the question of how big the trend is. It's not specific enough to be able to figure out the consequences.

13.4 The p-value

One of the consequences of randomness is that there isn't a completely clean way to say whether the observations fail to match the consequences of the null hypothesis. In principle, this is a problem even with simple statements like "the car is red." There is a continuous range of colors and at some point one needs to make a decision about how orange the car can be before it stops being red.

Figure 13.3 shows the probability distribution for the start-to-end stock price change under the null hypothesis that stock prices are a random walk. The observed value of the test statistic, $5446, falls under the tall part of the curve — it's a plausible outcome of a random draw from the probability distribution.

The conventional way to measure the plausibility of an outcome is by a **p-value**. The p-value of an observation is always calculated with reference to a probability distribution derived from the null hypothesis.

P-values are closely related to percentiles. The observed value $5446 falls at the 81rd percentile of the distribution. An observation that's at or beyond the extremes of the distribution is implausible. This would correspond to either very high percentiles or very low percentiles. Being at the 81rd percentile implies that 19 percent of draws would be even more extreme, falling even further to the right than $5446.

The p-value is the fraction of possible draws from the distribution that are as extreme or more extreme than the observed value. If the concern is only with values bigger than $5446, then the p-value is 0.19.

A small p-value indicates that the actual value of the test statistic is quite surprising as an outcome from the null hypothesis. A large p-value means that the test statistic value is run of the mill, not surprising, not enough to satisfy the "if" part of the contrapositive.

The convention in hypothesis testing is to consider the observation as being implausible when the p-value is less than 0.05. In the stock market example, the p-value is larger than 0.05, so the outcome is to fail to reject the null hypothesis that stock prices are a random walk with no trend.

13.5   Rejecting by Mistake

The p-value for the hypothesis test of the possible trend in stock-price was 0.19, not small enough to justify rejecting the null hypothesis that stock prices are a random walk with no trend. A smaller p-value, one less than 0.05 by convention, would have led to rejection of the null. The small p-value would have indicated that the observed value of the test statistic was implausible in a world where the null hypothesis is true.

Now turn this around. Suppose the null hypothesis really were true; suppose stock prices really are a random walk with no trend. In such a world, it's still possible to see an implausible value of the test statistic. But, if the null hypothesis is true, then seeing an implausible value is misleading; rejecting the null is a mistake. This sort of mistake is called a **Type I error**.

Such mistakes are not uncommon. In a world where the null is true — the only sort of world where you can falsely reject the null — they will happen 5% of the time so long as the threshold for rejecting the null is a p-value of 0.05.

The way to avoid such mistakes is to lower the p-value threshold for rejecting the null. Lowering it to, say, 0.01, would make it harder to mistakenly reject the null. On the other hand, it would also make it harder to correctly reject the null in a world where the null ought to be rejected.

The threshold value of the p-value below which the null should be rejected is a probability: the probability of rejecting the null in a world where the null hypothesis is true. This probability is called the **significance level** of the test.

It's important to remember that the significance level is a **conditional probability**. It is the probability of rejecting the null in a world where the null hypothesis is actually true. Of course that's a hypothetical world, not necessarily the real world.

13.6   Failing to Reject

In the stock-price example, the large p-value of 0.19 led to a failure to reject the null hypothesis that stock prices are a random walk. Such a failure doesn't mean that the null hypothesis is true, although it's encouraging news to people who want to believe that the null hypothesis is true.

You never get to "accept the null" because there are reasons why, even if the null were wrong, it might *not* have been rejected:

- You might have been unlucky. The randomness of the sample might have obscured your being able to see the trend in stock prices.

- You might not have had enough data. Perhaps the trend is small and can't easily be seen.

- Your test statistic might not be sensitive to the ways in which the system differs from the null hypothesis. For instance, suppose that there is an small average tendency for each day's activity on the stock market to undo the previous day's change: the walk isn't exactly random. Looking for large values of the start-to-end price difference will not reveal this violation of the null. A more sensitive test statistic would be the correlation between price changes on successive days.

A helpful idea in hypothesis testing is the **alternative hypothesis**: the pet idea of what the world is like if the null hypothesis is wrong. The alternative hypothesis plays the role of the thing that you would like to prove. In the hypothesis-testing drama, this is a very small role, since the only possible outcomes of a hypothesis test are (1) reject the null and (2) fail to reject the null. The alternative hypothesis is not directly addressed by the outcome of a hypothesis test.

The role of the alternative hypothesis is to guide you in interpreting the results if you do fail to reject the null. The alternative hypothesis is also helpful in deciding how much data to collect.

To illustrate, suppose that the stock market really does have a trend hidden inside the random day-to-day fluctuations with a standard deviation of $106.70. Imagine that the trend is $2 per day: a pet hypothesis.

Suppose the world really were like the alternative hypothesis. What is the probability that, in such a world, you would end up failing to reject the null hypothesis? Such a mistake, where you fail to reject the null in a world where the alternative is actually true, is called a **Type II error**.)

This logic can be confusing at first. It's tempting to reason that, if the alternative hypothesis is true, then the null must be false. So how could you fail to reject the null? And, if the alternative hypothesis is assumed to be true, why would you even consider the null hypothesis in the first place?

Keep in mind that neither the null hypothesis nore the alternative hypothesis should be taken as "true." They are just competing hypotheses, conjectures used to answer "what-if?" questions.

Aside. 13.1 Calculating a Power

Here are the steps in calculating the power of the hypothesis test of stock market prices. The null hypothesis is that prices are a pure random walk as illustrated in Figure 13.2. The alternative hypothesis is that in addition to the random component, the stock prices have a systematic trend of increasing by $2 per day.

1. Go back to the null hypothesis world and find the thresholds for the test statistic that would cause you to reject the null hypothesis. Referring to Figure 13.3, you can see that a test statistic of $11,000.00 would have produced a p-value of 0.05.

2. Now return to the alternative hypothesis world. In this world, what is the probability that the test statistic would have been bigger than $11,000? This question can be answered by the same sort of simulation as in Figure 13.2 but with a $2 price increase added each day. Doing the calculation gives a probability of 0.16.

Section 15.7 discusses power calculations for models.

The probability of rejecting the null in a world where the alternative is true is called the **power** of the hypothesis test. Of course, if the alternative is true, then it's completely appropriate to reject the null, so a large power is desirable.

A power calculation involves considering both the null and alternative hypotheses. Aside 13.1 shows the logic applied to the stock-market question. It results in a power of 16%.

The power of 16% for the stock market test means that even if the pet theory of the $2 daily trend were correct, there is only a 16% chance of rejecting the null. In other words, the study is quite weak.

When the power is small, failure to reject the null can reasonably be interpreted as a failure in the modeler (or in the data collection or in the experiment). The study has given very little information.

Just because the power is small is no reason to doubt the null hypothesis. Instead, you should think about how to conduct a better, more powerful study.

One way a study can be made more powerful is to increase the sample size. Fortunately, it's feasible to figure out how large the study should be to achieve a given power. The reason is that the power depends on the two hypotheses: the null and the alternative. In carrying out the simulations using the null and alternative hypotheses, it's possible to generate any desired amount of simulated data. It turns out that reliably detecting — a power of 80% — a $2 per day trend in stock prices requires about 75 years worth of data. This long historical period is probably not relevant to today's investor. Indeed, it's just about all the data that is actually available: the DJIA was started in 1928.

When the power is small for realistic amounts of data, the phenomenon you are seeking to find may be undetectable.

13.7   A Glossary of Hypothesis Testing

Null Hypothesis A statement about the world that you are interested to disprove. The null is almost always something that is clearly relevant and not controversial: that the conventional wisdom is true or that there is no relationship between variables. Examples: "The drug has no influence on blood pressure." "Smaller classes do not improve school performance."

The allowed outcomes of the hypothesis test relate only to the null:

- Reject the null hypothesis.
- Fail to reject the null hypothesis.

Alternative Hypothesis A statement about the world that motivates your study and stands in contrast to the null hypothesis. "The drug will reduce blood pressure by 5 mmHg on average." "Decreasing class size from 30 to 25 will improve test scores by 3%."

The outcome of the hypothesis test is not informative about the alternative. The importance of the alternative is in setting up the study: choosing a relevant test statistic and collecting enough data.

Test Statistic The number that you use to summarize your study. This might be the sample mean, a model coefficient, or some other number. Later chapters will give several examples of test statistics that are particularly appropriate for modeling.

Type I Error A wrong outcome of the hypothesis test of a particular type. Suppose the null hypothesis were really true. If you rejected it, this would be an error: a type I error.

Type II Error A wrong outcome of a different sort. Suppose the alternative hypothesis were really true. In this situation, failing to reject the null would be an error: a type II error.

Significance Level A conditional probability. In the world where the null hypothesis is true, the significance is the probability of making a type I error. Typically, hypothesis tests are set up so that the significance level will be less than 1 in 20, that is, less than 0.05. One of the things that makes hypothesis testing confusing is that you do not know whether the null hypothesis is correct; it is merely assumed to be correct for the purposes of the deductive phase of the test. So you can't say what is the probability of a type I error. Instead, the significance level is the probability of a type I error *assuming* that the null hypothesis is correct.

Ideally, the significance level would be zero. In practice, one accepts the risk of making a type I error in order to reduce the risk of making a type II error.

p-value This is the usual way of presenting the result of the hypothesis test. It is a number that summarizes how atypical the observed value of the test statistic would be in a world where the null hypothesis is true. The convention for rejecting the null hypothesis is $p < 0.05$.

The p-value is closely related to the significance level. It is sometimes called the **achieved significance level**.

Power This is a conditional probability. But unlike the significance, the condition is that the alternative hypothesis is true. The power is the probability that, in the world where the alternative is true, you will reject the null. Ideally, the power should be 100%, so that if the alternative really were true the null hypothesis would certainly be rejected. In practice, the power is less than this and sometimes much less.

In science, there is an accepted threshold for the p-value: 0.05. But, somewhat strangely, there is no standard threshold for the power. When you see a study which failed to reject the null, it is helpful to know what the power of the study was. If the power was small, then failing to reject the null is not informative.

13.8   An Update on Stock Prices

Figure 13.1 shows stock prices over the 10-year period from Dec. 5, 1997 to Nov. 14, 2007. For comparison, Figure 13.4 shows a wider time period, the 25-year period from 1985 to the month this section is being written in 2011.

When the first edition of this book was being written, in 2007, the 10-year period was a natural sounding interval, but a bit more information on the choice can help to illuminate a potential problem with hypothesis testing. I wanted to include a stock-price example because there is such a strong disconnection between the theories of stock prices espoused by professional economists — daily changes are a random walk — and the stories presented in the news, which wrongly provide a specific daily cause for each small change and see "bulls" and "bears" behind month- and year-long trends. I originally planned a time frame of 5 years — a nice round number. But the graph of stock prices from late 2002 to late 2007 shows a pretty steady upward trend, something that's visually inconsistent with the random-walk null hypothesis. I therefore changed my plan, and included 10-years worth of data. If I had waited another year, through the 2008 stock market crash, the upward trend would have been eliminated. In 2010 and early 2011, the market climbed up again, only to fall dramatically in mid-summer.

That change from 5 to 10 years was inconsistent with the logic of hypothesis testing. I was, in effect, changing my data — by selecting the start and end points — to make them more consistent with the claim I wanted to make. This is always a strong temptation, and one that ought to be resisted or, at least, honestly accounted for.

Reading Questions

- What is a "null hypothesis?" Why does it play a special role in hypothesis testing?
- Why is it good to have a hypothesis test with a low "significance level?"
- Why is it good to have a hypothesis test with a high "power?"
- What is a p-value?
- Why are there two kinds of potential errors in hypothesis testing, Type I and Type II?

For exercises, see www.mosaic-web.org/StatisticalModeling/Exercises.

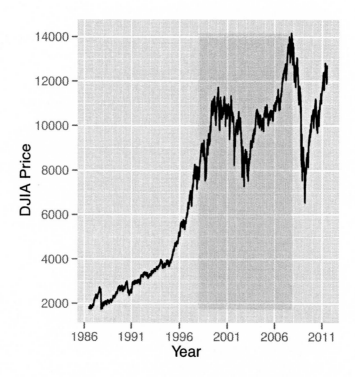

Figure 13.4:   Closing prices of the Dow Jones Industrial Average for the 25 years before July 9, 2011, the date on which the plot was made. The sub-interval used in this book's first edition is shaded.

14

Hypothesis Testing on Whole Models

A wise man ... proportions his belief to the evidence. — David Hume (1711 – 1776), Scottish philosopher

Fitted models describe patterns in samples. Modelers interpret these patterns as indicating relationships between variables in the population from which the sample was drawn. But there is another possibility. Just as the constellations in the night sky are the product of human imagination applied to the random scattering of stars within range of sight, so the patterns indicated by a model might be the result of accidental alignments in the sample.

Deciding how seriously to take the patterns identified by a model is a problem that involves judgment. Are the patterns consistent with well established understanding of how the system works? Are the patterns corroborated by other sources of data? Are the model results sensitive to trivial changes in the model design?

Before undertaking that judgment, it helps to apply a much simpler standard of evidence. The conventional interpretation of a model such as A $\sim$ B+C+... is that the variables on the right side of the modeler's tilde explain the response variable on the left side. The first question to ask is whether the explanation provided by the model is stronger than the "explanation" that would be arrived at if the variables on the right side were random — explanatory variables in name only without any real connection with the response variable A.

It's important to remember that in a hypothesis test, the null hypothesis is about the **population**. The null hypothesis claims that in the population the explanatory variables are unlinked to the response variable. Such a hypothesis does not rule out the possibility that, in the sample, the explanatory variables are aligned with the response variable. The hypothesis merely claims that any such alignment is accidental, due to the randomness of the sampling process.

14.1   The Permutation Test

The null hypothesis is that the explanatory variables are unlinked with the response variable. One way to see how big a test statistic will be in a world where
the null hypothesis holds true is to randomize the explanatory variables in the
sample to destroy any relationship between them and the response variable. To
illustrate how this can be done in a way that stays true to the sample, consider
a small data set:

A	B	C
3	37.1	M
4	17.4	M
5	26.8	F
7	44.3	F
5	19.7	F

Imagine that the table has been cut into horizontal slips with one case on each
slip. The response variable — say, A — has been written to the left of a dotted
line. The explanatory variables B and C are on the right of the dotted line, like
this:

A=3	B=37.1	C=M
A=4	B=17.4	C=M
A=5	B=26.8	C=F
A=7	B=44.3	C=F
A=5	B=19.7	C=F

To randomize the cases, tear each sheet along the dotted line. Place the right
sides — the explanatory variables — on a table in their original order. Then,
randomly shuffle the left halves — the response variable — and attach each to a
right half.

A=4	B=37.1	C=M
A=5	B=17.4	C=M
A=5	B=26.8	C=F
A=3	B=44.3	C=F
A=7	B=19.7	C=F

None of the cases in the shuffle are genuine cases, except possibly by chance.
Yet each of the shuffled explanatory variables is true to its distribution in the
original sample and the relationships among explanatory variables — collinearity
and multi-collinearity — are also authentic.

Each possible order for the left halves of the cards is called a **permutation**. A hypothesis test conducted in this way is called a **permutation test**.

The logic of a permutation test is straightforward. To set up the test, you need to choose a test statistic that reflects some aspect of the system of interest to you.

Here are the steps involved in permutation test:

Step 1 Calculate the value of the test statistic on the original data.

Step 2 Permute the data and calculate the test statistic again. Repeat this many times, collecting the results. This gives the distribution of the test statistic under the null hypothesis.

Step 3 Read off the p-value as the fraction of the results in (2) that are more extreme than the value in (1).

DATA FILE
galton.csv

To illustrate, consider a model of heights from Galton's data and a question Galton didn't consider: Does the number of children in a family help explain the eventual adult height of the children? Perhaps in families with large numbers of children, there is competition over food, so children don't grow so well. Or, perhaps having a large number of children is a sign of economic success, and the children of successful families have more to eat.

The regression report indicates that larger family size is associated with shorter children:

	Estimate	Std. Error	t value	Pr($>$|t|)
Intercept	67.800	0.296	228.96	0.0000
nkids	**-0.169**	0.044	-3.83	0.0001

For every additional sibling, the family's children are shorter by about 0.17 inches on average. The confidence interval is -0.169 ± 0.088.

Now for the permutation test, using the coefficient on nkids as the test statistic:

Step 1 Calculate the test statistic on the data without any shuffling. As shown above, the coefficient on nkids is −0.169.

Step 2 Permute and re-calculate the test statistic, many times. One set of 10000 trials gave values of −0.040, 0.037, −0.094, −0.069, 0.062, −0.045, and so on. The distribution is shown in Figure 14.1.

Step 3 The p-value is fraction of times that the values from (2) are more extreme than the value of −0.169 from the unshuffled data. As Figure 14.1 shows, few of the permutations produced an nkid coefficient anywhere near −0.169. The p-value is very small, $p < 0.001$.

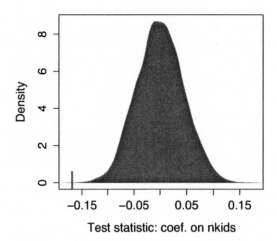

Figure 14.1: Distribution of the coefficient on `nkids` from the model `height` ∼ `1+nkids` from many permutation trials. Tick mark: the coefficient −0.169 from the unshuffled data.

Conclusion, the number of kids in a family accounts for somewhat more of the children's heights than is likely to occur with a random explanatory variable.

The idea of a permutation test is almost a century old. It was proposed originally by statistician Ronald Fisher (1890-1960). Permutation tests were infeasible for even moderately sized data sets until the 1970s when inexpensive computation became a reality. In Fisher's day, when computing was expensive, permutation tests were treated as a theoretical notion and actual calculations were performed using algebraic formulas and calculus. Such formulas could be derived for a narrow range of test statistics such as the sample mean, differences between group means, and the coefficient of determination R^2. Fisher himself derived the sampling distributions of these test statistics.[22]

Ronald Fisher

14.2 R^2 and the F Statistic

The coefficient of determination R^2 measures what fraction of the variance of the response variable is "explained" or "accounted for" or — to put it simply — "modeled" by the explanatory variables. R^2 is a comparison of two quantities: the variance of the fitted model values to the variance of the response variable. R^2 is a single number that puts the explanation in the context of what remains unexplained. It's a good test statistic for a hypothesis test.

Using R^2 as the test statistic in a permutation test would be simple enough. There are advantages, however, to thinking about things in terms of a closely related statistic invented by Fisher and named in honor of him: the **F statistic**.

Like R^2, the F statistic compares the size of the fitted model values to the size of the residuals. But the notion of "size" is somewhat different. Rather than measuring size directly by the variance or by the sum of squares, the F statistic takes into account the number of model vectors.

To see where F comes from, consider the **random model walk**. In a regular random walk, each new step is taken in a random direction. In a random model walk, each "step" consists of adding a new random explanatory term to a model. The "position" is measured as the R^2 from the model.

The starting point of the random model walk is the simple model A $\sim$ 1 with just $m = 1$ model vector. This model always produces $R^2 = 0$ because the all-cases-the-same model can't account for any variance. Taking a "step" means adding a random model vector, x_1, giving the model A $\sim$ 1+x_1. Each new step adds a new random vector to the model:

m	Model
1	A $\sim$ 1
2	A $\sim$ 1+x_1
3	A $\sim$ 1+x_1+x_2
4	A $\sim$ 1+x_1+x_2+x_3
$\vdots$	
n	A $\sim$ 1+x_1+x_2+x_3 + $\cdots$ + x_{n-1}

Figure 14.2 shows R^2 versus m for several random model walks in data with $n = 50$ cases. Each successive step adds in its own individual random explanatory term.

All the random walks start at $R^2 = 0$ for $m = 1$. All of them reach $R^2 = 1$ when $m = n$. Adding any more vectors beyond $m = n$ simply creates redundancy; $R^2 = 1$ is the best that can be done.

Notice that each step increases R^2 — none of the random walks goes down in value as m gets bigger.

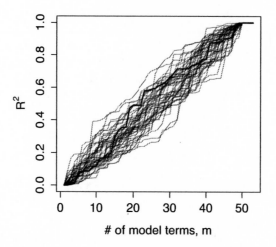

Figure 14.2:   Random model walks for $n = 50$ cases. The "position" of the walk is R^2. This is plotted versus number of model vectors m. The heavy line shows one simulation. The light lines show other simulations. All of the simulations reach $R^2 = 1$ when $m = n$.

Figure 14.3: The R^2 from a fitted model defines a model walk with two segments. The F statistic is the ratio of the slopes of these segments. Here a model with $m = 10$ has produced $R^2 = 0.65$ when fitted to a data set with $n = 50$ cases.

The R^2 from a fitted model gives a single point on the model walk that divides the overall walk into two segments, as shown in Figure 14.3. The slope of each of the two segments has a straightforward interpretation. The slope of the segmented labeled "Model" describes the rate at which R^2 is increased by a typical model vector. The slope can be calculated as $R^2/(m-1)$.

The slope of the segment labeled "Residuals" describes how adding a random vector to the model would increase R^2. From the figure, you can see that a typical model vector increases R^2 much faster than a typical random vector. Numerically, the slope is $(1-R^2)/(m-n)$.

The F statistic is the ratio of these two slopes:

$$F = \frac{\text{Slope of model segment}}{\text{Slope of residual segment}} = \frac{R^2}{m-1} \bigg/ \frac{1-R^2}{n-m}. \qquad (14.1)$$

In interpreting the F statistic, keep in mind that if the model vectors were no better than random, F should be near 1. When F is much bigger than 1, it indicates that the model terms explain more than would be expected at random. The p-value provides an effective way to identify when F is "much bigger than 1." Calculating the p-value involves knowing the exact shape of the F distribution. In practice, this is done with software.

The number $m-1$ in the numerator of F counts how many model terms there are other than the intercept. In standard statistical nomenclature, this is called the **degrees of freedom of the numerator**. The number $n-m$ in the denominator of F counts how many random terms would need to be added to make a "perfect" fit to the response variable. This number is called the **degrees of freedom of the denominator**.

Example 14.1: Marriage and Astrology

Does your astrological sign predict when you will get married? To test this possibility, consider a small set of data collected from an on-line repository of marriage licenses in Mobile County, Alabama in the US. The licenses contain a variety of information: age at marriage, years of college, date of birth, date of the wedding and so on. For those with mystical interests, date of birth can be converted to an astrological sign, resulting in a data set that looks like this:

DATA FILE
marriage.csv

Sign	Age	College
Aquarius	22.6	4
Sagittarius	25.1	0
Taurus	39.6	1
Cancer	45.8	6
Leo	26.4	1

... and so on for 98 cases altogether.

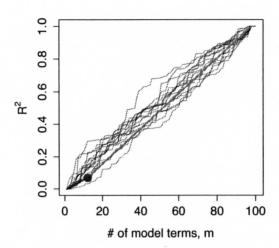

Figure 14.4: Random model walks compared to the model Age $\sim$ Sign. The actual model does not stand out from the set of random model walks.

There are, of course, 12 different astrological signs, so the model Age $\sim$ Sign has $m = 12$. With the intercept term, that leaves 11 vectors to represent Sign. Fitting the model produces $R^2 = 0.070$. To generate a p-value, this can be compared to the distribution of R^2 for random vectors with $n = 98$ and $m = 12$, giving $p = 0.885$. This large value is consistent with the null hypothesis that Sign is unlinked with Age.

The pair $m = 12, R^2 = 0.070$ gives one point on a model walk. This is compared to random model walks in the Figure 14.4. The 11 indicator vectors that arise from the 12 levels of Sign do not contribute more to R^2 than would be expected from 11 random vectors.

Now consider a different model, Age $\sim$ College. This model undertakes to explain age at marriage by whether the person went to college. The R^2 from this model is only 0.065 — the College variable accounts for somewhat less of the variability in Age than astrological Sign. Yet this small R^2 is statistically significant — $p = 0.017$. The reason is that College accomplishes its explanation using only a single model vector, compared to the 11 vectors in Sign. The model walk for the College model starts with a steep increase because the whole gain of 0.065 is accomplished with just one model vector, rather than being achieved using 11 vectors as in Sign.

14.3   The ANOVA Report

The F statistic compares the variation that is explained by the model to the variation that remains unexplained. Doing this involves taking apart the variation; partitioning it into a part associated with the model and a part associated with the residuals.

Such partitioning of variation is fundamental to statistical methods. When done in the context of linear models, this partitioning is given the name **analysis of variance** (ANOVA, for short). This name stays close to the dictionary definition of "analysis" as "the process of separating something into its constituent elements." [23]

The analysis of variance is often presented in a standard way: the ANOVA **report**. For example, here is the ANOVA report for the marriage-astrology model `Age ~ Sign`:

	Df	Sum Sq	Mean Sq	F value	Pr(>F)
Sign	11	1402	127	0.59	0.8359
Residuals	86	18724	218		

In this ANOVA report, there are two rows. The first refers to the explanatory variable, the second to the residual.

Since ANOVA is about variance, the mean of the response variable is subtracted out before the analysis is performed, just as it would be when calculating a variance.

The column labeled "Sum Sq" gives the sum of squares of the fitted model values and the residual vector. The column headed "Df" is the degrees of freedom of the term. This is simply the number of model vectors associated with that term or, for the residual, the total number of cases minus the number of explanatory vectors. For a categorical variable, the number of explanatory vectors is the number of levels of that variable minus one for each redundant vector. (For instance, every categorical variable has one degree of redundancy with the intercept). Because there are 12 levels in `Sign`, the 12 astrological signs, the `Sign` variable has 11 degrees of freedom.

The degrees of freedom of the residuals is the number of cases n minus the number of model terms m.

Example 14.2: Is height genetically determined?

Francis Galton's study of height in the late 1800s was motivated by his desire to quantify genetic inheritance. In 1859, Galton read Charles Darwin's *On the*

Aside. 14.1 F and R^2

The R^2 doesn't appear explicitly in the ANOVA report, but it's easy to calculate since the report does give the square lengths of the two legs of the model triangle. In the above ANOVA report for `Age ~ Sign`, the square length of the hypotenuse is, through the pythagorean relationship, simply the sum of the two legs: in this report, $1402 + 18724 = 20126$. The model's R^2 is the square length of the fitted-model-value leg divided into the square length of the hypotenuse: $1402/20126 = 0.070$.

The **mean square** in each row is the sum of squares divided by the degrees of freedom. The table's F value is the ratio of the mean square of the fitted model values to the mean square of the residuals: $\frac{127}{218} = 0.585$ in this example. This is the same as given by Equation 14.1, but the calculations are being done in a different order.

Finally, the F value is converted to a p-value by look-up in the appropriate F distribution with the indicated degrees of freedom in the numerator and the denominator.

Charles Darwin (1809-1882)   Francis Galton (1822-1911)

Origin of Species in which Darwin first put forward the theory of natural selection of heritable traits. (Galton and Darwin were half-cousins, sharing the same grandfather, Erasmus Darwin.)

The publication of *Origin of Species* preceded by a half-century any real understanding of the mechanism of genetic heritability. Today, of course, even elementary-school children hear about DNA and chromosomes, but during Darwin's life these ideas were unknown. Darwin himself thought that traits were transferred from the parents to the child literally through the blood, with individual traits carried by "gemmules." Galton tried to confirm this experimentally by doing blood-mixing experiments on rabbits; these were unsuccessful at transferring traits.

By collecting data on the heights of children and their parents, Galton sought to quantify to what extent height is determined genetically. Galton faced the challenge that the appropriate statistical methods had not yet been developed — he had to start down this path himself. In a very real sense, the development of

ANOVA by Ronald Fisher in the early part of the twentieth century was a direct outgrowth of Galton's work.

Had he been able to, here is the ANOVA report that Galton might have generated. The report summarizes the extent to which `height` is associated with inheritance from the `mother` and the `father` and by the genetic trait `sex`, using the model `height ~ 1 + sex + mother + father`.

	Df	Sum Sq	Mean Sq	F value	Pr(>F)
Genetic Terms	3	7366	2455	**529**	**0.000**
Residuals	894	4159	5		

The F value is huge and correspondingly the p-value is very small: the genetic variables are clearly explaining much more of `height` than random vectors.

If Galton had access to modern statistical approaches — even those from as long ago as the middle of the twentieth century — he might have wondered how to go further, for example how to figure out whether the mother and father each contribute to height, or whether it is a trait that comes primarily from one parent. Answering such questions involves partitioning the variance not merely between the model terms and the residual but *among* the individual model terms. This is the subject of Chapter 15.

Aside. 14.2 The shape of F

The shape of the F distribution depends on both n and m. Some of the distributions are shown for various m and n in Figure 14.5. Despite slight differences, the F distributions are all centered on 1. (In contrast, distributions of R^2 change shape substantially with m and n.) This steadiness in the F distribution makes it easy to interpret an F statistic by eye since a value near 1 is a plausible outcome from the null hypothesis. (The meaning of "near" reflects the width of the distribution: When n is much bigger than m, the the F distribution has mean 1 and standard deviation that is roughly $\sqrt{2/m}$.)

Presenting F with m and n as the parameters violates a convention. The F distribution is always specified in terms of the degrees of freedom of the numerator $m - 1$ and the degrees of freedom of the denominator $n - m$.

Example 14.3: F and Astrology   Returning to the attempt to model age at marriage by astrological sign ...

The model `Age ~ Sign` produced $R^2 = 0.070$ with $m = 12$ model vectors and $n = 98$ cases. The F statistic is therefore $\frac{0.070/11}{0.930/86} = 0.585$. Since F is somewhat less than 1, there is no reason to think that the `Sign` vectors are more effective

$$n = 10, m = 5 \qquad\qquad n = 50, m = 25$$

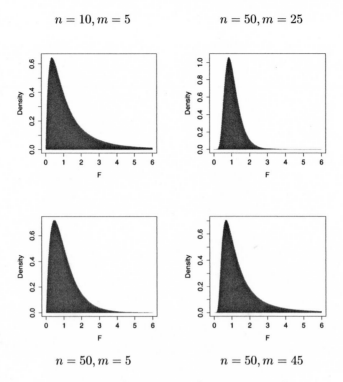

$$n = 50, m = 5 \qquad\qquad n = 50, m = 45$$

Figure 14.5: F distribution for various n and m.

than random vectors in explaining Age. Finding a p-value involves looking up the value F= 0.585 in the F distribution with $m - 1 = 11$ degrees of freedom in the numerator and $n - m = 86$ degrees of freedom in the denominator. Figure 14.6 (left) shows this F distribution.

The p-value is the probability of seeing an F value from this distribution that is larger than the observed value of $F = 0.585$. From the figure, it's easy to see that p is more than one-half since a majority of the distribution falls to the right of 0.585. Calculating it exactly using software gives $p = 0.836$.

14.4   Interpreting the p-value

The p-value is a useful format for summarizing the strength of evidence that the data provide. But statistical evidence, like any other form of evidence, needs to be interpreted in context.

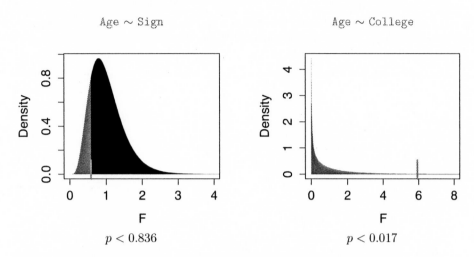

Figure 14.6: Finding a p-value from an F distribution always involves the area to the right of the test statistic, in this case marked by the ticks at $F = 0.585$ (for Age $\sim$ Sign) and $F = 5.93$ (for Age $\sim$ College).

14.4.1   Multiple Comparisons

Keep in mind that a hypothesis test, particularly when p is near the conventional $p < 0.05$ threshold for rejection of the null, is a very weak standard of evidence. Failure to reject the null may just mean that there isn't enough data to reveal the patterns, or that important explanatory variables have not been included in the model.

But even when the p-value is below 0.05, it needs to be interpreted in the context within which the tested hypothesis was generated. Often, models are used to explore data, looking for relationships among variables. The hypothesis tests that stem from such an exploration can give misleadingly low p-values.

To illustrate, consider an analogous situation in the world of crime. Suppose there were 20 different genetic markers evenly distributed through the population. A crime has been committed and solid evidence found on the scene shows that the perpetrator has a particular genetic marker, M, found in only 5% of the population. The police fan out through the city, testing passersby for the M marker. A man with M is quickly found and arrested.

Should he be convicted based on this evidence? Of course not. That this specific man should match the crime marker is unlikely, a probability of only 5%. But by testing large numbers of people who have no particular connection to the crime, it's a guarantee that someone who matches will be found.

Now suppose that eyewitnesses had seen the crime at a distance. The police arrived at the scene and quickly cordoned off the area. A man, clearly nervous and disturbed, was caught trying to sneak through the cordon. Questioning by the police revealed that he didn't live in the area. His story for why he was there did not hold up. A genetic test shows he has marker M. This provides much stronger, much more credible evidence. The physical datum of a match is just the same as in the previous scenario, but the context in which that datum is set is much more compelling.

The lesson here is that the p-value needs to be interpreted in context. The p-value itself doesn't reveal that context. Instead, the story of the research project come into play. Have many different models been fitted to the data? If so, then it's likely that one or more of them may have $p < 0.05$ even if the explanatory variables are not linked to the response.

It's a grave misinterpretation of hypothesis testing to treat the p-value as the probability that the null hypothesis is true. Remember, the p-value is based on the assumption that the null hypothesis is true. A low p-value may call that assumption into doubt, but that doubt needs to be placed into the context of the overall situation.

Consider the unfortunate researcher who happens to work in a world where the null hypothesis is always true. In this world, each study that the researcher performs will produce a p-value that is effectively a random number equally likely to be anywhere between 0 and 1. If this researcher performs many studies, it's highly likely that one or more of them will produce a p-value less than 0.05 even though the null is true.

Tempting though it may be to select a single study from the overall set based on its low p-value, it's a mistake to claim that this isolated p-value accurately depicts the probability of the null hypothesis. Statistician David Freedman writes, "Given a significant finding ... the chance of the null hypothesis being true is ill-defined — especially when publication is driven by the search for significance." [19]

One approach to dealing with multiple tests is to adjust the threshold for rejection of the null to reflect the multiple possibilities that chance has to produce a small p-value. A simple and conservative method for adjusting for multiple tests is the **Bonferroni correction**. Suppose you perform k different tests. The Bonferroni correction adjusts the threshold for rejection downward by a factor of $1/k$. For example, if you perform 15 hypothesis tests, rather than rejecting the null at a level of 0.05, your threshold for rejection should be $0.05/15 = 0.0033$.

Another strategy is to treat multiple testing situations as "hypothesis generators." Tests that produce low p-values are not to be automatically deemed as significant but as worthwhile candidates for further testing.[24]. Go out and collect a new sample, independent of the original one. Then use this sample to perform exactly one hypothesis test: re-testing the model whose low p-value originally prompted your interest. This common-sense procedure is called an **out-of-sample** test, since the test is performed on data outside the original sample used to form the hypothesis. In contrast, tests conducted on the data used to form the hypothesis are called **in-sample** tests. It's appropriate to be skeptical of in-sample tests.

When reading work from others, it can be hard to know for sure whether a test is in-sample or out-of-sample. For this reason, researchers value **prospective studies**, where the data are collected *after* the hypothesis has been framed. Obviously, data from a prospective study must be out-of-sample. In contrast, in **retrospective studies**, where data that have already been collected are used to test the hypothesis, there is a possibility that the same data used to form the hypothesis are also being used to test it. Retrospective studies are often disparaged for this reason, although really the issue is whether the data are in-sample or out-of-sample. (Retrospective studies also have the disadvantage that the data being analyzed might not have been collected in a way that optimally addresses the hypothesis. For example, important covariates might have been neglected.)

Example 14.4: Multiple Jeopardy

You might be thinking: Who would conduct multiple tests, effectively shopping around for a low p-value? It happens all the time, even in situations where wrong conclusions have important implications.[1]

To illustrate, consider the procedures adopted by the US Government's Office of Federal Contract Compliance Programs when auditing government contractors to see if they discriminate in their hiring practices. The OFCCP requires contractors to submit a report listing the number of applicants and the number of hires broken down by sex, by several racial/ethnic categories, and by job group. In one such report, there were 9 job groups (manager, professional, technical, sales workers, office/clerical, skilled crafts, operatives, laborers, service workers) and 6 discrimination categories (Black, Hispanic, Asian/Pacific Islander, American Indian/American Native, females, and people with disabilities).

According to the OFCCP operating procedures,[25] a separate hypothesis test with a rejection threshold of about 0.05 is to be undertaken for each job group and for each discrimination category, for example, discrimination against Black managers or against female sales workers. This corresponds to 54 different hypothesis tests. Rejection of the null in any one of these tests triggers punitive action by the OFCCP. Audits can occur annually, so there is even more potential for repeated testing.

Such procedures are not legitimately called hypothesis tests; they should be treated as **screening tests** meant to identify potential problem areas which can then be confirmed by collecting more data. A legitimate hypothesis test would require that the threshold be adjusted to reflect the number of tests conducted, or that a pattern identified by screening in one year has to be confirmed in the following year.

---

[1]See Section 13.8 for another example.

14.4.2   Significance vs Substance

It's very common for people to misinterpret the p-value as a measure of the strength of a relationship, rather than as a measure for the *evidence* that the data provide. Even when a relationship is very slight, as indicated by model coefficients or an R^2, the evidence for it can be very strong so long as there are enough cases.

Suppose, for example, that you are studying how long patients survive after being diagnosed with a particular disease. The typical survival time is 10 years, with a standard deviation of 5 years. In your research, you have identified a genetic trait that explains some of the survival time: modeling survival by the genetics produces an R^2 of 0.01. Taking this genetic trait into account makes the survival time more predictable; it reduces the standard deviation of survival time from 5 years to 4.975 years. Big deal! The fact is, an R^2 of 0.01 does not reduce uncertainty very much; it leaves 99 percent of the variance unaccounted for.

To see how the F statistic stems from both $R^2 = 0.01$ and the sample size n, re-write the formula for F in Equation 14.1:

$$F \;=\; \frac{R^2}{m-1} \,\bigg/\, \frac{1-R^2}{n-m} \tag{14.2}$$

$$=\; \left(\frac{n-m}{m-1}\right) \frac{R^2}{1-R^2} \tag{14.3}$$

$$=\; \text{``Sample size''} \times \text{``Substance''}. \tag{14.4}$$

The ratio $\frac{R^2}{1-R^2}$ is a reasonable way to measure the substance of the result: how forceful the relationship is. The ratio $\frac{n-m}{m-1}$ reflects the amount of data. Any relationship, even one that lacks practical substance, can be made to give a large F value so long as n is big enough. For example, taking $m = 2$ in your genetic trait model, a small study with $n = 100$ gives an F value of approximately 1: not significant. But if $n = 1000$ cases were collected, the F value would become a hugely significant $F = 10$.

When used in a statistical sense to describe a relationship, the word "significant" does not mean important or substantial. It merely means that there is evidence that the relationship did not arise purely by accident from random variation in the sample.

Example 14.5: The Significance of Finger Lengths

Example 9.4 (page 173) commented on a study that found $R^2 = 0.044$ for the relationship between finger-length ratios and aggressiveness. The relationship was hyped in the news media as the "key to aggression." (BBC News, 2005/03/04) The researchers who published the study[16] didn't characterize their results in this dramatic way. They reported merely that they found a statistically signficant result, that is, p-value of 0.028. The small p-value stems not from a forceful correlation but from number of cases; their study, at $n = 134$, was large enough to produce a value of F bigger than 4 even though the "substance", $R^2/(1 - R^2)$, is only 0.046.

The researchers were careful in presenting their results and gave a detailed presentation of their study. They described their use of four different ways of measuring aggression: physical, hostility, verbal, and anger. These four scales were each used to model finger-length ratio for men and women separately. Here are the p-values they report:

Sex	Scale	R^2	p-value
Males	Physical	0.044	0.028
	Hostility	0.016	0.198
	Verbal	0.008	0.347
	Anger	0.001	0.721
Females	Physical	0.010	0.308
	Hostility	0.001	0.670
	Verbal	0.001	0.778
	Anger	0.000	0.887

Notice that only one of the eight p-values is below the 0.05 threshold. The others seem randomly scattered on the interval 0 to 1, as would be expected if there were no relationship between the finger-length ratio and the aggressiveness scales. A Bonferroni correction to account for the eight tests gives a rejection threshold of $0.05/8 = 0.00625$. None of the tests satisfies this threshold.

14.5   Computational Technique

The chapter presents two ways of doing hypothesis tests on whole models: (1) permutation tests where the connection is severed between the explanatory and response variables, (2) tests such as ANOVA where the sampling distribution is calculated from first principles. In practice, first-principle tests are used most of the time. Still, the permutation test is useful for developing intuition about hypothesis testing — our main purpose here — and for those not-so-rare occasions where the assumptions behind the first-principle tests are dubious.

14.5.1   The Permutation Test

The idea of a permutation test is to enforce the null hypothesis that there is no connection between the response variables and the explanatory variables. An effective way to do this is to randomize the response variable in a way that is

consistent with sampling variability. When constructing confidence intervals, the
resampling() function was used. Re-sampling will typically repeat some cases
and omit others. Here, the shuffle() function will be used instead, to scramble
the order of one or more variables while leaving the others in their original state.

DATA FILE
galton.csv

To illustrate, consider a model for exploring whether sex and mother's height
are related to the height of the child:

```
> galton = fetchData("galton.csv")
> mod = lm(height ~ sex + mother, data=galton)
> coefficients(mod)
(Intercept)       sexM       mother
     41.450      5.177        0.353
```

The coefficients indicate that typical males are taller than typical females by
about 5 inches and that for each inch taller the mother is, a child will typically
be taller by 0.35 inches. A reasonable test statistic to summarize the whole model
is R^2. The summary report shows that to be $R^2 = 0.562$.

For confidence intervals, re-sampling was applied to the entire data frame. This
selects random cases, but each selected case is an authentic one that matches
exactly the original values for that case. The point of re-sampling is to get an
idea of the variability introduced by random sampling of authentic cases.

```
> do(5) * lm(height ~ sex + mother, data=resample(galton))
  Intercept sexM mother sigma r-squared
1      44.0 4.82  0.315  2.39     0.523
2      41.6 4.91  0.352  2.32     0.552
3      42.1 5.30  0.344  2.27     0.588
4      38.9 5.18  0.395  2.33     0.574
5      42.7 5.16  0.334  2.29     0.578
```

The sex**M** coefficients are tightly grouped near 5 inches, the mother coefficients
are around 0.3 to 0.4.

In order to carry out a permutation test, do not randomize the whole data frame.
Instead, shuffle just the response variable:

```
> do(5) * lm(shuffle(height) ~ sex + mother, data=galton)
  Intercept     sexM    mother sigma r-squared
1      64.3   0.1473   0.03650  3.59  0.000940
2      68.9  -0.2475  -0.03201  3.58  0.001567
3      69.0   0.0774  -0.03613  3.59  0.000676
4      69.4   0.1371  -0.04170  3.58  0.001124
5      66.9   0.2627  -0.00466  3.58  0.001361
```

Now the sex**M** and mother coefficients are close to zero, as would be expected
when there is no relationship between the response variable and the explanatory
variables.

In constructing the sampling distribution under the null hypothesis, you should
do hundreds of trials of fitting the model to the scrambled data, calculating the

test statistic (R^2 here) for each trial. Note that each trial itself involves all of the cases in your sample, but those cases have been changed so that the shuffled variable almost certainly takes on a different value in every case than in the original data.

```
> nulltrials = do(500) * lm(shuffle(height) ~ sex + mother, data=galton)
```

Notice that `do()` calculates R^2 from the model. The output of `do()` is a data frame:

```
> nulltrials

  Intercept    sexM  mother sigma r-squared
1      64.6  0.2746  0.0322  3.58   0.00184
2      69.9 -0.5056 -0.0448  3.58   0.00567
3      62.7  0.0886  0.0620  3.58   0.00171
... for 500 cases altogether ...
```

Naturally, all of the R^2 values for the trials are close to zero. After all, there is no relation between the response variable (after randomization with `shuffle()`) and the explanatory variables.

The p-value can be calculated directly from the trials, by comparison to the observed value in the actual data: R^2 was 0.5618.

```
> tally(~ r.squared > 0.5618, nulltrials)

 TRUE FALSE Total
    0   500   500
```

None of the 500 trials were greater than the value of the test statistic, 0.5618. It wouldn't be fair to claim that $p = 0$, since we only did 500 trials, but it is reasonable to say that the permutation test shows the p-value is $p \leq 1/500$.

14.5.2   First-Principle Tests

On modern computers, the permutation test is entirely practical. But a few decades ago, it was not. Great creativity was applied to finding test statistics where the sampling distribution could be estimated without extensive calculation. One of these is the F statistic. This is still very useful today and is a standard part of the regression report in many statistical packages.

Here is the regression report from the `height ~ sex+mother`:

```
> mod = lm( height ~ sex + mother, data=galton)
> summary(mod)

...
            Estimate Std. Error t value Pr(>|t|)
(Intercept)  41.4495     2.2095    18.8   <2e-16 ***
sexM          5.1767     0.1587    32.6   <2e-16 ***
mother        0.3531     0.0344    10.3   <2e-16 ***
```

```
---
Signif. codes:   0 '***' 0.001 '**' 0.01 '*' 0.05 '.' 0.1 ' ' 1

Residual standard error: 2.37 on 895 degrees of freedom
Multiple R-squared: 0.562,          Adjusted R-squared: 0.561
F-statistic:   574 on 2 and 895 DF,   p-value: <2e-16
```

The last line of the report shows an F statistic of 574 based on an R^2 of 0.562 and translates this to a p-value that is practically zero: `<2e-16`.

By way of showing that the regression report is rooted in the same approach shown in the chapter, you can confirm the calculations. There are $m = 3$ coefficients and $n = 898$ cases, producing $n - m = 895$ degrees of freedom in the denominator and $m - 1 = 2$ degrees of freedom in the numerator. The calculation of the F statistic from R^2 and the degrees of freedom follows the formula given in the chapter.

$$F = \frac{R^2}{m - 1} \left/ \frac{1 - R^2}{n - m} \right.$$

Plugging the values into the formula

```
> (0.562/2) / ((1-.562)/895)
```

```
[1] 574
```

F is the test statistic. To convert it to a p-value, you need to calculate how extreme the value of F= 574.2 is with reference to the F distribution with 895 and 2 degrees of freedom.

```
> 1 - pf( 574.2, 2, 895)
```

```
[1] 0
```

The calculation of p-values from F always follows this form. In the context of the F distribution, "extreme" always means "bigger than." So, calculate the area under the F distribution to the right of the observed value.

Reading Questions

- A permutation test involves randomizing in order to simulate eliminating the relationship, if any, between the explanatory variables and the response variable. What's the point of this?
- The F statistic compares two quantities. What are they?
- What is a "degree of freedom?"

For exercises, see www.mosaic-web.org/StatisticalModeling/Exercises.

15

Hypothesis Testing on Parts of Models

Everything should be made as simple as possible, but not simpler. — Albert Einstein

It often happens in studying a system that a single explanatory variable is of direct interest to the modeler. Other explanatory variables may be important in the way the system works, but they are not of primary interest to the modeler. As in previous chapters, call the explanatory variable of interest simply the "explanatory variable." The other explanatory variables, the ones that aren't of direct interest, are the **covariates**. The covariates are ordinary variables. Their designation as covariates reflects the interests of the modeler rather than any intrinsic property of the variables themselves.

The source of the interest in the explanatory variable might be to discover whether it is relevant to a model of a response variable. For example, in studying people's heights, one expects that several covariates, for instance the person's sex or the height of their father or mother, play a role. It would be interesting to find out whether the number of siblings a person has, nkids in Galton's dataset, is linked to the height. Studying nkids in isolation might be misleading since the other variables are reasonably regarded as influencing height. But doing a whole-model hypothesis test on a model that includes both nkids and the covariates would be uninformative: Of course one can account for a significant amount of the variation in height using sex and mother and father. (See Example 14.3 on page 263.) The question about nkids is whether it contributes something to the explanation that goes beyond the covariates. To answer this question, one needs a way of assessing the contribution of nkids on its own, but in the context set by the other variables.

Sometimes you may choose to focus on a single explanatory variable because a decision may hang on the role of that variable. Keep in mind that role of the explanatory variable of interest can depend on the context set by covariates. Those covariates might enhance, mask, or reverse the role of the variable of interest. For instance, it's legitimate that wages might vary according to the type of job and the worker's level of experience and education. It's also possible that wages might vary according to sex or race insofar as those variables happen to be correlated with the covariates, that is, correlated with the type of job or level of education and experience. But, if wages depend on the worker's sex or race *even taking into account* the legitimate factors, that's a different story and suggests a more sinister mechanism at work.

This chapter is about conducting hypothesis tests on a single explanatory variable in the context set by covariates. In talking about general principles, the text will refer to models of the form A $\sim$ B+C or A $\sim$ B+C+D where A is the response variable, B is the variable of interest, and C and D are the variables that you aren't directly interested in: the covariates.

Recall the definition of statistics offered in Chapter 1:

> *Statistics is the explanation of variation in the context of what remains unexplained.*

It's important to include covariates in a hypothesis test because they influence both aspects of this definition:

Explanation of variation When the covariates are correlated with the explanatory variable, as they often are, including the covariates in a model will change the coefficients on the explanatory variable.

What remains unexplained Including covariates raises the R^2 of a model. Or, to put it another way, including covariates reduces the size of the residuals. This can make the explanatory variable look better: smaller residuals generally mean smaller standard errors and higher F statistics. This is not an accounting trick, it genuinely reflects how much of the response variable remains unexplained.

15.1   The Term-by-Term ANOVA Table

The ANOVA table introduced in the Chapter 14 provides a framework for conducting hypothesis tests that include covariates. The whole-model ANOVA table lets you compare the "size" of the explained part of the model with the "size" of the residuals. Here is a whole-model report for the model height $\sim$ nkids + sex + father + mother fit to Galton's data:

DATA FILE
galton.csv

	Df	Sum Sq	Mean Sq	F value	Pr(>F)
Model terms	4	7377.9	1845.0	401	0.0000
Residuals	893	4137.1	4.6		

The square length of the residual vector is 4137.1, the square length of the fitted model vector is 7377.9. The F test takes into account the number of vectors involved in each — four explanatory vectors (neglecting the intercept term), leaving 893 residual degrees of freedom. The F value, 401, is the ratio of the mean square of the model terms to the residuals. Since 401 is much, much larger than 1 (which is the expected value when the model terms are just random vectors), it's appropriate to reject the null hypothesis; the p-value is effectively zero since F is so huge.

A term-by-term ANOVA report is much the same, but the report doesn't just partition variation into "modeled" and "residual," it goes further by partitioning the modeled variation among the different explanatory terms. There is one row in the report for each individual model term.

	Df	Sum Sq	Mean Sq	F value	Pr(>F)
nkids	1	185.5	185.5	40.0	0.0001
sex	1	5766.3	5766.3	1244.7	0.0001
father	1	937.6	937.6	202.4	0.0001
mother	1	488.5	488.5	105.5	0.0001
Residuals	893	4137.1	4.6		

Notice that the "Residuals" row is exactly the same in the two ANOVA reports. This is because that row just describes the square length of the residuals — it's the same model with the same residuals being analyzed in the two ANOVA reports. Less obvious, perhaps, is that the sum of squares of the individual model terms adds up across all the terms to give exactly the sum of squares from the whole-model ANOVA report: $185.5 + 5766.3 + 937.6 + 488.5 = 7377.9$. The same is true for the degrees of freedom of the model terms: $1 + 1 + 1 + 1 = 4$.

What's new in the term-by-term ANOVA report is that there is a separate mean square, F value, and p-value for each model term. These are calculated in the familiar way: the mean square for any term is just the sum of squares for that term divided by the degrees of freedom for that term. Similarly, the F value for each term is the mean square for that term divided by the mean square of the residuals. For instance, for nkids, the F value is $185.5/4.6 = 40$. This is translated to a p-value in exactly the same way as in Chapter 14 (using an F distribution with 1 degree of freedom in the numerator and 893 in the denominator — values that come from the corresponding rows of the ANOVA report).

15.2   Covariates Soak Up Variance

An important role of covariates is to account for variance in the response. This
reduces the size of residuals. Effectively, the covariates reduce the amount of
randomness attributed to the system and thereby make it easier to see patterns
in the data. To illustrate, consider a simple question relating to marriage: Do
men tend to be older than women when they get married?

The marriage-license dataset contains information on the ages of brides and
grooms at the time of their marriage as well as other data on education, race,
number of previous marriages, and so on. These data were collected from the
on-line marriage license records made available by Mobile County, Alabama in
the US. Here's an excerpt:

DATA FILE
marriage.csv

BookpageID	Person	Age
B230p539	Bride	28.7
B230p539	Groom	32.6
B230p677	Bride	52.6
B230p677	Groom	32.3
B230p766	Bride	26.7
B230p766	Groom	34.8
B230p892	Bride	39.6
B230p892	Groom	40.6

... and so on for 49
couples altogether

The Person and Age variables are obvious enough. The BookpageID variable
records the location of the marriage license in the Mobile County records as a
book number and page number. There is only one license on each page, so this
serves as a unique identifier of the couple.

It seems simple enough to test whether men tend to be older than women when
they get married, just fit the model Age ~ Person. Here it is:

	Estimate	Std. Error	t value	Pr($>$|t|)
Intercept	33.239	2.060	16.13	0.0001
PersonGroom	2.546	2.914	0.87	0.3845

The coefficient on person**Groom** indicates that men are typically 2.5 years older
than women when they get married. That's roughly what one would expect
from experience — husbands and wives tend to be roughly the same age, with
the husband typically a bit older. The confidence interval suggests a different
interpretation, however. It's 2.5 ± 5.8, giving reason to believe that a different
sample of licenses could give a coefficient of zero, indicating no age difference
between men and women. ANOVA tells much the same story

	Df	Sum Sq	Mean Sq	F value	Pr(>F)
Person	1	159	159	0.76	0.38
Residuals	96	19967	208.00		

The F value, 0.76, is smaller than one. Correspondingly, the p-value is big: 0.38. Based on these data, it's not appropriate to reject the null hypothesis that men and women are the same age when they get married.

No big deal. Perhaps there just isn't enough data. With some effort, more data could be collected and this might bring the p-value down to the point where the null could be rejected.

Actually, there's much more information in this sample than the hypothesis test suggests. The model `Age ~ Person` ignores a very important structure in the data: Who is married to whom. A person's age at marriage is very strongly related to the age of their spouse. That is, if you know the age of the wife, you have a lot of information about the age of the husband, and vice versa. This relationship between the husband and wife is carried by the variable `BookpageID`. Since the model `Age ~ Person` doesn't include `BookpageID` as a covariate, the model tends to overstate the unexplained part of `age`.

To fix things, add in `BookpageID` as a covariate and examine the model `Age ~ Person + BookpageID`. In this model the coefficient on `Person`**Groom** refers to the difference in age between males and females, *holding constant* the family. That is, this model looks at the difference between the husband and wife *within the family*. Here's the term-by-term ANOVA report:

	Df	Sum Sq	Mean Sq	F value	Pr(>F)
Person	1	159.0	159.0	9.07	0.0041
BookpageID	48	19127.0	398.5	22.77	0.0001
Residuals	48	840.0	17.5		

Notice that here the F value of `Person` is much larger than before, 9.07 versus 0.76 before. Correspondingly the p-value is much smaller: 0.004 versus 0.384. But the sum of squares of `Person` is exactly the same as it was for the previous model. What's happened is that the inclusion of `BookpageID` in the model has dramatically reduced the size of the residuals. The residual mean square is now 17.5 compared to 208 in the model that omitted `BookpageID` as a covariate.

It's not that `BookpageID` is a variable that's directly of interest. But that doesn't mean that you shouldn't include `BookpageID` in a model. It accounts for some of the variation in `Age` and in so doing makes it easier for the role of other variables to be seen above the random variation due to sampling.

The particular hypothesis test conducted here has a specific name, the **paired t-test**. The word "paired" reflects the natural pairing in the data: each family has a wife and a husband. Another context in which pairing arises is before-and-after studies, for example measuring a subject's blood pressure both before and after a drug is given.

A more general term is **repeated measures**. In a paired situation there are two measurements on each subject, but there can also be situations where there are more than two.

A still more general term is **analysis of covariance**, which refers simply to a situation where covariates are used to soak up the residuals.

Example 15.1: Wages and Race   The Current Population Survey data (from the mid-1980s) can be analyzed to look for signs that there is discrimination based on race in the wages people earn. That dataset has a variable, race, that encodes the race of each wage earner as either Black or White. The obvious, simple model is wage ~ race. Here's the coefficient report:

	Estimate	Std. Error	t value	Pr(>|t|)
Intercept	8.06	0.63	12.86	0.0001
raceW	1.10	0.67	1.65	0.1001

According to this report, Whites earned an average of $1.10 per hour more than Blacks. But the standard error is large: the confidence interval on this estimate is $1.10 ± 1.34. The ANOVA report on the model suggests that these data don't give enough evidence to reject the null hypothesis that race is a factor in wages:

	Df	Sum Sq	Mean Sq	F value	Pr(>F)
race	1	71.5	71.45	2.71	0.1001
Residuals	532	14005.3	26.33		

The F value is 2.7, bigger than the expected value of one, but not so big as to be compelling evidence. The p-value is 0.10, too large to reject the null.

Remember that the p-value compares the explanatory power of race to a typical random term in order to account for sampling variation. In this model, all of the variation in wage is considered random other than that attributed to race. This is not reasonable. There are other sources of variation in wage such as the education of the worker and the type of job. Consider now a model with educ and sector of the economy as covariates: wage ~ race+educ + sector:

	Df	Sum Sq	Mean Sq	F value	Pr(>F)
race	1	71.45	71.45	3.44	0.0641
educ	1	2017.67	2017.67	97.22	0.0001
sector	7	1112.92	158.99	7.66	0.0001
Residuals	524	10874.66	20.75		

Now the F value on `race` is increased, simply because the size of the residuals has been reduced by inclusion of the covariates.

The lesson here is, again, that including covariates can make the patterns of the explanatory variable of interest stand out more clearly. Admittedly, the change in F here is not huge, but it has come at a very small price: fitting a new model. Collecting data can be expensive. The modeler seeks to extract the most information from that data.

This example will be continued later in this chapter.

15.3   Measuring the Sum of Squares

At a superficial level, interpretation of the term-by-term ANOVA report is straight-forward. Use the p-value on each row to decide whether to reject the null hypothesis for that row. For instance, return to the height-model example from before: `height ∼ nkids+sex+father+mother`

	Df	Sum Sq	Mean Sq	F value	Pr(>F)
nkids	1	185.46	185.46	40.03	**0.0001**
sex	1	5766.33	5766.33	1244.67	0.0001
father	1	937.63	937.63	202.39	0.0001
mother	1	488.52	488.52	105.45	0.0001
Residuals	893	4137.12	4.63		

The very small p-value on `nkids` (it's actually 0.0000000004) prompts a rejection of the null hypothesis on the `nkids` term. But there are other ANOVA reports on exactly the same model fitted to exactly the same data. Here's one:

	Df	Sum Sq	Mean Sq	F value	Pr(>F)
sex	1	5874.57	5874.57	1268.03	0.0001
father	1	1001.11	1001.11	216.09	0.0001
mother	1	490.22	490.22	105.81	0.0001
nkids	1	12.04	12.04	2.60	**0.1073**
Residuals	893	4137.12	4.63		

According to this report, `nkids` is not making a significant contribution to the model.

Why do the two reports give such different results for nkids? Which is right, the second report's p-value on nkids of 0.107 or the first report's p-value of 0.0000000004? Obviously, they lead to different conclusions. But they are *both* right. It's just that there are two different null hypotheses involved. In the first report, the null is that nkids on its own doesn't contribute beyond what's typical for a random vector. In the second report, the null is that nkids doesn't contribute *beyond* the contribution already made by mother, father, and sex. The two reports give us different perspectives on nkids.

In understanding term-by-term ANOVA, it's helpful to start with an analogy. Suppose you have a sports team consisting of players B, C, D, and so on. As a whole, the team scores 30 points in a game. B scored 3 of these points, C 10 of them, D no points, and so on.

The score reflects the team as a whole but you want to be able to identify particularly strong or weak players as individuals. The obvious thing to do is give each player credit for the points that he or she actually scored: B gets 3 points of credit, C 10 points of credit, D no credit, and so on.

This system, though simple, has its flaws. In particular, the system doesn't acknowledge the role of teamwork. Perhaps D's role is primarily defensive; she contributes to the team even though she doesn't actually do the scoring. C scores a lot, but maybe this is because B does a great job of passing to her. In evaluating an individual player's contribution, it's important to take into account the context established by the other players.

Now consider two different ways of assigning credit to individual players. Each involves replaying the game with some changes; this is impractical in real-world game playing but quite feasible when it comes to fitting models.

Take out one player Play the game and record the score. Now take out one player and re-play the game. The player who was taken out gets credit for the difference in scores between the two games.

What's nice about this method is that it gives the player credit for how he or she they contributed to the score **beyond** what the other players could have accomplished on their own.

Take out multiple players Play the game with a subset of the players. Now replay the game, adding in one new player. The new player gets credit for the difference in scores between the two games.

As you can imagine, the result of this method will depend on which subset of players was in the game. In one extreme limit, the new player would be the **only** player: a one person team.

Now to translate this analogy back to ANOVA. First, the game is played with only one player: a single model term, as in the model height ~ 1. The game's score is recorded as the sum of squares of the fitted model values. Next, another player is put in and the game is replayed: as in `height ~ 1+nkids`. More and more games are played, each successive game adding in one more player: `height ~ 1+nkids+sex`, then `height ~ 1+nkids+sex+father` and so on . In each game, the score is measured as the sum of squares.

To illustrate the process, reconstruct term-by-term ANOVA on the model `height ~ 1+nkids + sex + father + mother`. Think of this as a set of nested models, as shown in the table. For each of the nested models a "score" — that is, a sum of squares — is found.

Model	Sum of Squares	Term added	Additional Sum of Sq.
height ~ 1	4002376.8	intercept	
height ~ 1+nkids	4002562.3	nkids	185.5
height ~ 1+nkids+sex	4008328.6	sex	5766.3
height ~ 1+nkids+sex+father	4009266.2	father	937.6
height ~ 1+nkids+sex+father+mother	4009754.7	mother	488.5

The "Additional Sum of Squares" assigned to each term reflects how much that term increased the sum of squares compared to the previous model. For instance, adding the `nkids` term in the second line of the table increased the sum of squares from 4002376.8 to 4002562.3, an increase of 185.5. It's the increase that's attributed to `nkids`.

Perhaps you're wondering, why did `nkids` go first? ANOVA can take the terms in any order you want. For example:

Model	Sum of Squares	Term added	Additional Sum of Sq.
height ~ 1	4002376.8	intercept	
height ~ 1+mother	4002845.1	mother	468.3
height ~ 1+mother+father	4003630.8	sex	785.7
height ~ 1+mother+father+sex	4009742.7	sex	6112.0
height ~ 1+mother+father+sex+nkids	4009754.7	nkids	12.0

Notice that with the new arrangement of terms, the sum of squares assigned to each term is different. In particular, the first report gave `nkids` a fairly large sum of squares: 185.5. The second report gave `nkids` only 12.0. This change plays out in the p-value on `nkids` given in the ANOVA report: it's 0.107 now compared to 0.0000000004.

15.4   ANOVA, Collinearity, and Multi-Collinearity

In sports, it's easy to see why the performance of one player on a team depends on the context set by the other players. Players specialize in offense and defense, they support one another by passing and blocking or by drawing away the opponent's defense. A poor defensive player may hurt his own team by depriving it of opportunities to go on the offense. A good team player improves the performance of other players on the team by creating opportunities for them to perform well.

With model terms, the situation is analogous but obviously lacking the aspect of personality and intentionality that shapes team dynamics.

In ANOVA, each model term is assigned a sum of squares: think of this that the term is a player "carries the ball" forward. When there are collinear model terms, it is as if each player could have carried the ball over the same ground. This raises the question of who should get credit.

The approach taken in ANOVA in a model like A ∼ B+C is to assign player B the credit for the amount the ball would have been carried without player C, so the credit from the simulated play A ∼ B. Then C gets the rest of the credit for A ∼ B+C.

It's important to do things this way to avoid double counting. Marching forward with this sport metaphor, imagine that the accounting were done in another way, measuring the actual distance that each player carries the ball. It might be that only B carries the ball, but C performs an important block that lets B go further. In the carry-the-ball accounting, C would get no credit. But with ANOVA, B gets the credit for the distance that he would have gone without the help of C's block, and C gets the credit for the extra distance that B was able to go because of the block.

Now imagine what will happen with A ∼ C+B. This is exactly the same model as before, but now ANOVA has been directed to consider first the play A ∼ C to assign credit to player C, then look at the result of A ∼ C+B to figure out how much credit to give to B. The model A ∼ C corresponds to the play in which C successfully makes his block, but since there is *no ball carrier* B, player C will get absolutely no credit. A block without a ball carrier is of no use whatsoever! Now add in player B — that is, model A ∼ C+B. With both the ball carrier and the blocker, the ball will be moved down the field. But B will get all the credit now, because there was no credit to be given to C in the play A ∼ C. This is why the credit assigned by ANOVA depends on the order of terms.

When model terms are orthogonal, it is as if the players had no influence on one another's performance. For orthogonal model terms, the results of ANOVA are the same, regardless of the order in which they are considered. This simplifies interpretation, since there is no decision to be made about the proper order. But, if your model terms are not orthogonal, you need to be thoughtful in interpreting the ANOVA report, considering the implications of the different possible orderings of model terms.

Example 15.2: Height and Siblings In fitting the model height $\sim$ nkids + sex + father + mother to Galton's data, the p-value on nkids depended substantially on where the term is placed in the ANOVA report. When nkids came first, the p-value was small, leading to rejection of the null hypothesis. But when nkids came last, the p-value was not small enough to justify rejection of the null.

As always, the order dependence of the term-by-term ANOVA results stems from collinearity. You can investigate this directly by modeling nkids as a function of the covariates. Here is the regression report on the model nkids $\sim$ sex + father + mother:

	Estimate	Std. Error	t value	Pr($>$|t|)
Intercept	19.2374	3.3772	5.70	0.0001
sexM	-0.3652	0.1770	-2.06	0.0394
father	-0.1751	0.0359	-4.88	0.0001
mother	-0.0123	0.0385	-0.32	0.7488

The model coefficients indicate that boys tend to have fewer siblings than girls. This may sound a bit strange, because obviously within any family every boy has exactly the same number of siblings as every girl. But the model applies *across* families, so this model is saying that families with boys tend to have fewer children than families with girls. This is a well known phenomenon. Depending on your point of view, you might like to interpret in either of two ways. Perhaps it's that parents with boys get worn out and stop having children. An alternative is that, particularly in Galton's time when women were definitely second-class citizens, parents who didn't have boys continued to have more children in the hopes of producing them. Either way, the model indicates that nkids is collinear with sex. It also appears to be related to father, as you will see later in Example 15.4.

A nice way to measure the extent of collinearity is with either the model R^2 or, equivalently but more directly geometrically, with the angle θ between nkids and the fitted model vector. For the model, $R^2 = 0.03$, corresponding to $\theta = 80°$. That's practially $90°$, hardly any alignment at all! How can that trivial amount of collinearity lead to the dramatic order-dependence of the ANOVA result on nkids?

To examine this, imagine splitting nkids into two vectors: a vector that is exactly aligned with the sex, father, mother subspace and the part that is exactly orthogonal to it. These two vectors correspond to the fitted model values and the residuals of the nkids model. Call them aligned and perp and add them to the height model in place of nkids. It's important to remember that neither of these vectors points in exactly the same direction as nkids, but nkids = aligned + perp.

Here's one ANOVA report, where `aligned` and `perp` have been placed first:

	Df	Sum Sq	Mean Sq	F value	Pr(>F)
aligned	1	3435.49	3435.49	741.55	0.0001
perp	1	12.04	12.04	2.60	0.1073
sex	1	3529.00	3529.00	761.74	0.0001
father	1	401.41	401.41	86.64	0.0001
Residuals	893	4137.12	4.63		

There are several interesting aspects to this report. First, `aligned` shows up as very significant, with a huge sum of squares compared to the original `nkids` — the original was only 185.5. This is because `aligned` happens to point in a very favorable direction, closely related to the very important variable `sex`. Second, `perp` gets a very small sum of squares: only 12. Third, `sex` is much reduced compared to the original ANOVA. This is because `aligned` has already grabbed much of the sum of squares originally associated with `sex`. Finally, the `mother` term gets absolutely no sum of squares and, indeed, has zero degrees of freedom. This is because there is one degree of redundancy among the set `aligned`, `sex`, `father`, and `mother`. Since `mother` came last in the report, it had absolutely nothing to contribute.

Now consider an ANOVA report on the same terms, but in a different order:

	Df	Sum Sq	Mean Sq	F value	Pr(>F)
sex	1	5874.57	5874.57	1268.03	0.0001
father	1	1001.11	1001.11	216.09	0.0001
mother	1	490.22	490.22	105.81	0.0001
aligned	0	0	NA	NA	NA
perp	1	12.04	12.04	2.60	0.1073
Residuals	893	4137.12	4.63		

Coming after `father`, `mother` and `sex`, the `aligned` vector is the one discarded as being redundant. Indeed, it was constructed to fit exactly into the subspace spanned by `father`, `mother` and `sex`. Coming before `aligned` in the ANOVA report, the term `sex` has regained its large sum of squares, indicating that `sex` is a strong predictor of height.

Now look at `perp`. Although it comes at the end of the list of terms, it has exactly the same set of values that it had when it came at the beginning of the list. This is because `perp` is exactly orthogonal to all the other terms in the report — it was constructed that way as the residual from fitting `nkids` to the other terms. Whenever a term is orthogonal to the others, the sum of squares for that term will not depend on where the term comes in order with respect to the others.

It's worth pointing out that the sum of squares, F value, and p-value on `perp` exactly matches that from the original ANOVA report using `nkids` when `nkids` came last. This is not a coincidence. It stems from putting `father`, `mother` and `sex` before `nkids` in the report — those other variables effectively stripped `nkids` of any component that was aligned with them, leaving only the part of `nkids` perpendicular to them.

All this may sound like an abstract exercise in geometrical thinking, but it actually carries a strong implication for interpreting the relationship between `nkids` and `height`. Earlier, a possible **causal** relationship was suggested; perhaps in families with many kids, competition for food and other resources caused the kids to be stunted in growth. Or it might be that families that had lots of kids back then were healthier or rich in resources that caused the kids to grow well.

The results with `aligned` and `perp` suggest something different. If `nkids` really did **cause** `height`, then the component of `nkids` perpendicular to `sex` and the other covariates ought to have some explanatory power with regard to height. On the other hand, if it's really `sex` and the other covariates that cause height, and `nkids` has nothing to do with it, then the perpendicular component of `nkids` ought to be no better than a random vector. The ANOVA report is consistent with this second scenario. The p-value of 0.107 isn't sufficiently small to justify rejecting the null that `perp` plays no role.

Even a very small alignment with genuinely important variables — `nkids` is at an angle of $\theta = 80°$ with respect to the `sex`, `father`, `mother` subspace — can create a sum of squares that's statistically significant. Keep in mind that "significance" in a hypothesis test is defined with respect not to how strong or substantial or authentic the variable's role is, but how it compares in size to a completely random variable. With large n, even a very small alignment can be much larger than expected for a random vector. There are n=898 cases in Galton's data, and in a space of dimension 898 it's very unlikely that a random vector would show even an alignment as far from perpendicular as 80°. (The 95% confidence interval for the angle that a random vector makes with another vector is 86° to 94°.)

15.4.1 Choosing the Order of Terms in ANOVA

The order-dependence of ANOVA results creates profound problems in interpretation. There is, unfortunately, no generally applicable way to identify a single correct ordering. This is because the order-dependence in ANOVA reflects genuine ambiguities in how to interpret data. Eliminating these ambiguities requires adding new information to the analysis, such as the modeler's assumptions or knowledge about the system under study. An illustration of this is given in Example 15.4, where it was assumed (reasonably enough) that the number of children in a family might be the result of covariates such as the children's sex or the height of the mother and father, but that the number of kids doesn't itself cause those covariates.

The mathematical analysis of the order-dependence of term-by-term ANOVA as it stems from collinearity can illuminate the situation, but doesn't resolve the ambiguity.

Here are some suggestions for dealing with the ambiguity of term-by-term ANOVA. It's important to remember that despite the problems with ANOVA, it offers the important advantage of allowing covariates to soak up unexplained variance. Other methods such as whole-model ANOVA or the regression report (the topic of Section 15.5) may avoid ambiguity but this is only because they don't offer the flexibility of ANOVA. Such methods also impose their own hidden assumptions.

Treat ANOVA as a screening method. In medicine, **screening tests** are ways to get a quick, inexpensive indication of whether a patient has an illness or condition. They tend to have relatively high error rates. Nonetheless, they can be genuinely useful for identifying situations where more invasive or expensive methods can be used to get a more definitive result.

ANOVA provides a quick, powerful, and effective way to assess the strength of evidence for a claim. You can use it to probe whether variables should be included in a model and what covariates might be included as well. The results shouldn't be taken as proof that a hypothesis is correct. Indeed, you should always keep in mind that hypothesis testing never offers a proof of a hypothesis. It can only produce a rejection of the null or a failure to reject the null.

Arrange the covariates so that they are orthogonal to the explanatory variable. If two explanatory vectors are not at all collinear, that is, if they are exactly orthogonal to each other, then the order of the terms has no effect.

If you are collecting data in the context of an experiment, you may well be able to arrange things so that the explanatory variables and covariates are orthogonal to one another. Chapter 18 on **experimental design** covers some of the techniques to do this.

Chapter 12 explains that collinearity between explanatory vectors increases standard errors, that is, worsens the precision of your coefficient estimates. This inflation of standard errors is another reason to try to create orthogonality, if you have the means to do so.

Adopt a skeptical attitude. If you are inclined to be skeptical about a variable, look for the arrangement of terms that produces the smallest sum of squares. If, despite this, the variable still has a significant sum of squares, the ambiguity of order-dependence won't influence your conclusions.

But in interpreting your results, keep in mind that there might be other covariates that weren't included in your models that might reduce your variable to insignificance.

Adopt an enthusiastic attitude of hypothesis formation. Although ANOVA is formally a mechanism for hypothesis testing, it can also be used for hypothesis formation. Explore your data using ANOVA. If you find an arrangement of explanatory variables that produces a significant result, that's a good reason to devote some time and energy to thinking more about that result and how to follow up on it.

But don't be complacent. Once you have formed a hypothesis, you will have to test it skeptically at some point.

Don't forget other ambiguities. The ambiguity of order dependence is readily seen in ANOVA reports. But there are other ambiguities and uncertainties that you won't necessarily be aware of. Why did you choose the particular covariates in your analysis? Why did you choose to measure certain variables and not others? Did you include interaction terms (which often introduce colinearities)? Did you consider transformation terms? For example, Example 15.4 treats the number of kids as a simple linear term. But there is reason to think that its effect might be nonlinear, that in small families height is associated with having more siblings, but in large families the reverse is true.

Even if there were no ambiguities of order dependence, there would still be ambiguities and uncertainties in your model results.

Think carefully about how your system works, and model the system rather than just the data. The source of order dependence is collinearity among the explanatory variables. Such collinearity is itself evidence that the explanatory variables are related in some way. A model like A ~ B+C+D is about the relationship between A and the explanatory variables; it doesn't describe the relationships among the explanatory variables, even though these may be important to understanding how the system works. If you want to understand the system as a whole, you need to model the system as a whole. This involves a set of models. For example, suppose that in the real system, A is caused by both B and C, and D exerts its influence only because it affects B. For such a system, it's appropriate to consider a set of models: A ~ B+C and B ~ D. Things can quickly get more complicated. For example, suppose C influences D. In that case, the model A ~ B+C would confuse the direct influence of C on A with the indirect influence that C has on A via D and therefore B.

The methods of **structural equation modeling** (SEM) are designed to deal with such complexity by creating structured sets of models. The structure itself is based in the modeler's knowledge or assumptions about how the system works.

Example 15.3: Wages and Race: Part 2

Example 15.2 looked at the Current Population Survey data to see if there is evidence that race is associated with wages. The simple model wage ~ race produced a p-value on race of 0.10, not strong evidence. However, including the covariates educ and sector made the role of race somewhat clearer as shown by the term-by-term ANOVA report:

	Df	Sum Sq	Mean Sq	F value	Pr(>F)
race	1	71.45	71.45	3.44	0.0641
educ	1	2017.67	2017.67	97.22	0.0001
sector	7	1112.92	158.99	7.66	0.0001
Residuals	524	10874.66	20.75		

Since the sum of squares in term-by-term ANOVA can be order dependent, it's worthwhile to look at a diferent ordering of terms. Here's one with race last:

	Df	Sum Sq	Mean Sq	F value	Pr(>F)
educ	1	2053.29	2053.29	98.94	0.0001
sector	7	1136.56	162.37	7.82	0.0001
race	1	12.19	12.19	0.59	0.4439
Residuals	524	10874.66	20.75		

This report suggests that the data provide no evidence that race plays any role at all.

Which conclusion is right? Do the data provide evidence for the importance of race or not? The answer is that it depends on your view of how the system is working.

Suppose, for instance, that race is really a causal influence in determining people's level of education or the sector of the economy that they are permitted to work in. In such a situation, it's appropriate to put race first in order to reflect the claim that race influences educ and sector and therefore race should get credit for any of the way it overlaps with educ and sector in accounting for wage.

Now consider an alternative perspective. It's certainly clear that educ and sector can't possibly be *causing* race. But it is possible that a person's race is correlated with education and sector without having caused them. How? Both education and sector can be influenced by the opportunities and role models that a person had as a child and these in turn are set by the situation in which that person's parents lived, including racial discrimination against the parents. According to this perspective, the person's race doesn't cause their level of education or the sector in which they work. Instead, all these things were causally influenced by other factors. In such a situation, it might be fair to assume in the null hypothesis that educ and sector are primary influences on wage independent of race. To test this null hypothesis, which treats the potential role of race with skepticism, race should come after educ and sector in the ANOVA breakdown.

There's also a third possibility here. Suppose you are looking for evidence that employers discriminate and you suspect that one mechanism for such discrimation is to restrict which sectors people can work in. That's not an unreasonable idea. But it's harder to believe that the employers have influenced the person's level of education. So, put educ *before* race and put sector *after* race:

	Df	Sum Sq	Mean Sq	F value	Pr($>$F)
educ	1	2053.29	2053.29	98.94	0.0001
race	1	35.83	35.83	1.73	0.1894
sector	7	1112.92	158.99	7.66	0.0001
Residuals	524	10874.66	20.75		

This set of assumptions leads to failure to reject the null on race: the skeptic's attitude toward race is supported by the analysis.

The core of the matter is whether covariates such as sector or educ are mechanisms through which the effects of race plays out, or whether they provide alternative, non-racial explanations for the variation in wage. Depending on which one of these you believe, you can get very different results from ANOVA.

In this wages and race example, people with different views can each see that the data are consistent with those views. The data provide evidence for the person who thinks that race influences wages through the mechanism of educ and sector. Similarly, for the person who says that educ and sector are the determinants of wage, the data are consistent with the view that race doesn't play a role.

15.5   Hypothesis Tests on Single Coefficients

ANOVA treats a covariate as either previous to or subsequent to the explanatory variable. In contrast, model fitting takes both the explanatory variable and the covariates simultaneously.

The **coefficient t-test** is a hypothesis test on a coefficient in a model. The null hypothesis is that, in the population, that coefficient is zero but all the other coefficients are exactly as given by the model fit. Under this null hypothesis, the sampling distribution of the coefficient of interest is centered on zero. The standard deviation of the sampling distribution is the standard error found in the model regression report.

To illustrate, consider the model `height ~ nkids + sex + mother + father` fitted to Galton's height data:

	Estimate	Std. Error	t value	$\Pr(>|t|)$
Intercept	16.1877	2.7939	5.79	0.0001
nkids	-0.0438	0.0272	-1.61	0.1073
sexM	5.2099	0.1442	36.12	0.0001
mother	0.3210	0.0313	10.27	0.0001
father	0.3983	0.0296	13.47	0.0001

According to this model, the coefficient on `nkids` is -0.0438 with a standard error of 0.0272. Under the null hypothesis for `nkids`, the sampling distribution of the coefficient has a mean of zero and a standard devation of 0.0272. The p-value of the observed coefficient, 0.107, tells how likely it is for that value or a more extreme value to be observed as a random draw from the sampling distribution. In this model, the p-value for `nkids` is not so small to justify rejecting the null hypothesis.

A nice feature of the regression report is that it is conducting a hypothesis test on each of the coefficients at the same time. This makes it easy to scan for coefficients that are statistically non-zero. On the other hand, this also introduces the need to adjust the rejection threshold to take into account the multiple hypothesis tests that are being conducted simultaneously. For example, in the above report, a Bonferroni adjustment would change the rejection threshold from the conventional 0.05 to 0.0125, since there are four coefficients being tested. (The hypothesis test on the intercept would not be of interest, since it doesn't relate to any of the explanatory variables.)

A not-so-nice feature of the regression report is that collinearity tends to produce high p-values on the coefficients of *all* of the collinear vectors; there's no hint from the report itself in the p-values that any of the collinear vectors might have a low p-value if the others were dropped from the model. To find this out, you need to try various orderings of the terms in the ANOVA report.

As always, the easiest situation for interpretation is when there is no collinearity at all between the explanatory variable and the covariates. In such a case, the regression report p-value is exactly the same as the p-value from ANOVA. However, when there is a correlation between the explanatory variable and the covariates, the regression report suffers from the same sorts of ambiguities as ANOVA, it's just that these are hidden because a simple re-arrangement of terms doesn't change the regression report.

Example 15.4: Wages and Race: Part 3   Earlier in this chapter, the Current Population Survey data was explored using term-by-term ANOVA to investigate the potential role of race. The conclusions reached differed depending on the assumptions made by the modeler as reflected by the order of terms in the ANOVA report.

Here is yet another analysis, using the regression report:

	Estimate	Std. Error	t value	Pr(>|t|)
Intercept	0.2083	1.4298	0.15	0.8842
raceW	0.4614	0.6021	0.77	0.4439
educ	0.5274	0.0965	5.47	0.0001
sectorconst	3.0204	1.1320	2.67	0.0079
sectormanag	4.3935	0.7857	5.59	0.0001
sectormanuf	1.5382	0.7400	2.08	0.0381
sectorother	1.6285	0.7301	2.23	0.0261
sectorprof	3.0602	0.6947	4.41	0.0001
sectorsales	-0.0085	0.8734	-0.01	0.9922
sectorservice	-0.1574	0.6940	-0.23	0.8206

That raceW comes first in this report doesn't signify anything. In a regression report, the values don't depend at all on the order of the terms.

The valuable thing about the regression report is that it gives not just the statistical significance of the term, but a measure of the actual strength of the term. This report indicates that Whites earned $0.46 ± 1.20 more than Blacks, after adjusting for the sector of the economy and the educational level of the worker. The p-value reflects the wide confidence interval: at 0.44 there's no basis for rejecting the null hypothesis that the population coefficient on raceW is zero.

Because the regression report is independent of the order of terms, it's tempting to think that it's somehow more objective than term-by-term ANOVA. That's wrong. The causal model implicit in the regression report has it's own point of view, that each of the terms in the model contributes to the response variable directly, not through the mediation of another variable. Thus, for the person who thinks that sector is merely a mechanism for discrimination by race, the regression report is not an appropriate form of analysis. Similarly, the regression report isn't appropriate for the person who thinks that it's really educ and sector that determine wages and that race only appears to come into play because it happens to be correlated with those other variables. The regression report is appropriate only for the person for whom causation isn't an issue. This might be because they want to construct a prediction model or because they believe that none of the explanatory variables cause others.

Example 15.5: Testing Universities

University students are used to being given tests and graded as individuals. But who grades the universities to find out how good a job the institutions are doing?

This need not be hard. Most universities require an entrance test — the SAT is widely used in the US for undergraduate admissions, the GRE, LSAT, MCAT, etc. for graduate school. Why not give students the entrance test a second time when they leave and compare the two results? If students at Alpha University show a large increase compared to students at Beta University, then there is evidence that Alpha does a better job than Beta.

There are good and bad reasons why such testing is not widely done. University faculty as a group are notoriously independent and don't like being evaluated. They are suspicious of standardized tests for evaluation of their teaching (although the don't often oppose using them for admissions purposes). They point out that there are many factors outside of their control that influence the results, such as the students' preparedness, motivation, and work ethic. (On the other hand, universities are happy to take credit for the students who succeed).

One legitimate obstacle to meaningful testing of universities is that students are not required to take an exit test and not motivated to perform well on it. A student who is applying to university has to take the entrance exam and has good reason to try to do well on it — favorable admissions decisions and scholarship awards often follow good test results. But the student who is soon to graduate has no such motivation, either to take the exit exam or to do well on it. So what does the difference between the entrance and exit scores show: How much the students learned or that the graduating students have something better to do with their time than take an exit exam?

The Collegiate Learning Assessment (CLA) is a standardized test consisting of several essay questions that probe a student's critical thinking skills.[26] (See `www.cae.org`.) As of 2008, more than 200 universities and colleges have been testing the exam. The CLA is given to one group of first-year students and another group of final-year students. The scores of the two groups are then compared.

Ideally, the same students would be tested in both their first and last years. If this were done, each student could be compared to himself or herself and covariates such as previous preparation or overall aptitude would be held constant within each entry-to-exit comparison. Unfortunately, such **longitudinal** designs were used at only 15% of the CLA schools. At the remaining schools, for reasons of cost and administrative complexity, a **cross-sectional** design was used, where the two groups consist of different students. When the study is cross-sectional, it can be important to adjust for covariates that may differ from one group to another.

In the case of the CLA, the students' performance on other standardized tests (such as the entrance SAT) is used for the adjustment. As it happens, there is a strong correlation between the SAT score and other explanatory variables. This collinearity tends to increase the standard error of the estimate of school-to-school differences.

Two studies of the CLA adjustment methodology concluded that they so increased standard errors that no clear inference can be made of school-to-school differences.[27] The studies called for longitudinal testing to be done in order to increase the reliability of the results. But, short of requiring students to take both the entrance and exit exams, it's not clear how the longitudinal approach can be implemented.

15.6 Non-Parametric Statistics

It sometimes happens that one or more of your variables have outliers or a highly skew distribution. In this situation, the extreme values of the variable can have an unduly strong influence on the fit of the model. As a result, the p-values calculated from ANOVA can be misleading.

Common sense suggests deleting the outliers or extreme values from the data used to fit the model. Certainly this is an appropriate step if you have good reason to think that the extreme values are bogus.

A more moderate approach is to fit two models: one with and one without the extreme values. If the two models give similar results, then you can reasonably conclude that the extreme values are not having an undue effect.

But if the two models give very different results, you have a quandry. Which model should you use? On the one hand, you don't want some cases to have an "undue" influence. On the other hand, those cases might be telling you something about the system and you need to be able to guard against the criticism that you have altered your data.

There is a simple and effective way to deal with this situation for the purpose of deciding whether the extreme values are dominating p-value calculations. The approach is to transform your data in a way that is genuine to the extreme values by keeping them on the edge of the distribution, but which brings them closer to the mainstream. The easiest such transform is called the **rank transform**. It replaces each value in a variable with the position of the value in the set of values. For example, suppose you have a variable with these values:

$$23.4, 17.3, 26.8, 32.8, 31.3, 34.5, 7352.3.$$

It's obvious that the seventh value is quite different from the other six. Applying the rank transform, this variable becomes

$$2, 1, 3, 5, 4, 6, 7.$$

That is, 23.4 is the 2nd smallest value, 17.3 is the 1st smallest value, 26.8 is the 3rd smallest, and so on. With the rank transform, the extreme value of 7352.3 becomes nothing special: it has rank 7 because it is the seventh smallest value. There are never outliers in a rank transformed variable. Nevertheless, the rank transformed data are honest to the original data in the sense that each value retains its position relative to the other values.

Analysis of rank-transformed data is called **non-parametric statistics**. The co-efficients from models of rank-transformed data are hard to interpret, because they describe how the response value changes do to a 1-step increase in rank rather than a one-unit increase the value of the variable. Still, the p-values can be interpreted in a standard way.

When outliers or extreme values are a concern, it's worth comparing the p-values from the original (parametric) model and the non-parametric model fitted to the rank-transformed data. If the p-values lead to the same conclusion, you know that the extreme values are not shaping the results. If the p-values for the two models lead to different conclusions then your work is just beginning and you need to think carefully about what is going on.

15.7   Sample Size and Power

If the p-value on your explanatory variable of interest is small enough, you're entitled to reject the null. If it's not so small, you are left in the ambiguous situation of "failing to reject." This failure might be because the explanatory variable is indeed irrelevant to the response variable. That's a valuable finding. On the other hand, there can be a much more mundane explanation for the failure: your sample size was not large enough.

In ANOVA, the p-value gets smaller as F gets bigger. In turn, F is a product of both the substance of the effect and the sample size n: larger n produces larger F as described in Equation 14.3 on page 270.

The fundamental issue, however, is not F, but the **power** of your study. In picking a sample size n for your study, your goal should be to produce a study with a large enough power so that, if you do fail to reject the null, you will have good reason to prefer the null hypothesis to the alternative hypothesis as a reasonable representation of your system.

Typically, you start a study with some working hypothesis about how the explanatory variable is related to the response. This working hypothesis is given the name **alternative hypothesis**. (The word "alternative" is simply the statistical vocabulary for distinguishing the working hypothesis from the "null" hypothesis.) The goal of this section is to show how to translate your alternative hypothesis into a decision about the appropriate sample size n to produce good power.

It may seem odd to be thinking about sample size here, at the end of a chapter on analyzing data. After all, you have to have your data already in hand before you can analyze it! But modeling is a process of asking questions. That process often involves going back and collecting more or different data based on the results of the analysis of earlier data.

When deciding on a sample size, think ahead to the analysis you will eventually do on the data you collect. It's likely that your analysis will be analysis of covariance or something like it. So you will end up with an ANOVA table, looking perhaps like this:

Term	Df	Sum Sq	Mean Sq	F value	p value
Intercept	1	500			
Covariates	3	200			
Explanatory Var	1	50	50	2	0.19
Residuals	10	250	25		
TOTAL	15	1000			

From your knowledge of the covariates and the explanatory variable, you should know the degrees of freedom of each model term even before you collect the data. But until you actually have the data, you won't be able to fill in the actual values for the sums of squares. What's been done here is to guess — hopefully an informed guess based on your working hypothesis.

What information might you have to work from? Perhaps you have already done a preliminary study and collected just a bit of data — the $n = 15$ cases here. Then you have the ANOVA report from those data. Or perhaps there is an existing study in the literature from a study of the same explanatory variable or an analogous one in a setting similar to the one you are working on. You'll need to be creative, but realistic.

For the present, assume that the above ANOVA table came from a preliminary study with $n = 15$ cases. The F value of 2 is suggestive, but the p-value is large; you cannot reject the null based on this data set. But perhaps a larger study would be able to reveal what's merely suggested in the preliminary study.

Imagine what the table would look like for larger n. For simplicity here, consider what would happen if you doubled the number of cases, to $n = 30$. (In reality, you might need to consider some number much larger than the $n = 30$ used in this example.) Of course, you can't know exactly what the larger n will give until you actually collect the data. But, for planning, it's sensible to assume that your extended study might look something like the preliminary study. If that's so, doubling the number of cases will typically double the total sum of squares. (Why? Because you're adding up twice as many cases. For instance, the sum of squares of 3, 4, 5 is 50; the sum of squares of 3, 4, 5, 3, 4, 5 is 100.)

Increasing the number of cases doesn't change the degrees of freedom of the explanatory variables. The intercept, the covariates, and the explanatory variable terms still have the same degrees of freedom as before. As a result, for these terms the mean square will double.

In contrast, the degrees of freedom of the residual will increase with the number of cases in the sample. The sum of squares of the residual will also increase, but the net effect is that the mean square of the residual will stay roughly the same.

To illustrate, the following table shows the ANOVA tables side by side for a preliminary study with $n = 15$ and an expanded study with $n = 30$.

Term	Prelim. Study $n = 15$				New Study $n = 30$			
	D.F.	Sum Sq.	Mean Sq.	F	D.F.	Sum Sq.	Mean Sq.	F
Intercept	1	500	500		1	1000	1000	
Covariates	3	200	67		3	400	133	
Explan. Var.	1	50	50	2	1	100	100	5
Residuals	10	250	25		25	500	20	
TOTAL	15	1000			30	2000		

Overall, by doubling n you can anticipate that the F value will be more than doubled. If n were increased even further, the anticipated F value would similarly be increased further, as in Equation 14.3.

The goal in setting the sample size n is to produce statistical significance — a small p-value. As a rule of thumb for the F distribution, F above 4 or 5 will give a small p-value when the sample size n is around 25 or bigger. (More precisely, when the degrees of freedom of the denominator is around 25 or bigger.)

But targeting such an F value would be a mistake. The reason is that F itself is subject to sampling fluctuations. If your sample size is such to produce a p-value of 0.05 when you hit the target F, then there's a roughly 50% probability that sampling fluctuations will produce an F that's too small and consequently a p-value that's too large.

To avoid suffering from a mishap, it's appropriate to choose the sample size n large enough that sampling fluctuations are unlikely to produce an unsatisfactory p-value. Recall that the **power** is the probability that your study will lead to rejection of the null hypothesis *if the alternative hypothesis were true*. Your goal in choosing n is to produce a large power.

The calculation behind power is somewhat complicated, but the table gives an idea of the power for studies with different sample sizes n and different anticipated F.

Anticipated F	Power			
	$n = 10$	$n = 20$	$n = 100$	$n \to \infty$
3	17%	23%	28%	29%
5	33%	42%	49%	51%
10	64%	76%	83%	85%
20	92%	97%	99%	99%

This table was constructed for an explanatory variable with one degree of freedom. This could be a quantitative variable (for example, family income) or a categorical variable with two levels (for example, sex). As the table indicates the anticipated F must be quite high — 10 or so — to achieve a power of 90% or higher. When the degrees of freedom in the numerator is higher, so long as n is large, high power can be achieved with considerably smaller F. For example, with five degrees of freedom in the denominator, $F = 5$ gives roughly 90% power.

If your study has low power, then failing to reject the null doesn't give much reason to take the null as reasonable: your study is likely to be inconclusive. When you aim for an F of about 5, your power will be only about 50%. If you want a high power, say 90%, your study should be designed to target a high F.

Studies are often expensive and difficult to conduct and so you want to be careful in designing them. The table above gives only a rough idea about power. Since the power calculations are complicated, you may want to consult with a professional to do the calculation that will be appropriate for your specific study design.

15.8   Computational Technique

The basic software for hypothesis testing on parts of models involves the familiar `lm` and `summary` operators for generating the regression report and the `anova` operator for generating an ANOVA report on a model.

15.8.1   ANOVA reports

The `anova` operator takes a model as an argument and produces the term-by-term ANOVA report. To illustrate, consider this model of wages from the Current Population Survey data.

DATA FILE
cps.csv

```
> cps = fetchData("cps.csv")
> mod1 = lm(wage ~ married + age + educ, data=cps)
> anova(mod1)

Analysis of Variance Table

Response: wage
          Df Sum Sq Mean Sq F value  Pr(>F)
married    1    142     142    6.74  0.0097 **
age        1    338     338   16.02 7.2e-05 ***
educ       1   2399    2399  113.54 < 2e-16 ***
Residuals 530  11197      21
---
Signif. codes:  0 '***' 0.001 '**' 0.01 '*' 0.05 '.' 0.1 ' ' 1
```

Note the small p-value on the `married` term: 0.0097.

To change the order of the terms in the report, you can create a new model with the explanatory terms listed in a different order. For example, here's the ANOVA on the same model, but with `married` last instead of first:

```
> mod2 = lm(wage ~ age + educ + married, data=cps)
> anova(mod2)

Analysis of Variance Table

Response: wage
          Df Sum Sq Mean Sq F value  Pr(>F)
age        1    441     441    20.9 6.1e-06 ***
educ       1   2403    2403   113.7 < 2e-16 ***
married    1     36      36     1.7    0.19
Residuals 530 11197      21
---
Signif. codes:  0 '***' 0.001 '**' 0.01 '*' 0.05 '.' 0.1 ' ' 1
```

Now the p-value on `married` is large. This suggests that much of the variation in `wage` that is associated with `married` can also be accounted for by `age` and `educ` instead.

15.8.2   Non-Parametric Statistics

Consider the model of world-record swimming times plotted on page 116. It shows pretty clearly the interaction between `year` and `sex`.

It's easy to confirm that this interaction term is statistically significant:

```
> swim = fetchData("swim100m.csv")
> anova( lm(time ~ year*sex, data=swim) )

Analysis of Variance Table

Response: time
          Df Sum Sq Mean Sq F value  Pr(>F)
year       1   3579    3579   324.7 < 2e-16 ***
sex        1   1484    1484   134.7 < 2e-16 ***
year:sex   1    297     297    26.9 2.8e-06 ***
Residuals 58    639      11
---
Signif. codes:  0 '***' 0.001 '**' 0.01 '*' 0.05 '.' 0.1 ' ' 1
```

The p-value on the interaction term is very small: 2.8×10^{-6}.

To check whether this result might be influenced by the shape of the distribution of the `time` or `year` data, you can conduct a non-parametric test. Simply take the rank of each quantitative variable:

```
> mod = lm(rank(time) ~ rank(year)*sex, data=swim)
> anova(mod)
```

```
Analysis of Variance Table

Response: rank(time)
              Df Sum Sq Mean Sq F value Pr(>F)
rank(year)     1  14320   14320 3755.77 <2e-16 ***
sex            1   5313    5313 1393.41 <2e-16 ***
rank(year):sex 1      1       1    0.23   0.63
Residuals     58    221       4
---
Signif. codes:  0 '***' 0.001 '**' 0.01 '*' 0.05 '.' 0.1 ' ' 1
```

With the rank-transformed data, the p-value on the interaction term is much larger: no evidence for an interaction between year and sex. You can see this directly in a plot of the data after rank-transforming time:

```
> xyplot(rank(time) ~ year, groups=sex, data=swim)
```

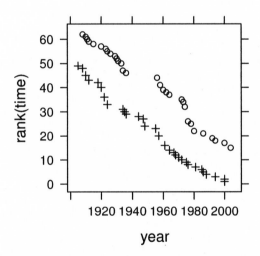

The rank-transformed data suggest that women's records are improving in about the same way as men's.

Reading Questions

- What is a "covariate" and how does it differ from any other kind of variable?

- Why is there a separate F statistic for each explanatory term in a model?

- How can covariates make an explanatory term look better (e.g., more significant) in an F test?

- How can covariates make an explanatory term look worse (e.g., less significant) in an F test?

- Why does the the sum of squares of the various model terms change when there is collinearity among the model terms?

For exercises, see www.mosaic-web.org/StatisticalModeling/Exercises.

16

Models of Yes/No Variables

The techniques studied up until now are intended to model *quantitative* response variables, those where the value is a number, for example height, wage, swimming times, or foot size. Categorical variables have been used only in the role of explanatory variables.

But sometimes the variation that you want to model occurs in a categorical variable. For instance, you might want to know what dietary factors are related to whether a person develops cancer. The variable "develops cancer" isn't a number: it's a yes-or-no matter.

There are good technical reasons why it's easier to build and interpret models with quantitative response variables. For one, a residual from such a model is simply a number. The size of a typical residual can be described using a variance or a mean square. In contrast, consider a model that tries to predict whether a person will become an businessman or an engineer or a farmer or a lawyer. There are many different ways for the model to be wrong, e.g., it predicts farmer when the outcome is lawyer, or engineer when the outcome is businessman. The "residual" is not a number, so how do you measure how large it is?

This chapter introduces one technique for building and evaluating models where the response variable is categorical. The technique handles a special case, where the categorical variable has only two levels. Generically, these can be called **yes/no** variables, but the two levels could be anything you like: alive/dead, success/failure, engineer/not-engineer, and so on.

16.1   The 0-1 Encoding

The wonderful thing about yes/no variables is that they are always effectively quantitative; they can be naturally encoded as 0 for no and 1 for yes. Given this encoding, you could if you want just use the standard linear modeling approach of quantitative response variables. That's what I'll do at first, showing what's good and what's bad about this approach before moving on to a better method.

DATA FILE
whickham.csv

To illustrate using the linear modeling approach, consider some data that relate smoking and mortality. The table below gives a few of the cases from a data frame where women were interviewed about whether they smoked.

Case	Outcome	Smoker	Age
1	Alive	Yes	23
2	Alive	Yes	18
3	Dead	Yes	71
4	Alive	No	67
5	Alive	No	64
6	Alive	Yes	38

... and so on for 1314 cases altogether.

Of course, all the women were alive when interviewed! The outcome variable records whether each woman was still alive 20 years later, during a follow-up study. For instance, case 3 was 71 years old at the time of the interview. Twenty years later, she was no longer alive.

Outcome is the Yes/No variable I'm interested in understanding; it will be the response variable and smoker and age will be the explanatory variables. I'll encode "Alive" as 1 and "Dead" as 0, although it would work just as well do to things the other way around.

The simplest model of the outcome is all-cases-the-same: outcome $\sim$ 1. Here is the regression report from this model:

	Estimate	Std. Error	t value	Pr($>$|t|)
Intercept	0.7192	0.0124	57.99	0.0000

The intercept coefficient in the model outcome $\sim$ 1 has a simple interpretation; it's the mean of the response variable. Because of the 0-1 coding, the mean is just the fraction of cases where the person was alive. That is, the coefficient from this model is just the probability that a random case drawn from the sample has an outcome of "Alive."

At first that might seem a waste of modeling software, since you could get exactly the same result by counting the number of "Alive" cases. But notice that there is a bonus to the modeling approach — there is a standard error given that tells how precise is the estimate: 0.719 ± 0.024 with 95% confidence.

The linear modeling approach also works sensibly with an explanatory variable. Here's the regression report on the model `outcome ~ smoker`:

	Estimate	Std. Error	t value	Pr(>|t|)
(Intercept)	0.6858	0.0166	41.40	0.0000
smokerYes	0.0754	0.0249	3.03	0.0025

You can interpret the coefficients from this model in a simple way — the intercept is group-wise means of `outcome` for the non-smokers. The other coefficient gives the difference in the means between the smokers and the non-smokers. Since `outcome` is a 0-1 variable encoding whether the person was alive, the coefficients indicate the proportion of people in each group who were alive at the time of the follow-up study. In other words, it's reasonable to interpret the intercept as the probability that a non-smokers was alive, and the other coefficient as the difference in probability of being alive between the non-smokers and smokers.

Again, you could have found this result in a simpler way: just count the fraction of smokers and of non-smokers who were alive.

The advantage of the modeling approach is that it produces a standard error for each coefficient and a p-value. The intercept says that 0.686 ± 0.033 of non-smokers were alive. The `smoker`**Yes** coefficient says that an additional 0.075 ± 0.05 of smokers were alive.

This result might be surprising, since most people expect that mortality is higher among smokers than non-smokers. But the confidence interval does not include 0 or any negative number. Correspondingly, the p-value in the report is small: the null hypothesis that `smoker` is unrelated to `outcome` can be rejected.

Perhaps it's obvious that a proper model of mortality and smoking should adjust for the `age` of the person. After all, `age` is strongly related to mortality and smoking might be related to `age`. Here's the regression report from the model `outcome ~ smoker+age`:

	Estimate	Std. Error	t value	Pr(>|t|)
(Intercept)	1.4726	0.0301	48.92	0.0000
smokerYes	0.0105	0.0196	0.54	0.5927
age	**-0.0162**	0.0006	-28.95	0.0000

It seems that the inclusion of `age` has had the anticipated effect. According to the coefficient -0.016, there is a negative relationship between `age` and being alive. The effect of `smoker` has been greatly reduced; the p-value 0.59 is much too large to reject the null hypothesis. These data in fact give little or no evidence that smoking is associated with mortality. (It's well established that smoking

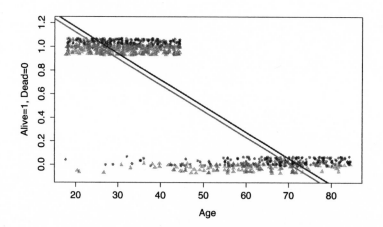

Figure 16.1: Top: The smoking/mortality data along with a linear model. Bottom: A thought experiment which eliminates the "Alive" cases above age 45.

increases mortality, but the number of people involved in this study, combined with the relatively young ages of the smokers, means that the power of the study was small.)

There is also a mathematical issue. Consider the fitted model value for a 20-year old smoker: $1.47 + 0.010 - 0.016 \times 20 = 1.16$. This value, 1.16, can't be interpreted as a probability that a 20-year old smoker would still be alive at the time of the follow-up study (when she would have been 40). Probabilities must always be between zero and one.

The top panel of Figure 16.1 shows the fitted model values for the linear model

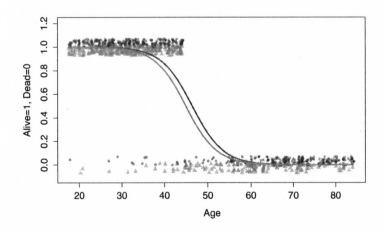

Figure 16.2: Logistic forms for outcome ~ age + smoker. Top: The smoking/mortality data. Bottom: The thought experiment in which the "Alive" cases above age 45 were eliminated.

along with the actual data. (Since the outcome variable is coded as 0 or 1, it's been jittered slightly up and down so that the density of the individual cases shows up better. Smokers are at the bottom of each band, plotted as small triangles.) The data show clearly that older people are more likely to have died. Less obvious in the figure is that the very old people tended not to smoke.

The problem with the linear model is that it is too rigid, too straight. In order for the model to reflect that the large majority of people in their 40s and 50s were alive, the model overstates survival in the 20-year olds. This isn't actually a problem for the 20-year olds — the model values clearly indicate that they are very likely to be alive. But what isn't known is the extent to which the line has been pulled down to come close to 1 for the 20-year olds, thereby lowering the model values for the middle-aged folks.

To illustrate how misleading the straight-line model can be, I'll conduct a small thought experiment and delete all the "alive" cases above the age of 45. The resulting data and the best-fitting linear model are shown in the bottom panel of Figure 16.1.

The thought-experiment model is completely wrong for people in their 50s. Even though there are no cases whatsoever where such people are alive, the model value is around 50%.

What's needed is a more flexible model — something not quite so rigid as a line, something that can bend to stay in the 0-to-1 bounds of legitimate probabilities. There are many ways that this could be accomplished. The one that is most widely used is exceptionally effective, clever, and perhaps unexpected. It consists of a two-stage process:

1. Construct a model value in the standard linear way — multiplication of coefficients times model vectors. The model outcome ~ age+smoker would involve the familiar terms: an intercept, a vector for age, and the indicator vector for smoker**Yes**. The output of the linear formula — I'll call it Y — is not a probability but rather a **link value**: an intermediary of the fitting process.

2. Rather than taking the link value Y as the model value, transform Y into another quantity P that it is bounded by 0 and 1. A number of different transformations could do the job, but the most widely used one is called the **logistic transformation**: $P = \frac{e^Y}{1+e^Y}$.

This type of model is called a **logistic regression** model. The choice of the best coefficients — the model fit — is based not directly on how well the link values Y match the data but on how the probability values P match.

Figure 16.2 illustrates the logistic form on the smoking/mortality data. The logistic transformation lets the model fit the outcomes for the very young and the very old, while maintaining flexibility in the middle to match the data there.

The two-stage approach to logistic regression makes it straightforward to add explanatory terms in a model. Whatever terms there are in a model — main terms, interaction terms, nonlinear terms — the logistic transformation guarantees that the model values P will fall nicely in the 0-to-1 scale.

Figure 16.3 shows how the link value Y is translated into the 0-to-1 scale of P for different "shapes" of models.

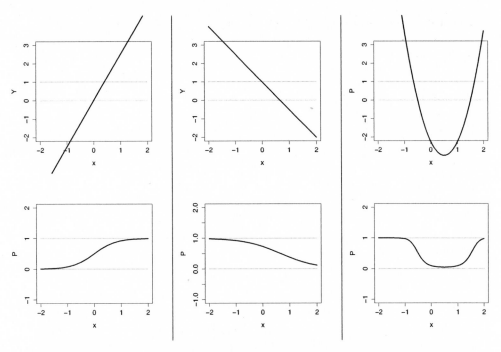

Figure 16.3: Comparing the link values Y with the probability values P for three different models, each with an explanatory variable x. Top: Link values. Bottom: Probability values.

16.2   Inference on Logistic Models

The interpretation of logistic models follows the same logic as in linear models. Each case has a model probability value. For example, the model probability value for a 64-year old non-smoker is 0.4215, while for a 64-year old smoker it is 0.3726. These model values are in the form of probabilities; the 64-year old non-smoker had a 42% chance of being alive at the time of the follow-up interview.

There is a regression report for logistic models. Here it is for `outcome ~ age+smoker`:

	Estimate	Std. Error	z value	$\Pr(>|z|)$
Intercept	**7.5992**	0.4412	17.22	0.0000
age	**-0.1237**	0.0072	-17.23	0.0000
smokerYes	-0.2047	0.1684	-1.22	0.2242

The coefficients refer to the link values Y, so for the 64-year old non-smoker the value is $Y = 7.59922 - 0.12368 \times 64 = -0.3163$. This value is not a probability; it's negative, so how could it be? The model value is the output of applying the logistic transform to Y, that is, $\frac{e^{-0.3163}}{1+e^{-0.3163}} = 0.4215$.

The logistic regression report includes standard errors and p-values, just as in the ordinary linear regression report. Even if there were no regression report, you could generate the information by resampling, using bootstrapping to find confidence intervals and doing hypothesis tests by permutation tests or by resampling the explanatory variable.

In the regression report for the model above, you can see that the null hypothesis that age is unrelated to outcome can be rejected. (That's no surprise, given the obvious tie between age and mortality.) On the other hand, these data provide only very weak evidence that there is a difference between smokers and non-smokers; the p-value is 0.22.

An ANOVA-type report can be made for logistic regression. This involves the same sort of reasoning as in linear regression: fitting sequences of nested models and examining how the residuals are reduced as more explanatory terms are added to the model.

It's time to discuss the residuals from logistic regression. Obviously, since there are response values (the 0-1 encoding of the response variable) and there are model values, there must be residuals. The obvious way to define the residuals is as the difference between the response values and the model values, just as is done for linear models. If this were done, the model fit could be chosen as that which minimizes the sum of square residuals.

Although it would be possible to fit a logistic-transform model in this way, it is not the accepted technique. To see the problem with the sum-of-square-residuals approach, think about the process of comparing two candidate models. The table below gives a sketch of two models to be compared during a fitting process. The first model has one set of model values, and the second model has another set of model values.

	Model Values		
	First	Second	Observed
Case	Model	Model	Value
1	0.8	1.0	1
2	0.1	0.0	1
3	0.9	1.0	1
4	0.5	0.0	0
Sum. Sq. Resid.	1.11	1.00	

Which model is better? The sum of square residuals for the first model is $(1 - 0.8)^2 + (1-0.1)^2 + (1-0.9)^2 + (0-0.5)^2$, which works out to be 1.11. For the second model, the sum of square residuals is $(1-1.0)^2 + (1-0.0)^2 + (1-1.0)^2 + (0-0.0)^2$, or 1.00. Conclusion: the second model is to be preferred.

However, despite the sum of squares, there is a good reason to prefer the first model. For Case 2, the Second Model gives a model value of 0 — this says that it's *impossible* to have an outcome of 1. But, in fact, the observed value was 1;

according to the Second Model the impossible has occurred! The First Model has a model value of 0.1 for Case 2, suggesting it is merely *unlikely* that the outcome could be 1.

The actual criterion used to fit logistic models penalizes heavily — infinitely in fact — candidate models that model as impossible events that can happen. The criterion for fitting is called the **likelihood** and is defined to be the probability of the observed values according to the probability model of the candidate. When the observed value is 1, the likelihood of the single observation is just the model probability. When the observed value is 0, the likelihood is 1 minus the model probability. The overall likelihood is the product of the individual likelihoods of each case. So, according to the First Model, the likelihood of the observations $1, 1, 1, 0$ is $0.8 \times 0.1 \times 0.9 \times (1 - 0.5) = 0.036$. According to the Second Model, the likelihood is $1 \times 0 \times 1 \times (1 - 0) = 0$. The First Model wins.

It might seem that the likelihood criterion used in logistic regression is completely different from the sum-of-square-residuals criterion used in linear regression. It turns out that they both fit into a common framework called **maximum likelihood estimation**. A key insight is that one can define a probability model for describing residuals and, from this, compute the likelihood of the observed data given the model.

In the maximum likelihood framework, the equivalent of the sum of squares of the residuals is a quantity called the **deviance**. Just as the linear regression report gives the sum of squares of the residual, the logistic regression report gives the deviance. To illustrate, here is the deviance part of the logistic regression report for the `outcome ~ age+smoker` model:

```
    Null deviance: 1560.32  on 1313   degrees of freedom
Residual deviance:  945.02  on 1311   degrees of freedom
```

The **null deviance** refers to the simple model `outcome ~ 1`: it's analogous to the sum of squares of the residuals from that simple model. The reported degrees of freedom, 1313, is the sample size n minus the number of coefficients m in the model. That's $m = 1$ because the model `outcome ~ 1` has a single coefficient. For the smoker/mortality data in the example, the sample size is $n = 1314$. The line labelled "Residual deviance" reports the deviance from the full model: `outcome ~ age+smoker`. The full model has three coefficients altogether: the intercept, `age`, and `smoker`**Yes**, leaving $1314 - 3 = 1311$ degrees of freedom in the deviance.

According to the report, the `age` and `smoker`**Yes** vectors reduced the deviance from 1560.32 to 945.02. The deviance is constructed in a way so that a random, junky explanatory vector would, on average, consume a proportion of the deviance equal to 1 over the degrees of freedom. Thus, if you constructed the `outcome ~ age+smoker + junk`, where `junk` is a random, junky term, you would expect the deviance to be reduced by a fraction $1/1311$.

To perform a hypothesis test, compare the actual amount by which a model term reduces the deviance to the amount expected for random terms. This is analogous to the F test, but involves a different probability distribution called the χ^2 (chi-squared). The end result, as with the F test, is a p-value which can be interpreted in the conventional way, just as you do in linear regression.

16.3   Model Probabilities

The link values Y in a logistic regression are ordinary numbers that can range from $-\infty$ to ∞. The logistic transform converts Y to numbers P on the scale 0 to 1, which can be interpreted as probabilities. I'll call the values P **model probabilities** to distinguish them from the sorts of model values found in ordinary linear models. The model probabilities describe the chance that the Yes/No response variable takes on the level "Yes."

To be more precise, P is a **conditional probability**. That is, it describes the probability of a "Yes" outcome conditioned on the explanatory variables in the model. In other words, the model probabilities are probabilities *given* the value of the explanatory variables. For example, in the model outcome ~ age + smoker, the link value for a 64-year old non-smoker is $Y = -0.3163$ corresponding to a model probability $P = 0.4215$. According to the model, this is the probability that a person who was 64 and a non-smoker was still alive at the time of the follow-up interview. That is to say, the probability is 0.4215 of being alive at the follow-up study conditioned on being age 64 and non-smoking at the time of the original interview. Change the values of the explanatory variables — look at a 65-year old smoker, for instance — and the model probability changes.

There is another set of factors that conditions the model probabilities: the situation that applied to the selection of cases for the data frame. For instance, fitting the model outcome ~ 1 to the smoking/mortality data gives a model probability for "Alive" of $P = 0.672$. It would not be fair to say that this is the probability that a person will still be alive at the time of the follow-up interview. Instead, it is the probability that a person will still be alive *given* that they were in the sample of data found in the data frame. Only if that sample is representative of a broader population is it fair to treat that probability as applying to that population. If the overall population doesn't match the sample, the probability from the model fitted to the sample won't necessarily match the probability of "Alive" in the overall population.

Often, the interest is to apply the results of the model to a broad population that is not similar to the sample. This can sometimes be done, but care must be taken.

To illustrate, consider a study done by researchers in Queensland, Australia on the possible link between cancer of the prostate gland and diet.   Pan-fried and grilled meats are a source of carcinogenic compounds such as heterocyclic amines and polycyclic aromatic hydrocarbons. Some studies have found a link between eating meats cooked "well-done" and prostate cancer.[28] The Queensland researchers[29] interviewed more than 300 men with prostate cancer to find out how much meat of various types they eat and how they typically have their meat cooked. They also interviewed about 200 men without prostate cancer to serve as controls. They modeled whether or not each man has prostate cancer (variable `pcancer`) using both `age` and `intensity` of meat consumption as the explanatory variables. Then, to quantify the effect of meat consumption, they compared high-intensity eaters to low-intensity eaters; the model probability at the 10th percentile of `intensity` compared to the model probability at the 90th percentile. For example, for a 60-year old man, the model probabilities are 69.8% for low-meat intensity eaters, and 82.1% for high-meat intensity eaters.

It would be a mistake to interpret these numbers as the probabilities that a 60-year old man will have prostate cancer. The prevalence of prostate cancer is much lower. (According to one source, the prevalence of clinically evident prostate cancer is less than 10% over a lifetime, so many fewer than 10% of 60-year old men have clinically evident prostate cancer.[30])

The sample was collected in a way that intentionally overstates the prevalence of prostate cancer. More than half of the sample was selected specifically because the person had prostate cancer. Given this, the sample is not representative of the overall population. In order to make a sample that matches the overall population, there would have had to be many more non-cancer controls in the sample.

However, there's reason to believe that the sample reflects in a reasonably accurate way the diet practices of those men with prostate cancer and also of those men without prostate cancer. As such, the sample can give information that might be relevant to the overall population, namely how meat consumption could be linked to prostate cancer. For example, the model indicates that a high-intensity eater has a higher chance of having prostate cancer than a low-intensity eater. Comparing these probabilities — 82.1% and 69.8% — might give some insight.

There is an effective way to compare the probabilities fitted to the sample so that the results can be generalized to apply to the overall population. It will work so long as the different groups in the sample — here, the men with prostate cancer and the non-cancer controls — are each representative of that same group in the overall population.

It's tempting to compare the probabilities directly as a ratio to say how much high-intensity eating increases the risk of prostate cancer compared to low-intensity eating. This ratio of model probabilities is 0.821/0.698, about 1.19. The interpretation of this is that high-intensity eating increases the risk of cancer by 19%.

Unfortunately, because the presence of prostate cancer in the sample doesn't match the prevalence in the overall population, the ratio of model probabilities usually will not match that which would be found from a sample that does represent the overall population.

Rather than taking the ratio of model probabilities, it turns out to be better to consider the **odds ratio**. Even though the sample doesn't match the overall population, the odds ratio will (so long as the two groups individually accurately reflect the population in each of those groups).

Odds are just another way of talking about probability P. Rather than being a number between 0 and 1, an odds is a number between 0 and ∞. The odds is calculated as $P/(1-P)$. For example, the odds that corresponds to a probability $P = 50\%$ is $0.50/(1 - 0.50) = 1$. Everyday language works well here: the odds are fifty-fifty.

The odds corresponding to the low-intensity eater's probability of $P = 69.8\%$ is $0.698/0.302 = 2.31$. Similarly, the odds corresponding to high-intensity eater's $P = 82.1\%$ is $0.821/0.179 = 4.60$. The odds ratio compares the two odds: $4.60/2.31 = 1.99$, about two-to-one.

Why use a ratio of odds rather than a simple ratio of probabilities? Because the sample was constructed in a way that doesn't accurately represent the prevalence of cancer in the population. The ratio of probabilities would reflect the prevalence of cancer in the sample: an artifact of the way the sample was collected. The odds ratio compares each group — cancer and non-cancer — to itself and doesn't depend on the prevalence in the sample.

Example 16.1: Log-odds ratios of Prostate Cancer   One of the nice features of the logistic transformation is that the link values Y can be used directly to read off the logarithm of odds ratios.

In the prostate-cancer data, the coefficients on the model `pcancer ~ age + intensity` are these:

	Estimate	Std. Error	z value	Pr(>|z|)
Intercept	4.274	0.821	5.203	0.0000
Age	-0.057	0.012	-4.894	0.0000
Intensity	**0.172**	0.058	2.961	0.0031

These coefficients can be used to calculate the link value Y which corresponds to a log odds. For example, in comparing men at 10th percentile of `intensity` to those at the 90th percentile, you multiply the `intensity` coefficient by the difference in intensities. The bottom 10th percentile is 0 `intensity` and the top 10th percentile is an `intensity` of 4. So the difference in Y score for the two percentiles is $0.1722 \times (4 - 0) = 0.6888$. This value, 0.6888, is the log odds ratio. To translate this to an odds ratio, you need to undo the log. That is, calculate $e^{0.6888} = 1.99$. So, the odds ratio for the risk of prostate cancer in high-intensity eaters versus low-intensity eaters is approximately 2.

Note that the model coefficient on `age` is negative. This suggests that the risk of prostate cancer *goes down* as people age. This is wrong biologically as is known from other epidemiological work on prostate cancer, but it does reflect that the sample was constructed rather than randomly collected. Perhaps it's better to say that it reflects a weakness in the way the sample was constructed: the prostate cancer cases tend to be younger than the non-cancer controls. If greater care had been used in selecting the control cases, they would have matched exactly the age distribution in the cancer cases. Including `age` in the model is an attempt to adjust for the problems in the sample — the idea is that including `age` allows the model's dependence on `intensity` to be treated *as if* `age` were held constant.

16.4 Computational Technique

Fitting logistic models uses many of the same ideas as in linear models.

16.4.1 Fitting Logistic Models

The `glm` operator fits logistic models. (It also fits other kinds of models, but that's another story.) `glm` takes model design and data arguments that are identical to their counterparts in `lm`. Here's an example using the smoking/mortality data:

DATA FILE
`whickham.csv`

```
> whickham = fetchData("whickham.csv")
> mod = glm( outcome ~ age + smoker, data=whickham,
      family="binomial")
```

The last argument, `family="binomial"`, simply specifies to `glm()` that the logistic transformation should be used. `glm()` is short for Generalized Linear Modeling, a broad label that covers logistic regression as well as other types of models involving links and transformations.

The regression report is produced with the **summary** operator, which recognizes that the model was fit logistically and does the right thing:

```
> summary(mod)
```

	Estimate	Std. Error	z value	Pr(>|z|)
(Intercept)	-7.5992	0.4412	-17.22	0.0000
age	0.1237	0.0072	17.23	0.0000
smokerYes	0.2047	0.1684	1.22	0.2242

Keep in mind that the coefficients refer to the intermediate model values Y. The probability P will be $e^Y/(1 + e^Y)$.

16.4.2   Fitted Model Values

Logistic regression involves two different kinds of fitted values: the intermediate "link" value Y and the probability P. The `fitted` operator returns the probabilities:

```
> probs = fitted(mod)
```

There is one fitted probability value for each case.

To use a logistic regression model for estimation of a probability, you should turn the model into a function that accepts the explanatory variables as inputs. This is done with `makeFun()`.

```
> pf = makeFun(mod)
```

Calculating the model probability is a matter of providing inputs to the function. For instance, here is the model probability for a 70-year old smoker:

```
> pf( age=70, smoker="Yes" )
    1
0.78
```

As always, make sure to use the appropriate levels for categorical variables.

By default, `makeFun()` will produce a function that gives the model probabilities. If you want to calculate the link values, you need to tell `makeFun()` that you want this type of output from the function.

```
> linkf = makeFun(mod, type="link")
> linkf(age=70, smoker="Yes")
    1
1.26
```

Notice that the link values are not necessarily between zero and one, although the probability determined by the link value will always be.

16.4.3   Which Level is "Yes"?

In fitting a logistic model, it's crucial that the response variable be categorical, with two levels. It happens that in the `whickham` data, the `outcome` variable fits the bill: the levels are `Alive` and `Dead`.

The `glm` software will automatically recode the response variable as 0/1. The question is, which level gets mapped to 1? In some sense, it makes no difference since there are only two levels. But if you're talking about the probability of dying, it's nice not to mistake that for the probability of staying alive. So make sure that you know which level in the response variable corresponds to 1: it's the second level.

Here is an easy way to make sure which level has been coded as "Yes". First, fit the all-cases-the-same model, `outcome ~ 1`. The fitted model value P from this model will be the proportion of cases for which the outcome was "Yes."

```
> mod2 = glm( outcome ~ 1, data=whickham, family="binomial")

> fitted(mod2)

    1     2     3     4     5
0.281 0.281 0.281 0.281 0.281
... for 1314 cases altogether ...
```

So, 28% of the cases were "Yes." But which of the two levels is "Yes?" You can check by looking at the proportion of each level in the response variable:

```
> tally( ~ outcome, data=whickham, format="proportion" )

Alive  Dead Total
0.719 0.281 1.000
```

Evidently, "Yes" means **Dead**.

If you want to dictate which of the two levels is going to be encoded as 1, you can use a comparison operation to do so:

```
> mod3 = glm( outcome=="Alive" ~ 1, data=whickham, family="binomial")

    1     2     3     4     5
0.719 0.719 0.719 0.719 0.719
... for 1314 cases altogether ...
```

In this model, "Yes" means **Alive**.

16.4.4 Analysis of Deviance

The same basic logic used in analysis of variance applies to logistic regression, although the quantity being broken down into parts is not the sum of squares of the residuals but, rather, the **deviance**.

The **anova** software will take apart a logistic model, term by term, using the order specified in the model.

```
> anova(mod, test="Chisq")
```

	Df	Deviance	Resid. Df	Resid. Dev	Pr(>Chi)
NULL			1313	1560.32	
age	1	613.81	1312	946.51	0.0000
smoker	1	1.49	1311	945.02	0.2228

Notice the second argument, `test="Chisq"`, which instructs `anova` to calculate a p-value for each term. This involves a slightly different test than the F test used in linear-model ANOVA.

The format of the ANOVA table for logistic regression is somewhat different from that used in linear models, but the concepts of degrees of freedom and partitioning still apply. The basic idea is to ask whether the reduction in deviance accomplished with the model terms is greater than what would be expected if random terms were used instead.

Reading Questions

- What's the difference between a "link value" and a "probability value" in a logistic regression model? How are they related to one another?

- How does the logistic function serve to keep the fitted probability values always within the range 0 to 1?

- What is maximum likelihood and how is it used as a criterion to fit a model?

For exercises, see www.mosaic-web.org/StatisticalModeling/Exercises.

17

Causation

If the issues at hand involve responsibilities or decisions or plans, causal reasoning is necessary. — Edward Tufte (1942 -), statistician and information artist

Knowing what causes what makes a big difference in how we act. If the rooster's crow causes the sun to rise we could make the night shorter by waking up our rooster earlier and make him crow - say by telling him the latest rooster joke. — Judea Pearl (1936 -), computer scientist

Starting in the 1860s, Europeans expanded rapidly westward in the United States, settling grasslands in the Great Plains. Early migrants had passed through these semi-arid plains, called the Great American Desert, on the way to habitable territories further west. But unusually heavy rainfall in the 1860s and 1870s supported new migrants who homesteaded on the plains rather than passing through.

The homesteaders were encouraged by a theory that the act of farming would increase rainfall. In the phrase of the day, "Rain follows the plow."

The theory that farming leads to rainfall was supported by evidence. As farming spread, measurements of rainfall were increasing. Buffalo grass, a species well adapted to dry conditions, was retreating. Other grasses more dependent on moisture were advancing. The exact mechanism of the increasing rainfall was uncertain, but many explanations were available. In a phrase-making book published in 1881, Charles Dana Wilber wrote,

> *Suppose now that a new army of frontier farmers ... could, acting in concert, turn over the prairie sod, and after deep plowing and receiving the rain and moisture, present a new surface of green, growing*

crops instead of the dry, hard-baked earth covered with sparse buffalo grass. No one can question or doubt the inevitable effect of this cool condensing surface upon the moisture in the atmosphere as it moves over by the Western winds. A reduction in temperature must at once occur, accompanied by the usual phenomena of showers. The chief agency in this transformation is agriculture. To be more concise. Rain follows the plow. [31, p. 68]

Seen in the light of subsequent developments, this theory seems hollow. Many homesteaders were wiped out by drought. The most famous of these, the Dust Bowl of the 1930s, rendered huge areas of US and Canadian prairie useless for agriculture and led to the displacement of hundreds of thousands of families.

Wilber was correct in seeing the association between rainfall and farming, but wrong in his interpretation of the causal connection between them. With a modern perspective, you can see clearly that Wilber got it backwards; there was indeed an association between farming and rainfall, but it was the increased rainfall of the 1870s that lead to the growth of farming. When the rains failed, so did the farms.

The subject of this chapter is the ways in which data and statistical models can and cannot appropriately be used to support claims of causation. When are you entitled to interpret a model as signifying a causal relationship? How can you collect and process data so that such an interpretation is justified? How can you decide which covariates to include or exclude in order to reveal causal links?

The answers to these questions are subtle. Model results can be interpreted only in the context of the researcher's beliefs and prior knowledge about how the system operates. And there are advantages when the researcher becomes a participant, not just collecting observations but actively intervening in the system under study as an experimentalist.

17.1   Interpreting Models Causally

Interpreting statistical models in terms of causation is done for a purpose. It is well to keep that purpose in mind so you can apply appropriate standards of evidence. When causation is an issue, typically you have in mind some intervention that you are considering performing. You want to use your models to estimate what will be the effect of that intervention.

For example, suppose you are a government health official considering the approval of flecainide, a drug intended for the treatment of overly fast heart rhythms such as atrial fibrillation. Your interest is improving patient outcomes, perhaps as measured by survival time. The purpose of your statistical models is to determine whether prescribing flecainide to patients is likely to lead to improved outcomes and how much improvement will typically be achieved.

Or suppose you are the principal of a new school. You have to decide how much to pay teachers but you have to stay within your budget. You have three options: pay relatively high salaries but make classes large, pay standard salaries and make classes the standard size, pay low salaries and make classes small. Your interest is in the effective education of your pupils, perhaps as measured by standardized test scores. The purpose of your statistical models is to determine whether the salary/class-size options will differ in their effects and by how much.

Or suppose you are a judge hearing a case involving a worker's claim of sex discrimination against her employer. You need to decide whether to find for the worker or the employer. This situation is somewhat different. In the education or drug examples, you planned to take action to change the variable of interest — reduce class sizes or give patients a drug — in order to produce a better outcome. But you can't change the worker's sex to avoid the discrimination. Even if you could, what's past is past. In this situation, you are dealing with a **counterfactual**: you want to find out how pay or working conditions would have been different if you changed the worker's sex and left everything else the same. This is obviously a hypothetical question. But that doesn't mean it isn't a useful one to answer or that it isn't important to answer the question correctly.

Example 17.1: Greenhouse Gases and Global Warming

Global warming is in the news every day. Warming is not a recent trend, but one that extends over decades, perhaps even a century or more, as shown in Figure 17.1. The cause of the increasing temperatures is thought to be the increased atmospheric concentration of greenhouse gases such as CO_2 and methane. These gases have been emitted at a rapidly growing rate with population growth and industrialization.

In the face of growing consensus about the problem, skeptics note that such temperature data provides support but not proof for claims about greenhouse-gas induced global warming. They point out that climate is not steady; it changes over periods of decades, over centuries, and over much longer periods of time. And it's not just CO_2 that's been increasing over the last century; lots of other variables are correlated with temperature. Why not blame global warming, if it does exist, on them?

Imagine that you were analyzing the data in Figure 17.1 without any idea of a possible mechanism of global temperature change. The data look something like a random walk; a sensible null hypothesis might be exactly that. The typical year-to-year change in temperature is about 0.05°, so the expected drift from a random walk over the 130 year period depicted in the graph is about 0.6°, roughly the same as that observed.

The data in the graph do not themselves provide a compelling basis to reject the null hypothesis that global temperatures change in a random way. However, it's important to understand that climatologists have proposed a physical **mechanism** that relates CO_2 and methane concentration in the atmosphere to

Figure 17.1: Global temperature since 1880 as reported by NASA. http://data. giss.nasa.gov/gistemp/graphs/ accessed on July 7, 2009.

global climate change. At the core of this mechanism is the increased absorption of infra-red radiation by greenhouse gases. This core is not seriously in doubt: it's solidly established by laboratory measurements. The translation of that absorption mechanism into global climate consequences is somewhat less solid. It's based on computer models of the physics of the atmosphere and the ocean. These models have increased in sophistication over the last couple of decades to incorporate more detail: the formation of clouds, the thermohaline circulation in the oceans, etc. It's the increasing confidence in the models that drives scientific support for the theory that greenhouse gases cause global warming.

It's not data like Figure 17.1 that lead to the conclusion that CO_2 is causing global warming. It's the data insofar as they support models of mechanisms.

17.2   Causation and Correlation

It's often said, "Correlation is not causation." True enough. But it's an odd thing to say, like saying, "A movie is not a train."

In the earliest days of the cinema, a Lumière brothers film showing a train arriving at a station caused viewers to rise to their feet as if the train were real. Reportedly, some panicked from fear of being run over.[32, p. 222]

Modern viewers would not be fooled; we know that a movie train is incapable of causing us harm. The Lumière movie authentically represented a real train — the movie is a kind of model, a representation for a purpose — but the representation is not the mechanical reality of the train itself. Similarly, correlation is a representation of the relationship between variables. It captures some aspects of that relationship, but it is not the relationship itself and it doesn't fully reflect the mechanical realities, whatever they may be, of the real relationships that drive the system.

Correlation, along with the closely related idea of model coefficients, is a concept that applies to data and variables. The correlation between two variables depends on the data set, and how the data were collected: what sampling frame was used, whether the sample was randomly taken from the sampling frame, etc.

In contrast, causation refers to the influence that components of a system exert on one another. I write "component" rather than "variable" because the variables that are measured are not necessarily the active components themselves. For example, the score on an IQ test is not intelligence itself, but a reflection of intelligence.

As a metaphor for the differences between correlation and causation, consider a chain hanging from supports. (Figure 17.3.) Each link of the chain is mechanically connected to its two neighbors. The chain as a whole is a collection of such local connections. Its shape is set by these mechanical connections together with outside forces: the supports, the wind, etc. The overall system — both internal connections and outside forces — determines the global shape of the chain. That overall shape sets the correlation between any two links in the chain, whether they be neighboring or distant.

In this metaphor, the shape of the chain is analogous to correlation; the mechanical connections between neighboring links is causation.

One way to understand the shape of the chain is to study its overall shape: the correlations in it. But be careful; the lessons you learn may not apply in different circumstances. For example, if you change the location of the supports, or add a new support in the middle, the shape of the chain can change completely as can

Figure 17.2: A frame from the 1895 film, "L'Arrivée d'un train en gare de La Ciotat"

the correlation between components of the chain.

Another way to understand the shape of the chain is to look at the local relationships between components: the causal connections. This does not directly tell you the overall shape, but you can use those local connections to figure out the global shape in whatever circumstances may apply. It's important to know about the mechanism so that you can anticipate the response to actions you take: actions that might change the overall shape of the system. It's also important for reasoning about counterfactuals: what would have happened had the situation been different (as in the sex discrimination example above) even if you have no way actually to make the system different. You can't change the plaintiff's sex, but you can play out the consequences of doing so through the links of causal connections.

One of the themes of this book has been that correlation, as measured by the correlation coefficient between two variables, is a severely limited way to describe relationships. Instead, the book has emphasized the use of model coefficients. These allow you to incorporate additional variables — covariates — into your interpretation of the relationship between two variables. Model coefficients provide more flexibility and nuance in describing relationships than does correlation. They make it possible, for instance, to think about the relationship between variables A and B *while adjusting for* variable C.

Even so, model coefficients describe the global properties of your data. If you

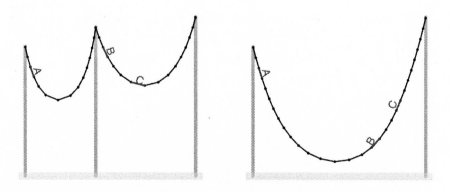

Figure 17.3: A metaphor for causation and correlation: the links of a chain with external supports. It's the same chain in both pictures but supported differently. The relationship between link orientations — links A and B are aligned in the picture on the left, but not in the picture on the right — depends both on the mechanical connections between links and on the external forces at work. So the alignment itself (correlation) is not a good signal for the mechanical connections (causation).

want to use them to examine the local, mechanistic connections, there is more work to be done. Presumably, what people mean in saying "correlation is not causation" is that correlation is not on its own compelling evidence for causation.

An example of the difference between local causal connections and global correlations comes from political scientists studying campaign spending. Analysis of data on election results and campaign spending in US Congressional elections shows that increased spending by those running for re-election — incumbents — is associated with lower vote percentages. This finding is counter-intuitive. Can it really be that an incumbent's campaign spending causes the incumbent to lose votes? Or is it that incumbents spend money in elections that are closely contested for other reasons? When the incumbent's election is a sure thing, there is no need to spend money on the campaign. So the negative correlation between spending and votes, although genuine, is really the result of external forces shaping the election and not the mechanism by which campaign spending affects the outcome.[33]

17.3   Hypothetical Causal Networks

In order to think about how data can be used as evidence for causal connections, it helps to have a notation for describing local connections. The notation I will use involves simple, schematic diagrams. Each diagram depicts a **hypothetical causal network**: a theory about how the system works. The diagrams consist of **nodes** and **links**. Each node stands for a variable or a component of the system. The nodes are connected by links that show the connections between them. A one-way arrow refers to a causal mechanistic connection. To illustrate, Figure 17.4 shows a hypothetical causal network for campaign spending by an incumbent.

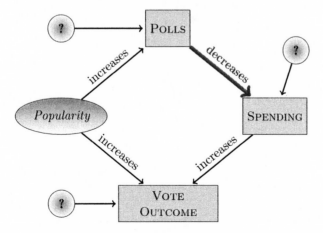

Figure 17.4:   A hypothetical causal network describing how campaign spending by an incumbent candidate for political office is related to the vote outcome.

The hypothetical causal network in Figure 17.4 consists of four main components: spending and the vote outcome are the two of primary interest, but the incumbent candidate's popularity and the pre-election poll results are also included. According to the network, an incumbent's popularity influences both the vote outcome and the pre-election polls. The polls indicate how close the election is and this shapes the candidate's spending decisions. The amount spent influences the vote total.

A complete description of the system would describe how the various influences impinging on each node shape the value of the quantity or condition represented by the node. This could be done with a model equation, or less completely by saying whether the connection is positive or negative (as in the above diagram). For now, however, focus on the topology of the network: what's connected to what and which way the connection runs.

Nodes in the diagrams are drawn in two shapes. A square node refers to a variable that can be measured: poll results, spending, vote outcomes. Round nodes are for unmeasured quantities. For example, it seems reasonable to think about a candidate's popularity, but how to measure this outside of the context set by a campaign? So, in the diagram, popularity itself is not directly measured. Instead, there are poll results and the vote outcome itself. Specific but unmeasured variables such as "popularity" are sometimes called **latent variables**.

Often the round, unmeasured nodes will be drawn ⓘ, which stands for the idea the *something* is involved, but no description is being given about what that something is; perhaps it's just random noise.

The links connecting nodes indicate causal influence. Note that every line has a arrow that tells which way causation works. The diagram

means that B causally influences A. The diagram

is the opposite: A is causally influencing B.

It's possible to have links running both ways between nodes. For instance, A causes B and B causes A. This is drawn as two different links. Such two way causation produces loops in the diagrams, but it is not necessarily illogical circular reasoning. In economics, for instance, it's conventional to believe that price influences production and that production influences price.

Why two causal links? When some outside event intervenes to change production, price is affected. For example, when a factory is closed due to a fire, production will fall and price will go up. If the outside event changes price — for instance, the government introduces price restrictions — production will change in response. Such outside influences are called **exogenous**. The Ⓠ stands for an unknown exogenous input.

A hypothetical causal network is a model: a representation of the connections between components of the system. Typically, it is incomplete, not attempting to represent all aspects of the system in detail. When an exogenous influence is marked as Ⓠ, the modeler is saying, "I don't care to try to represent this in detail." But even so, by marking an influence with Ⓠ, the modeler is making an affirmative claim that the influence, whatever it be, is not itself caused by any of the other nodes in the system: it's exogenous. In contrast, nodes with a causal input — one or more links pointing to them — are **endogenous**, meaning that they are determined at least in part by other components of the system.

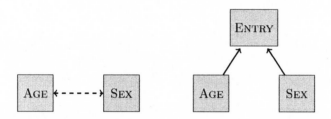

Figure 17.5: A non-causal link and its expansion into a diagram with causal links.

Often modelers decide not to represent all the links and components that might causally connect two nodes, but still want to show that there is a connection. Such **non-causal links** are drawn as double-headed dashed lines as in Figure 17.5. For instance, in many occupations there is a correlation between age and sex: older workers tend to be male, but the population of younger workers is more balanced. It would be silly to claim a direct causal link from age to sex: a person's sex doesn't change as they age! Similarly, sex doesn't determine age. Instead, women historically were restricted in their professional options. There is an additional variable — entry into the occupation — that is determined by both the person's age and sex. The use of a non-causal link to indicate the connection between age and sex allows the connection to be displayed without including the additional variable.

It's important not to forget the word "hypothetical" in the name of these diagrams. A hypothetical causal network depicts a state of belief. That belief might be strongly informed by evidence, or it might be speculative. Some links in the network might be well understood and broadly accepted. Some links, or the absence of some links, might be controversial and disputed by other people.

17.4   Networks and Covariates

Often, you are interested in only some of the connections in a causal network; you want to use measured data to help you determine if a connection exists and to describe how strong it is. For example, politicians are interested to know how much campaign spending will increase the vote result. Knowing this would let them decide how much money they should try to raise and spend in an election campaign.

It's wrong to expect to be able to study just the variables in which you have a direct interest. As you have seen, the inclusion of covariates in a model can affect the coefficients on the variables of interest.

For instance, even if the direct connection between `spending` and `vote outcome` is positive, it can well happen that using data to fit a model `vote outcome` ~ `spending` will produce a negative coefficient on spending.

There are three basic techniques that can be used to collect and analyze data in order to draw appropriate conclusions about causal links.

Experiment, that is, intervene in the system to set or influence certain variables and then examine how your intervention relates to the observed outcomes.

Include covariates in order to adjust for other variables.

Exclude covariates in order to prevent those variables from unduly influencing your results.

Experimentation provides the strongest form of evidence. Indeed, many statisticians and scientists claim that experimentation provides the only compelling evidence for a causal link. As the expression goes, "No causation without experimentation."

This may be so, but in order to explain why and when experimentation provides compelling evidence, it's helpful to examine carefully the other two techniques: including and excluding covariates. And, in many circumstances where you need to draw conclusions about causation, experimentation may be impossible.

Previous chapters have presented many examples of Simpson's paradox: the coefficient on an explanatory variable changing sign when a covariate is added to a model. Indeed, it is inevitable that the coefficient will change — though not necessarily change in sign — whenever a new covariate is added that is correlated with the explanatory variable.

An important question is this: Which is the right thing to do, include the covariate or not?

To answer this question, it helps to know the right answer! That way, you can compare the answer you get from a modeling approach to the known, correct answer, and you can determine which modeling approaches work best, which rules for including covariates are appropriate. Unfortunately, it's hard to learn such lessons from real-world systems. Typical systems are complex and the actual causal mechanisms are not completely known. As an alternative, however, you can use simulations: made-up systems that let you test your approaches and pick those that are appropriate for the structure of the hypothetical causal network that you choose to work with.

To construct a simulation, you need to add details to the hypothetical causal networks. What's left out of the notation for the networks is a quantitative description of what the link arrows mean: how the variable at the tail of the link influences the variable at the arrowhead. One way to specify this is with a formula. For instance, the formula

$$\texttt{vote} \leftarrow 0.75 \ \texttt{popularity} + 0.25 \ \texttt{spending} + \texttt{Normal}(0,5)$$

says that the vote outcome can be calculated by adding together weighted amounts of the level of popularity and spending and the exogenous random component (which is set to be a normal random variable with mean 0 and standard deviation 5).

Notice that I've used $\leftarrow$ instead of $=$ in the formula. The formula isn't just a statement that vote is related to popularity and spending but a description of what causes what. Changing popularity changes vote, but not *vice versa*.

Usually, modelers are interested in deducing the formula from measured data. In a simulation, however, the formula is pre-specified and used to create the simulated data.

Such a simulation can't directly tell you about real campaign spending. It can, however, illuminate the process of modeling by showing how the choice of covariates shapes the implications of a model. Even better, the simulations can guide you to make *correct* choices, since you can compare the results of your modeling of the simulated data to the known relationships that were set up for the simulation.

A simulation can be set up for the campaign spending hypothetical network. Here's one that accords pretty well with most people's ideas about how campaign spending works:

popularity is endogenous, simulated by a random variable with a uniform distribution between 15 and 85 percent, indicating the amount of support the incumbent has.

polls echo popularity, but include a random exogenous component as well: $\texttt{polls} \leftarrow \texttt{popularity} + \texttt{Normal}(0,3)$.

spending is set based on the poll results. The lower the polls, the more the incumbent candidate spends: $\texttt{spending} \leftarrow 100 - \texttt{polls} + \texttt{Normal}(0,10)$.

vote is the result of popularity, spending, and an exogenous random input:
$$\texttt{vote} \leftarrow 0.75 \ \texttt{popularity} + 0.25 \ \texttt{spending} + \texttt{Normal}(0,5)$$

Remember, these formulas are hypothetical. It's not claimed that they represent the mechanics of actual campaign spending in any detailed way, or that the coefficients reflect the real world (except, perhaps, in sign), or that the size of the random, exogenous influences are authentic. But by using the formulas you can generate simulated data that allows you to test out various approaches to modeling. Then you can compare your modeling results with the formulas to see which approaches are best.

The simulation outlined above was used to generate data on `polls`, `spending`, and `vote`. Then, this simulated data was used to fit two different models: one with covariates and one without them. Here are the results from a simulation with $n = 1000$:

	Model	Coef. on spending
1	vote $\sim$ spending	-0.33 ± 0.02
2	vote $\sim$ spending+ polls	0.23 ± 0.03

In the first model, vote $\sim$ spending, the fitted coefficient on `spending` is negative, meaning that higher spending is associated with lower `vote`. This negative coefficient correctly summarizes the pattern shown by the data but it is incorrect causally. According to the formulas used in the simulation, higher spending leads to higher vote outcome.

On the other hand, the model vote $\sim$ spending+polls that incorporates `polls` as a covariate gets it right: the coefficient on `spending` is positive (as it should be) and is even the right size numerically: about 0.25.

It's tempting to draw this conclusion: always add in covariates. But this general rule is premature and, in fact, wrong. To see why, consider another simulation based on another hypothetical causal network.

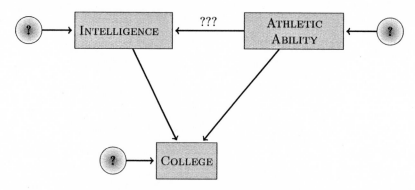

Figure 17.6: A hypothetical causal network about college admissions and athletics.

Figure 17.6 shows a simple hypothetical causal network that might be used to describe college admissions. This network depicts the hypothesis that whether or not a student gets into college depends on both the intelligence and athletic ability of the applicant. But, according to the hypothetical causal network, there may also be a link between intelligence and athletic ability.

Suppose someone wants to check whether the link marked ??? in Figure 17.6 actually exists, that is, whether athletic ability affects intelligence. An obvious approach is to build the simple model intelligence ∼ athletic ability. Or, should the covariate college be included in the model?

A simulation was set up with no causal connection at all between between athletic ability and intelligence. However, both athletic ability and intelligence combine to determine whether a student gets into college.

Using data simulated from this network (again, with $n = 1000$), models with and without covariates were fit.

	Model	Coef. on spending
1	IQ ∼ Athletic	0.03 ± 0.30
2	IQ ∼ Athletic+ College	-1.33 ± 0.24

The first model, without college as a covariate, gets it right. The coefficient, 0.03 ± 0.30, shows no connection between athletic and intelligence. The second model, which includes the covariate, is wrong. It falsely shows that there is a negative relationship between athletic ability and intelligence. Or, rather, the second model is false in that it fails to reproduce the causal links that were present in the simulation. The coefficients are actually correct in showing the correlations among athletic, intelligence, and college that are present in the data generated by the simulation. The problem is that even though college doesn't cause intelligence, the two variables are correlated.

The situation is confusing. For the campaign spending system, the right thing to do when studying the direct link between spending and vote outcome was to *include* a covariate. For the college admissions system, the right thing to do when studying the direct link between intelligence and athletic ability was to *exclude* a covariate.

The heart of the difficulty is this: In each of the examples you want to study a single link between variables, for instance these:

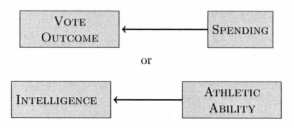

But the nature of networks is that there is typically more than one pathway that connects two nodes. What's needed is a way to focus on the links of interest while avoiding the influence of other connections between the variables.

17.4.1   Pathways

A hypothetical causal network is like a network of roads. The causal links are one-way roads where traffic flows in only one direction. In hypothetical causal networks, as in road networks, there is often more than one way to get from one place to another.

A **pathway** between two nodes is a route between them, a series of links that connects one to another, perhaps passing through some other nodes on the way.

It's helpful to distinguish between two kinds of pathways:

- **Correlating pathways** follow the direction of the causal links.

- **Non-correlating pathways** don't.

To help develop a definition of the two kinds of pathways, consider a simple network with three nodes, A, B, and C, organized with A connected to C, and C connected to B.

There is a pathway connecting A to B, but in order to know whether it is correlating or non-correlating, you need to know the causal directions of the links. If the links flow as A⇒C⇒B, then the pathway connecting A to B is correlating. Similarly if the pathway is A⇐C⇐B. Less obviously, the pathway connecting A to B in the network A⇐C⇒B is correlating, since from node C you can get to both A and B. But if the flows are A⇒C⇐B, the pathway connecting A and B is non-correlating.

The general rule is that a pathway connecting two variables A and B is correlating if there is some node on the pathway from which you can get to both A and B by following the causal flow. So, in A⇒C⇒B, you can start at A and reach B. Similarly, in A⇐C⇐B, you can start at B and reach A. In A⇐C⇒B you can start at C and reach both A and B. But in A⇒C⇐B, there is no node you can start at from which the flow leads both to A and B.

A non-correlating pathway is one where it is not possible to get from one of the nodes on the pathway to the end-points by following the causal links. So, A⇒C⇐B is a non-correlating pathway: Although you can get from B to C by

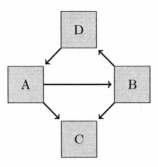

Figure 17.7: A hypothetical causal network with three pathways connecting nodes A and B.

following the causal link, you can't get to A. Similarly, starting at A will get you to C, but you can't get from C to B.

Hypothetical causal networks often involve more than one pathway between variables of interest. To illustrate, consider the network shown in Figure 17.7. There are three different pathways connecting A to B:

- The direct pathway A⇒B. This is a correlating pathway. Starting at A leads to B.

- The pathway through C, that is, A⇒C ⇐B. A non-correlating pathway. There is no node where you can start that leads to both endpoints A and B by following the causal flows.

- The pathway through D, that is, A⇐D ⇐B. This is a correlating pathway — start at B and the flow leads to A.

Of course, correlating pathways can be longer and can involve more intermediate nodes. For instance A⇐C ⇐D ⇒B is a correlating pathway connecting A and B. Starting at D, the flow leads to both A and B.

Pathways can also involve links that display correlation and not causation. When correlations are involved (shown by a double-headed arrow: ⇔), the test of whether a pathway is correlating or non-correlating is still the same: check whether there is a node from which you can get to both end-points by following the flows. For the correlation link, the flows go in both directions. So A ⇔C⇒D ⇒B is correlating; starting at C, the flow leads to both endpoints A and B.

Some hypothetical causal networks include pathways that are causal loops, that is, pathways that lead from a node back to itself following only the direction of causal flow. These are called **recurrent networks**. The analysis of recurrent networks requires more advanced techniques that are beyond the scope of this introduction. Judea Pearl gives a complete theory.[34]

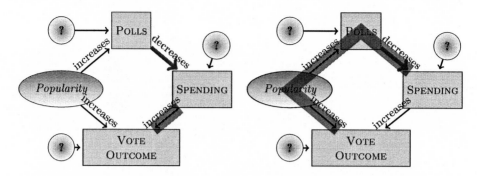

Figure 17.8: Two distinct pathways connecting spending to vote outcome, shaded with a thick line. Both of these are correlating pathways.

17.4.2   Pathways and the Choice of Covariates

Understanding the nature of the pathways connecting two variables helps in deciding which covariates to include or exclude from a model. Suppose your goal is to study the direct relationship between two nodes, say between A and B in Figure 17.7. To do this, you need to **block** all the other pathways between those variables. So, to study the direct relationship A⇒B, you would need to block the "backdoor" pathways A⇐D⇐B and A⇒C⇐B.

The basic rules for blocking a pathway are simple:

- For a **correlating pathway**, you must **include** at least one of the interior nodes on the pathway as a covariate.

- For a **non-correlating pathway**, you must **exclude** all the interior nodes on the pathway; do not include any of them as covariates.

Typically, there are some pathways in a hypothetical causal network that are of interest and others that are not. Suppose you are interested in the direct causal effect of A on B in the network shown in Figure 17.7. This suggests the model B ~ A. But which covariates to include in order to block the two backdoor pathways A⇐D ⇐B and A⇒C⇐B? Including D as a covariate will block the correlating pathway A⇐D⇐B, so you should include D in your model. On the other hand, in order to block A⇒C⇐B you need to *exclude* C from your model. So, the correct model is B ~ A+D.

Returning to the campaign spending example, there are two pathways between spending and vote outcome. The pathway of interest is vote⇐spending. The backdoor pathway, pathway vote⇐popularity⇒polls⇒spending is not of direct interest to those concerned with the causal effect of spending on the vote outcome. This backdoor pathway is correlating; starting at node popularity leads to both endpoints of the pathway, spending and vote. To block it, you need to include one of the interior nodes, either polls or popularity. The obvi-

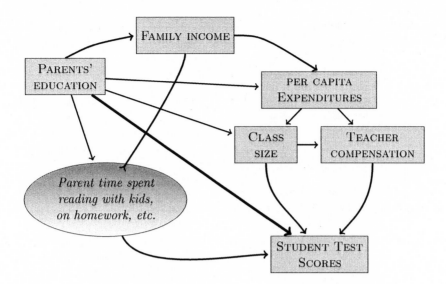

Figure 17.9: A hypothetical causal network relating student test scores to various educational policies and social conditions.

ous choice is `polls`, since this is something that can be measured and used as a covariate in a model. So, an appropriate model for studying the causal connection between `vote` and `spending` is the model `vote ~ spending + polls`.

In the college admission network shown in Figure 17.6, there are two pathways connecting `athletic` ability to `intelligence`. The direct one is of interest. The backdoor route is not: `intelligence⇒college⇐athletic`. The backdoor pathway is non-correlating: there is no node from which the flow leads to both `intelligence` and `athletic`. In order to block this non-correlating pathway, you must avoid including any interior node, so `college` cannot be used as a covariate.

Example 17.2: Learning about Learning

Suppose you want to study whether increasing expenditures on education will improve outcomes. You're going to do this by comparing different districts that have different policies. Of course, they likely also have different social conditions. So there are covariates. Which ones should be included in your models?

Figure 17.9 shows what's actually a pretty simple hypothetical causal network. It suggests that there is a link between family income and parents' education, and between parents' education the test scores of their children. It also suggests that school expenditures and policy variables such as class size relate to family income and parents' education. Perhaps this is because wealthier parents tend to live in higher-spending districts, or because they are more active in making sure that their children get personalized attention in small classes.

It hardly seems unreasonable to believe that things work something like the way they are shown in Figure 17.9. So reasonable people might hold the beliefs depicted by the network.

Now imagine that you want to study the causal relationship between per capita expenditures and pupil test scores. In order to be compelling to the people who accept the network in Figure 17.9, you need to block the backdoor pathways between expenditures and test scores. Blocking those backdoor pathways, which are correlating pathways, means including both `parents' education` and `family income` as covariates in your models. That, in turn, means that data relating to these covariates need to be collected.

Notice also that both `class size` and `teacher compensation` should not be included as covariates. Those nodes lie on correlating pathways that are part of the causal link between `expenditures` and `test scores`. They are not part of a backdoor correlating pathway; they are the actual means by which the variable `expenditures` does it's work. You do not want to block those pathways if you want to see how `expenditures` connects causally to `test scores`.

In summary, a sensible model, consistent with the hypothetical causal network in Figure 17.9, is this:

    `test scores ~ expenditures + family income + parents' education.`

17.4.3 Sampling Variables

Sometimes a variable is used to define the sampling frame when collecting data. For example, a study of intelligence and athletic ability might be based on a sampling frame of college students. This seems innocent enough. After all, colleges can be good sources of information about both variables. Of course, your results will only be applicable to college students; you are effectively holding the variable `college` constant. Note that this is much the same as would have happened if you had included both college and non-college students in your sample and then included `college` as a covariate, the standard process for adjusting for a covariate when building a model. The implication is that sampling only college students means that the variable `college` will be implicitly included as a covariate in all your models based on that data. A variable that is used to define your sampling frame is called a **sampling variable**.

In terms of blocking or unblocking pathways, using data based on a sampling variable is equivalent to including that variable in the model. To see this, recall that in the model $B \sim A + C$, the presence of the variable C means that the relationship between A and B can be interpreted as a *partial relationship*: how B is related to A while holding C constant. Now imagine that the data have been collected using C as a sampling variable, that is, with C constant for all the cases. Fitted to such data, the model $B \sim A$ still shows the relationship between B and

A while holding C constant.

In drawing diagrams, the use of a sampling variable to collect data will implicitly change the shape of the diagram. For example, consider the correlating pathway A⇒C⇒D⇒B. Imagine that the data used to study the relationship between A and B were collected from a sampling frame where all the cases had the same value of C. Then the model A ∼ B is effectively giving a coefficient on B with C held constant at the level in the sampling frame. That is, A ∼ B will give the same B coefficient as A ∼ B + C. Since C is an interior variable on the pathway from A to B, and since the pathway is correlating, the inclusion of C as a sampling variable blocks the entire pathway. This effectively disconnects A from B.

Now consider a non-correlating backdoor pathway like A⇒F⇐G⇒B. When F is used as a sampling variable, this pathway is unblocked. Effectively, this translates the pathway into A⇔G⇒B, which is a correlating pathway. (You can get to both endpoints A and B by starting either at G or at A.) So, a sampling variable can unblock a backdoor pathway that you might have wanted to block.

You need to be careful in thinking about how your sampling frame is based on a sampling variable that might be causally connected to other variables of interest. For instance, sampling just college students when studying the link between `intelligence` and `athletic ability` in the network shown in Figure 17.6 opens up the non-correlating, backdoor pathway via `college`. Thus, even if there were no relationship between `intelligence` and `athletic ability`, your use of `college` as a sampling variable could create one.

17.4.4 Disagreements about Networks

The appropriate choice of covariates to include in a model depends on the particular hypothetical causal network that the modeler accepts. The network reflects the modeler's beliefs, and different modelers can have different beliefs. Sometimes this will result in different modelers drawing incompatible conclusions about which covariates to include or exclude. What to do about this?

One possible solution to this problem is for you to adopt the other modeler's network. This doesn't mean that you have to accept that network as true, just that you reach out to that modeler by analyzing your data in the context set by that person's network. Perhaps you will find that, even using the other network, your data don't provide support for the other modeler's claims. Similarly, the other modeler should try to convince you by trying an analysis with your network.

It's particularly important to be sensitive to other reasonable hypothetical causal networks when you are starting to design your study. If there is a reasonable network that suggests you should collect data on some covariate, take that as a good reason to do so even if the details of your own network do not mandate that the covariate be included. You can always leave out the covariate when you analyze data according to your network, but you will have it at hand if it becomes important to convince another modeler that the data are inconsistent with his or her theory.

Sometimes you won't be able to agree. In such situations, being able to contrast the differing networks can point to origins of the dispute and can help you to figure out a way to resolve them.

Example 17.3: Sex Discrimination in Salary

The college where I work is deeply concerned to avoid discrimination against women. To this end, each year it conducts an audit of professors' salaries to see if there is any evidence that the college pays women less than men.

Regrettably, there is such evidence; female faculty earn on average less than male faculty. However, there is a simple explanation for this disparity. Salaries are determined almost entirely by the professor's rank: instructors earn the least, assistant professors next, then associate professors and finally "full" professors. Until recently, there have been relative few female full professors and so relatively few women earning the highest salaries.

Why? It takes typically about 12 years to move from being a starting assistant professor to being a full professor, and another 25 years or so until retirement. It takes five to ten years to go from a college graduate to being a starting assistant professor. Thus, the population of full professors reflects the opportunities for entering graduate students 20 to 45 years ago.

I am writing this in 2009, so 45 years ago was the mid 1960s. This was a very different time from today; women were discouraged even from going to college and certainly from going to graduate school. There was active discrimination against women. The result is that there are comparatively few female full professors. This is changing because discrimination waned in the 1970s and many women are rising up through the ranks.

In analyzing the faculty salary data, you need to make a choice of two simple models. Salary is the response variable and sex is certainly one of the explanatory variables. But should you include rank?

Here's one possible hypothetical causal network:

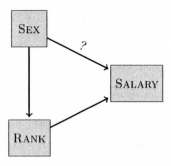

This hypothetical network proposes that there is a direct link between sex and salary — that link is marked with a question mark because the question is whether the data provide support for such a link. At the same time, the network proposes that sex is linked with rank and the network shows this as a causal link.

The consequence of this diagram is that to understand the total effect of sex on salary, you need to include both of the pathways linking the two variables: sex⇒salary as well as the pathway sex⇒rank⇒salary. In order to avoid blocking the second pathway, we should **not** include rank as an explanatory variable. Result: The data do show that being female has a negative impact on salary.

In the above network, the causal direction has been drawn from sex to rank. This might be simply because it's hard to imagine that a person's rank can determine their sex. Besides, in the above comments I already stipulated that there have been historical patterns of discrimination on the basis of sex that determine the population of the different ranks.

On the other hand, discrimination against people in the past doesn't mean that there is discrimination against the people who currently work at the institution. So imagine some other possibilities.

What would happen if the causal direction were reversed? I know this sounds silly, that rank can't cause sex, but suspend your disbelief for a moment. If rank caused sex, there is no causal connection from sex to salary via rank. As such, the pathway from sex to salary via rank ought to be blocked in your models. This is a correlating pathway, so you would block it by including rank as a covariate. Result: The data show that being female does not have a negative impact on salary.

Unfortunately, this means that the result of the modeling depends strongly on your assumptions. If you imagine that sex does not influence rank, then there is no evidence for salary discrimination. But if you presume that sex does influence rank, then the model does provide evidence for salary discrimination. Stalemate.

Fortunately, there is a middle ground. Perhaps rank and sex are not causally related, but are merely correlated. In this situation, too, you would want to block the indirect correlating pathway because it does not tell you about the causal effect of sex on salary. The result would remain that sex does not have a negative impact on salary.

Is your intuition kicking at you? Sex is determined at conception, it can't possibly be caused by anything else in this network. If it can't be caused by anything, it must be the cause of things. Right? Well, not quite. The reason is that all of the people being studied are professors, and this selection can create a correlation.

Here's a simple causal network describing who becomes a professor:

Whether a person became a professor depends on both sex and age. Putting aside the question of whether there is still sex discrimination in graduate studies and hiring, there is no real dispute that there was a relationship in the past. Perhaps this could be modeled as an interaction between sex and age in shaping who becomes a professor. There might be main effects as well.

With this in mind, an appropriate hypothetical causal network might look like this:

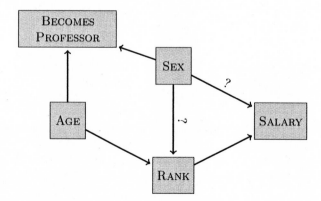

In this network, which people on both sides of the dispute would find reasonable, there is a new backdoor pathway linking sex and salary. This is the pathway sex⇒becomes professor⇐age⇒rank ⇒salary. This pathway is not about our present mechanisms for setting salary, it's about how people became professors in the past. Since the pathway is not of direct interest to studying sex discrimination in today's salaries, it should be blocked when examining the relationship between sex and salary.

The backdoor pathway sex⇒becomes professor⇐age⇒rank ⇒salary is a non-correlating pathway. There is no node on the pathway that flows to the two endpoints. (Of course you can reach salary from sex directly — there is a sex⇒salary pathway — but that is not involved in the backdoor pathway that is under consideration here.)

Here's the catch. Since the data used for the salary audit include only the people working at the college, the variable becomes professor is already included implicitly as a *sampling variable*. This means that the backdoor pathway is unblocked in the model sex ~ salary. That is, the use of becomes professor as a sampling variable creates a correlation between sex and age. The pathway then is equivalent to sex⇔age⇒rank⇒salary. This is a correlating pathway, since you can get from sex to salary by following the flows.

To block the correlating pathway, you need to include as a covariate one of the variables on the pathway. Age offers some interesting possibilities here. Including age as a covariate blocks the backdoor pathway but allows you to avoid including rank. By leaving rank out of the model, it becomes possible for the model to avoid making any assumption about whether there is sex discrimination in setting rank. Thus, it's possible to build a model that will be satisfactory both to those who claim that rank is not the product of sex discrimination and those who claim it is.

Reading Questions

1. Why does an observed correlation between two variables not provide compelling evidence that one causes the other?

2. What is a hypothetical causal network? What does the word "hypothetical" signify about these networks?

3. What is the difference between a correlating pathway and a non-correlating pathway?

4. How is the appropriate choice of covariates in models to study causation influenced by the structure of the modeler's hypothetical causal network?

5. When might two modelers legitimately disagree about which covariates to include in a model?

18

Experiment

The true method of knowledge is experiment. — William Blake (1757-1827), English poet, painter, and print-maker

A theory is something nobody believes, except the person who made it. An experiment is something everybody believes, except the person who made it. — Albert Einstein (1879-1955), physicist

18.1   Experiments

The word "experiment" is used in everyday speech to mean *a course of action tentatively adopted without being sure of the eventual outcome.* [23] You can experiment with a new cookie recipe; experiment by trying a new bus route for getting to work; experiment by planting some new flowers to see how they look.

Experimentation is at the core of the scientific method. Albert Einstein said, "[The] development of Western Science is based on two great achievements — the invention of the formal logical system (in Euclidean geometry) by the Greek philosophers, and the discovery of the possibility to find out causal relationships by systematic experiment (during the Renaissance)." [35, p.1]

Scientific experimentation is, as Einstein said, systematic. In the everyday sense of experimentation, to try out a new cookie recipe, you cook up a batch and try them out. You might think that the experiment becomes scientific when you measure the ingredients carefully, set the oven temperature and timing precisely, and record all your steps in detail. Those are certainly good things to do, but a crucial aspect of systematic experimentation is **comparison**.

Two distinct forms of comparison are important in an experiment. One form of comparison is highlighted by the phrase "**controlled experiment**". A controlled experiment involves a comparison between two interventions: the one you are interested in trying out and another one, called a **control**, that provides a baseline or basis for comparison. In the cookie experiment, for instance, you would compare two different recipes: your usual recipe (the control) and the new recipe (called the **treatment**). Why? So that you can put the results for the new recipe in an appropriate context. Perhaps the reason you wanted to try a new recipe is that you were particularly hungry. If so, it's likely that you will like the new recipe even if were not so good as your usual one. By comparing the two recipes side by side, a controlled experiment helps to reduce the effects of factors such as your state of hunger. (The word "controlled" also suggests carefully maintained experimental conditions: measurements, ingredients, temperature, etc. While such care is important in successful experiments, the phrase "controlled experiment" is really about the comparison of two or more different interventions.)

Another form of comparison in an experiment concerns intrinsic variability. The different interventions you compare in a controlled experiment may be affected by factors other than your intervention. When these factors are unknown, they appear as **random variation**. In order to know if there is a difference between your interventions — between the treatment and the control — you have to do more than just compare treatment and control. You have to compare the observed treatment-vs-control difference to that which would be expected to occur at random. The technical means of carrying out such a comparison is, for instance, the F statistic in ANOVA. When you carry out an experiment, it's important to establish the conditions that will enable such a comparison to be carried out.

A crucial aspect of experimentation involves causation. An experiment does not necessarily eliminate the need to consider the structure of a hypothetical causal network when selecting covariates. However, the experiment actually changes the structure of the network and in so doing can radically simplify the system. As a result, experiments can be much easier to interpret, and much less subject to controversy in interpretation than an observational study.

18.1.1 Experimental Variables and Experimental Units

In an experiment, you, the experimenter, intervene in the system.

- You choose the **experimental units**, the material or people or animals to which the control and treatment will be applied. When the "unit" is a person, a more polite term is **experiment subject**.

- You set the value of one or more variables — the **experimental variables** — for each experimental unit.

The experimenter then observes or measures the value of one or more variables for each experimental unit: a response variable and perhaps some covariates.

The choice of the experimental variables should be based on your understanding of the system under study and the questions that you want to answer. Often, the choice is straightforward and obvious; sometimes it's clever and ingenious. For example, suppose you want to study the possibility that the habit of regularly taking a tablet of aspirin can reduce the probability of death from stroke or heart attack in older people. The experimental variable will be whether or not a person takes aspirin daily. In addition to setting that variable, you will want to measure the response variable — the person's outcome, e.g., the age of their eventual death — and covariates such as the person's age, sex, medical condition at the onset of the study, and so on.

Or, suppose you want to study the claim that keeping a night-light on during sleeping hours increases the chances that the child will eventually need glasses for near-sightedness. The experimental variable is whether or not the child's night light is on, or perhaps how often it is left on. Other variables you will want to measure are the response — whether the child ends up needing glasses — and the relevant covariates: the child's age, sex, whether the parents are nearsighted, and so on.

In setting the experimental variable, the key thing is to create variability, to establish a contrast between two or more conditions. So, in the aspirin experiment, you would want to set things up so that some people regularly take aspirin and others do not. In the nearsightedness experiment, some children should be set to sleep in bedrooms with nightlights on and others in bedrooms with nightlights off.

Sometimes there will be more than one variable that you want to set experimentally. For instance, you might be interested in the effects of both vitamin supplements and exercise on health outcomes. Many people think that an experiment involves setting only one experimental variable and that you should do a separate experiment for each variable. There might be situations where this is sensible, but there can be big advantages in setting multiple experimental variables in the same experiment. (Later sections will discuss how to do this effectively — for instance it can be important to arrange things so that the experimental variables are mutually orthogonal.) One of the advantages of setting experimental variables simultaneously has to do with the amount of data needed to draw informative conclusions. Another advantage comes in the ability to study interactions between experimental variables. For example, it might be that exercise has different effects on health depending on a person's nutritional state.

The choice of experimental *units* depends on many factors: practicality, availability, and relevance. For instance, it's not so easy to do nutritional experiments on humans; it's hard to get them to stick to a diet and it often takes a long time to see the results. For this reason, many nutritional experiments are done on short-living lab animals. Ethical concerns are paramount in experiments involving potentially harmful substances or procedures.

Often, it's sensible to choose experimental units from a population where the effect of your intervention is likely to be particularly pronounced or easy to measure. So, for example, the aspirin experiment might be conducted in people at high risk of stroke or heart attack.

On the other hand, you need to keep in mind the **relevance** of your experiment. Studying people at the very highest risk of stroke or heart attack might not give useful information about people at a normal level of risk.

Some people assume that the experimental units should be chosen to be as homogeneous as possible; so that covariates are held constant. For example, the aspirin experiment might involve only women aged 70. Such homogeneity is not necessarily a good idea, because it can limit the relevance of the experiment. It can also be impractical because there may be a large number of covariates and there might not be enough experimental units available to hold all of them approximately constant.

One argument for imposing homogeneity is that it simplifies the analysis of the data collected in the experiment. This is a weak argument; analysis of data is typically a very small amount of the work and you have the techniques that you need to adjust for covariates. In any event, even when you attempt to hold the covariates constant by your selection of experimental units, you will often find that you have not been completely successful and you'll end up having to adjust for the covariates anyway. It can be helpful, however, to avoid experimental units that are outliers. These outlying units can have a disproportionate influence on the experimental results and increase the effects of randomness.

A good reason to impose homogeneity is to avoid accidental correlations between the covariates and the experimental variables. When such correlations exist, attempts to untangle the influence of the covariates and experimental variables can be ambiguous, as described in Section 15.4. For instance, if all the subjects who take aspirin are women, and all the subjects who don't take aspirin are men, how can you decide whether the result is due to aspirin or to the person's sex?

There are other ways than imposing homogeneity, however, to avoid correlations between the experimental variables and the covariates. Obviously, in the aspirin experiment, it makes sense to mix up the men and women in assigning them to treatment or control. More formally, the general idea is to make the experimental variables orthogonal to covariates — even those covariates that you can't measure or that you haven't thought to measure. Section 18.1.5 shows some ways to do this.

Avoiding a confounding association between the experimental variables and the covariates sometimes has to be done through the experimental protocol. A *placebo*, from the Latin "I will please," is defined as "a harmless pill, medicine, or procedure prescribed more for the psychological benefit to the patient than for any physiological effect." [23] In medical studies, placebos are used to avoid the confounding effects of the patient's attitude toward their condition.

If some subjects get aspirin and others get nothing, they may behave in different ways. Think of this in terms of covariates: Did the subject take a pill (even if it didn't contain aspirin)? Did the subject believe he or she was getting treated? Perhaps the subjects who don't get aspirin are more likely to drink alcohol, upset at having been told not to take aspirin and having heard that a small amount of daily alcohol consumption is protective against heart attacks. Perhaps the patients told to take aspirin tend not to take their vitamin pills: "It's just too much to deal with."

Rather than having your control consist of no treatment at all, use a placebo in order to avoid such confounding. Of course, it's usually important that the subjects be unaware whether they have been assigned to the placebo group or to the treatment group. An experiment in which the subjects are in this state of ignorance is called a **blind experiment**.

There is evidence that for some conditions, particularly those involving pain or phobias, placebos can have a positive effect compared to no treatment. [36, 37] This is the **placebo effect**. Many doctors also give placebos to avoid confrontation with patients who demand treatment. [38] This often takes the form of prescribing antibiotics for viral infections.

It can also be important to avoid accidental correlations created by the researchers between the experimental variables and the covariates. It's common in medical experiments to keep a subject's physicians and nurses ignorant about whether the subject is in the treatment or the control group. This prevents the subject from being treated differently depending on the group they are in. Such experiments are called **double blind**. (Of course, someone has to keep track of whether the subject received the treatment or the placebo. This is typically a statistician who is analyzing the data from the study but is not involved in direct contact with the experimental subjects.)

In many areas, the measured outcome is not entirely clear and can be influenced by the observer's opinions and beliefs. In testing the Salk polio vaccine in 1952, the experimental variable was whether the child subject got the vaccine or not. (See the account in [39].) It was important to make the experiment double-blind and painful measures were taken to make it so; hundreds of thousands of children were given placebo shots of saline solution. Why? Because in many cases the diagnosis of mild polio is ambiguous; it might be just flu. The diagnostician might be inclined to favor a diagnosis of polio if they thought the subject didn't get the vaccine. Or perhaps the opposite, with the physician thinking to himself, "I always thought that this new vaccine was dangerous. Now look what's happened."

Example 18.1: The Virtues of Doing Surgery while Blind   In order to capture the benefits of the placebo effect and, perhaps more important, allow studies of the effectiveness of surgery to be done in a blind or double-blind manner, **sham surgery** can be done. For example, in a study of the effectiveness of surgery for osteoarthritis of the knee, some patients got actual arthroscopic surgery while the placebo group had a simulated procedure that included actual skin incisions.[40] Sham brain surgery has even been used in studying a potential treatment for Parkinson's disease.[41] Needless to say, sham surgery challenges the notion that a placebo is harmless. A deep ethical question arises: Is the harm to the individual patient sufficiently offset by the gains in knowledge and the corresponding improvements in surgery for future patients?

Example 18.2: Oops! An accidental correlation!   You are a surgeon who wants to test out a new and difficult operation to cure a dangerous condition. Many of the subjects in this condition are in very poor health and have a strong risk of not surviving the surgery, no matter how effective the surgery is at resolving the condition. So you decide, sensibly, to perform the operation on those who are in good enough health to survive and use as controls those who aren't in a position to go through the surgery. You've just created a correlation between the experimental variable (surgery or not) and a covariate (health).

18.1.2   Choosing levels for the experimental variables

In carrying out an experiment, you set the experimental variables for each experimental unit. When designing your experiment, you have to decide what levels to impose on those variables. That's the subject of this section. A later section will deal with how to assign the various levels among the experimental units.

Keep in mind these two principles:

- **Comparison**. The point of doing a systematic experiment is to contrast two or more things. Another way of thinking about this is that in setting your experimental variable, you create variability. In analyzing the data from your experiment you will use this variability in the experimental variables.

- **Relevance**. Do the levels provide a contrast that guides meaningful conclusions. Is the difference strong enough to cause an observable difference in outcomes?

It's often appropriate to set the experimental variable to have a "control" level and a "treatment" level. For instance, placebo vs aspirin, or night-light off vs night-light on. When you have two such levels, a model "response $\sim$ experimental variable" will give one coefficient that will be the difference between the treatment and the control and another coefficient — the intercept — that is the baseline.

Make sure that the control level is worthwhile so that the difference between the treatment and control is informative for the question you want to answer. Try to think what is the interesting aspect of the treatment and arrange a control that highlights that difference. For example, in studying psychotherapy it would be helpful to compare the psychotherapy treatment to something that is superficially the same but lacking the hypothesized special feature of psychotherapy. A comparison of the therapy with a control that involves no contact with the subject whatsoever may really be an experiment about the value of human contact itself rather than the value of psychotherapy.

Sometimes it's appropriate to arrange more than two levels of the experimental variables, for instance more than one type of treatment. This can help tease apart effects from different mechanisms. It also serves the pragmatic purpose of checking that nothing has gone wrong with the overall set-up. For instance, a medical experiment might involve a placebo, a new treatment, and an established treatment. In experiments in biology and chemistry, where the measurement involves complicated procedures where something can go wrong (for instance, contamination of the material being studied) it's common to have three levels of the experimental variable: a treatment, a **positive control**, and a **negative control** that gives a clear signal if something is wrong in the procedure or materials.

Often, the experimental variable is naturally quantitative: something that can be adjusted in magnitude. For instance, in an aspirin experiment, the control would be a daily dose of 0mg (delivered *via* placebo pill) and the treatment might be a standard dose of 325 mg per day. Should you also arrange to have treatments that are other levels, say 100 mg per day or 500 mg per day? It's tempting to do so. But for the purposes of creating maximal variability in the experimental variable, it's best to set the treatment and control at opposite ends of whatever the relevant range is: say 0 and 325 mg per day.

It can be worthwhile, however, to study the **dose-response** relationship. For example, it appears that a low dose of aspirin (about 80 mg per day) is just as effective as higher dosages in preventing cardiovascular disease.[42] Put yourself in the position of a researcher who wants to test this hypothesis. You start with some background literature — previous studies have established that a dose of 325 mg per day is effective. You want to test a dose of one-quarter of that: 80 mg per day. It's helpful if your experimental variable involves at least *three* levels: 0 mg (the control, packaged in a placebo), 80 mg, and 325 mg. Why not just use two levels, say 0 and 80 mg, or perhaps 80 and 325 mg? So that you can demonstrate that your overall experimental set up is comparable to that of the background literature and so that you can, in your own experiment, compare the responses to 80 and 325 mg.

When you analyze the data from such a multi-level experimental variable, make sure to include nonlinear transformation terms in your model. The model "response ~ dose" will not be able to show that 80 mg is just as effective as 325 mg; the linear form of the model is based on the assumption that 80 mg will be only about one-quarter as effective as 325 mg. If your interest is to show that 80 can be just as effective as 325 mg, you must include additional terms, for instance response ~ (dose > 0) + (dose > 80)

18.1.3 Replication

Perhaps it seems obvious that you should include multiple experimental units: **replication**. For example, in studying aspirin, you want to include many subjects, not just a single subject at the control level and a single subject at the treatment level.

But how many? To answer this question, you need to understand the purposes of replication. There are at least two:

- Be able to compare the variability associated with the experimental variables from the background variability that arises from random sampling. This is done, for instance, when looking at statistical significance using an F statistic. (See Section 14.2.)

- Increase the ability of your experiment to detect a difference if it really does exist: the **power** of your experiment.

In setting the number of cases in your experiment, you need first to ensure that you have some non-zero degree of freedom in your residual. If not, you won't be able to compute an F value at all, or, more generally, you won't be able to compare the variability associated with your experimental variables with the variability described as random.

Second, you should arrange things so that the p-value that you would expect, assuming that the experimental variable acts as you anticipate, is small enough to give you a significant result. This relates to the issue of the **power** of your experiment: the probability that you would get a significant result in a world where the experimental variable acts as you anticipate. The relationship between sample size and power is described in Section 15.7.

18.1.4 Experiments vs Observations

Why do an experiment when you can just observe the "natural" relationships? For example, rather than dictating to people how much aspirin they take, why not just measure the amount they take on their own, along with appropriate covariates, and then use modeling to find the relationships?

To illustrate, here is a hypothetical causal network that models the relationship between aspirin intake and stroke:

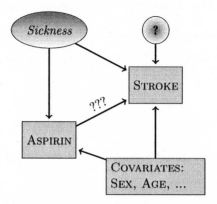

Included in this network is a latent (unmeasured, and perhaps unmeasurable) variable: sickness. The link between sickness and aspirin is intended to account for the possibility that sicker subjects — those who believe themselves to be at a higher risk of stroke — might have heard of the hypothesized relationship between aspirin and risk of stroke and are medicating themselves at a higher rate than those who don't believe themselves to be sick.

There are three pathways between aspirin and stroke. The direct pathway, marked ???, is of principal interest. One backdoor pathway goes through the sickness latent variable: aspirin⇐sickness⇒stroke. Another backdoor pathway goes through the covariates: aspirin⇐covariates⇒stroke.

If you want to study the direct link between aspirin and stoke, you need to block the backdoor pathways. If you don't, you can get misleading results. For instance, the increased risk of stroke indicated by the sickness variable might make it look as if aspirin consumption itself increases the risk of stroke, even if the direct effect of aspirin is to decrease the risk. Both the backdoor pathways are correlating pathways. To block them, you need to include sickness and the covariates (sex, age, etc.) in your model, e.g., a model like this:

$$\text{stroke} \sim \text{aspirin} + \text{sickness} + \text{age} + \text{sex}$$

But how do you measure sickness? The word itself is imprecise and general, but it might be possible to find a measurable variable that you think is strongly correlated with sickness, for instance blood pressure or cholesterol levels. Such a variable is called a **proxy** for the latent variable.

Even when there is a proxy, how do you know if you are measuring it in an informative way? And suppose that the hypothetical causal network or the proxy has left something out that's important. Perhaps there is a genetic trait that both increases the risk of stroke and improves the taste of aspirin or reduces negative side effects or increases joint inflammation for which people often take aspirin as a treatment. Any of these might increase aspirin use among those at higher risk. Or perhaps the other way around, decreasing aspirin use among the high risk so that aspirin's effects look better than they really are.

You don't know.

A proper experiment simplifies the causal network. Rather than the possibility of `sickness` or some other unknown variable setting the level of `aspirin` use, you know for sure that the level was set by you, the experimenter. This is not a hypothesis; it's a demonstrable fact. With this fact established by the experimenter, the causal network looks like this:

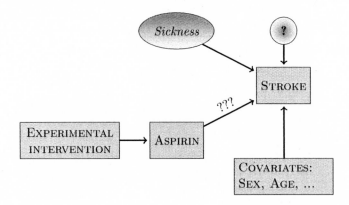

Experimental intervention has broken the link between `sickness` and `aspirin` since the experimenter, rather than the subject, sets the level of aspirin. There is no longer a backdoor correlating pathway. All the other possibilities for backdoor pathways — e.g., genetics — are also severed. With the experimental intervention, the simple model `stroke ~ aspirin` is relevant to a wide range of different researchers' hypothetical causal networks.

Details, however, are important. You need to make sure that the way you assign the values of `aspirin` to the experimental units doesn't accidentally create a correlation with other explanatory variables. Techniques for doing this are described in Section 18.1.5. Another possibility is that your experimental intervention doesn't entirely set the experimental variable. You can tell the subject how much aspirin to take, but they may not comply! You'll need to have techniques for dealing with that situation as well. (See Section 18.2.1.)

18.1.5   Creating Orthogonality

In setting the experimental intervention, it's your intention to eliminate any connections between the experimental variables and other variables in the causal network. Doing this requires some care. It's surprisingly easy to create accidental correlations.

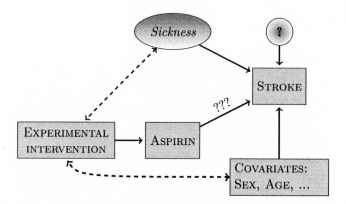

Figure 18.1: If the experimental intervention is influenced by or correlated with other variables in the system, new backdoor pathways will be created.

For instance, suppose the person assigning the subjects to either aspirin or placebo thinks it would be best to avoid risk to the sicker people by having them take only the placebo, effectively correlating the treatment with `sickness`. If such correlations are created, the experimental system will not be so simple: there will still be back doors to be dealt with.

There are two main ways to avoid accidental correlations: random assignment and blocking.

Random Assignment

In **random assignment**, you use a formal random process to determine what level of the experimental variable is to be assigned to each experimental unit. When there are just two levels, treatment and control, this can be as simple as flipping a coin. (It's better to do something that can be documented, such as having a computer generate a list of the experimental units and the corresponding randomly assigned values.)

Random assignment is worth emphasizing, even though it sounds simple:

Random assignment is of fundamental importance.

Randomization is important because it works for any potential covariate — so long as n is large enough. Even if there is another variable that you do not know or cannot measure, your random assignment will, for large enough n, guarantee that there is no correlation between your experimental variable and the unknown variable. If n is small, however, even random assignment may produce accidental correlations. For example, for $n = 25$, there's a 5% chance of the accidental R^2 being larger than 0.15, whereas for $n = 1000$, the R^2 is unlikely to be bigger than 0.005.

Blocking in Experimental Assignment

If you do know the value of a covariate, then it's possible to do better than randomization at producing orthogonality. The technique is called **blocking** . The word "blocking" in this context does not refer to disconnecting a causal pathway; it's a way of assigning values of the experimental variable to the experimental subjects.

To illustrate blocking in assignment, imagine that you are looking at your list of experimental subjects and preparing to assign each of them a value for the experimental variable:

Sex	Age	Aspirin
F	71	aspirin
F	70	placebo
F	69	placebo
F	65	aspirin
F	61	aspirin
F	61	placebo
M	71	placebo
M	69	aspirin
M	67	aspirin
M	65	placebo

Notice that the subjects have been arranged in a particular order and divided into blocks. There are two subjects in each block because there are two experimental conditions: treatment and control. The subjects in each block are similar: same sex, similar age.

Within each block of two, assign one subject to aspirin and the other to placebo. For the purpose of establishing orthogonality of aspirin to sex, it would suffice to make that assignment in any way whatsoever. But since you also want to make aspirin orthogonal to other variables, perhaps unknown, you should do the assignment within each block at random.

The result of doing assignment in this way is that the experimental variable will be **balanced**: the women will be divided equally between placebo and aspirin, as will the men. This is just another way of saying that the indicator vectors for sex will be orthogonal to the indicator vectors for aspirin.

When there is more than one covariate — the table has both age and sex — the procedure for blocking is more involved. Notice that in the above table, the male-female pairs have been arranged to group people who are similar in age. If the experimental subjects had been such that the two people within each pair had identical ages, then the aspirin assignment would be exactly orthogonal to age and to sex. But because the age variable is not exactly balanced, the orthogonality created by blocking will be only approximate. Still, it's as good as it's going to get.

Blocking becomes particularly important when the number of cases n is small. For small n, randomization may not give such good results.

Whenever possible, assign the experimental variable by using blocking against the covariates you think might be relevant, and using randomization within blocks to deal with the potential latent variables and covariates that might be relevant, even if they are not known to you.

Within each block, you are comparing the treatment and control between individuals who are otherwise similar. In an extreme case, you might be able to arrange things so that the individuals are identical. Imagine, for example, that you are studying the effect of background music on student test performance. The obvious experiment is to have some students take the test with music in the background, and others take it with some other background, for instance, quiet.

Better, though, if you can have each student take the test twice: once with the music and once with quiet. Why? Associated with each student is a set of latent variables and covariates. By having the student take the test twice, you can block against these variables. Within each block, randomly assign the student to which background condition to use the first time, with the other background condition being used the second time. This means to pick each student's assignment at random from a set of assignments that's balanced: half the students take the test with music first, the other half take the test with quiet first.

18.2   When Experiments are Impossible

Often you can't do an experiment.

The inability to do an experiment might stem from practical, financial, ethical or legal reasons. Imagine trying to investigate the link between campaign spending and vote outcome by controlling the amount of money candidates have to spend. Where would you get the money to do that? Wouldn't there be opposition from those candidates who were on the losing side of your random assignment of the experimental variables? Or, suppose you are an economist interested in the effect of gasoline taxes on fuel consumption. It's hardly possible to set gasoline taxes experimentally in a suitably controlled way. Or, consider how you would do an experiment where you randomly assign people to smoke or to not smoke in order to understand better the link between smoking, cancer, and other illnesses such as emphysema. This can't be done in an ethical way.

Even when you can do an experiment, circumstances can prevent your setting the experimental variables in the ways that you want. Subjects often don't comply in taking the pills they have been assigned to take. The families randomly admitted to private schools may decline to go. People drop out in the middle of a study,

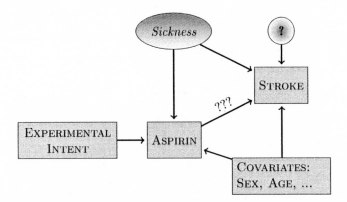

Figure 18.2: In an imperfect experiment, the experimental intent influences the treatment (`aspirin`, here), but the treatment may be influenced by the covariates and latent variables.

destroying the balance in your experimental variables. Some of your experimental units might be lost due to sloppy procedures or accidents.

When you can't do an experiment, you have to rely on modeling techniques to deal with covariates. This means that your assumptions about how the system works — your hypothetical causal networks — play a role. Rather than the data speaking for themselves, they speak with the aid of your assumptions.

Section 18.2.2 introduces two technical approaches to data analysis that can help to mitigate the impact of your assumptions. This is not to say that the approaches are guaranteed to make your results as valid as they might be if you had been able to do a perfect experiment. Just that they can help. Unfortunately, it can be hard to demonstrate that they actually have helped in any study. Still, even if the approaches cannot recreate the results of an experiment, they can be systematically better than doing your data analysis without using them.

18.2.1   Intent to Treat

Consider an experiment where the assignment of the experimental variables has not gone perfectly. Although you, the experimenter, appropriately randomized and blocked, the experimental subjects did not always comply with your assignments. Unfortunately, there is often reason to suspect that the compliance itself is related to the outcome of the study. For example, sick subjects might be less likely to take their experimentally assigned aspirin.

A hypothetical causal network describing the imperfect compliance aspirin experiment looks like Figure 18.2, with the value of `aspirin` determined both by the experimental intervention and the subject's state of `sickness`.

In such a network, the model `stroke ~ aspirin` describes the total connection between `aspirin` and `stroke`. This includes three parts: (1) the direct link `aspirin`⇒`stroke`, (2) the backdoor pathway through `sickness`, and (3) the backdoor pathway through the covariates. By including the covariates as explanatory variables in your model, you can block pathway (3). The experimental intervention has likely reduced the influence of backdoor pathway (2), but because the subjects may not comply perfectly with your assignment, you cannot be sure that your random assignment has eliminated it.

Consider, now, another possible model: `stroke` ∼ `experimental intent`. Rather than looking at the actual amount of `aspirin` that the subject took and relating that to `stroke`, the explanatory variable is the *intent* of the experimenter. This intent, however it might have been ignored by the subjects, remains disconnected from any covariates; the intent is the set of values assigned by the experimenter using randomization and blocking in order to avoid any connection with the covariates.

The hypothetical causal network still has three pathways from `experimental intent` to `stroke`. One pathway is `experimental intent`⇒`aspirin`⇒`stroke`. This is a correlating pathway that subsumes the actual pathway of interest: `aspirin`⇒`stroke`. As such, it's an important pathway to study, the one that describes the impact of the experimenter's intent on the subjects' outcomes.

The other two pathways connecting `intent` to `stroke` are the backdoor pathway via `sickness` and the backdoor pathway via the `covariates`. These two pathways cause the trouble that the experiment sought to eliminate but that non-compliance by the experimental subjects has re-introduced. Notice, though, that the backdoor pathways connecting `experimental intent` to `stroke` are non-correlating rather than correlating. To see why, examine this backdoor pathway:

`experimental intent` ⇒`aspirin` ⇐`sickness` ⇒`stroke`

There's no node from which the causal flow reaches both end points. This non-correlating pathway will be blocked so long as `sickness` is not included in the model. Similarly the back door pathway through the `covariates` is blocked when the covariates are not included in the model.

As a result, the model `stroke` ∼ `experimental intent` will describe the causal chain from `experimental intent` to `stroke`. This chain reflects the effect of the **intent to treat**. That chain is not just the biochemical or physiological link between `aspirin` and `stoke`, it includes all the other influences that would cause a subject to comply or not with the experimenter's intent. To a clinician or to a public health official, the intent to treat can be the proper thing to study. It addresses this question: How much will prescribing patients to take aspirin reduce the amount of stroke, taking into account non-compliance by patients with their prescriptions? This is a somewhat different question than would have been answered by a perfect experiment, which would be the effect of aspirin presuming that the patients comply.

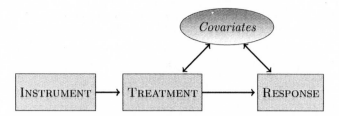

Figure 18.3: An instrument is a variable that is unrelated to the covariates but is connected to the treatment.

Intent to treat analysis can be counter-intuitive. After all, if you've measured the actual amount of aspirin that a patient took, it seems obvious that this is a more relevant variable than the experimenter's intent. That may be, but `aspirin` is also connected with other variables (`sickness` and the `covariates`) which can have a confounding effect. Even though `intent` is not perfectly correlated with `aspirin`, it has the great advantage of being uncorrelated with `sickness` and the `covariates` — so long as the experimental variables were properly randomized and blocked.

Of course, pure intent is not enough. In order for there to be an actual connection between `intent` and the outcome variable, some fraction of the patients has to comply with their assignment to aspirin or placebo.

18.2.2 Destroying Associations

In intent-to-treat analysis, the explanatory variable was changed in order to avoid unwanted correlations between the explanatory variable and covariates and latent variables. The techniques in this section — **matched sampling** and **instrumental variables** — allow you to keep your original explanatory variables but instead modify the data in precise ways in order to destroy or reduce those unwanted correlations.

Figure 18.3 shows the general situation. You're interested in the direct relationship between some `treatment` and a `response`, for instance aspirin and stroke. There are some covariates, which might be known or unknown. Also, there can be another variable, an `instrumental variable`, that is related to the treatment but not directly related to any other variable in the system. An example of an instrumental variable is `experimental intent` in Figure 18.2, but there can also be instrumental variables relevant to non-experimental systems.

A key question for a modeler is how to construct an appropriate model of the relationship between the `treatment` and the `response`. The two possibilities are:

1. `response ~ treatment`

2. `response ~ treatment + covariates`

The first model is appropriate if the backdoor pathway involving the `covariates` is a non-correlating pathway; the second model is appropriate if it is a correlating pathway. But it's not so simple; there can be multiple covariates, some of which are involved in correlating pathways and some not. Beyond that, some of the covariates might be unknown or unmeasured — latent variables — in which case the second form of model isn't possible; you just don't have the data.

In a proper experimental design, where you can assign the value of `treatment`, you use randomization and blocking to arrange `treatment` to be orthogonal to the `covariates`. Given such orthogonality, it doesn't matter whether or not the `covariates` are included in the model; the coefficient on `treatment` will be the same either way. That's the beauty of orthogonality.

In the absence of an experiment, or when the experimental intervention is only partially effective, then `treatment` will typically not be orthogonal to the `covariates`. The point of matched sampling and of instrumental variables is to arrange things, by non-experimental means, to make them orthogonal.

Instrumental Variables

An **instrumental variable** is a variable that is correlated with the treatment variable, but uncorrelated with any of the covariates. Its effect on the response variable, if any, is entirely indirect, via the treatment variable.

Perhaps the simplest kind of instrumental variable to understand is the experimenter's intent. Assuming that the intent has some effect on the treatment — for instance, that some of the subjects comply with their assigned treatment — then it will be correlated with the treatment. But if the intent has been properly constructed by randomization and blocking, it will be uncorrelated with the covariates. And, the intent ordinarily will affect the response only by means of the treatment. (It's possible to imagine otherwise, for example, if being assigned to the aspirin group caused people to become anxious, increased their blood pressure, and caused a stroke. Placebos avoid such statistical problems.)

An instrumental variable is orthogonal to the covariates but not to the treatment, and thus it provides a way to restructure the data in order to eliminate the need to include covariates when estimating the relationship between the treatment variable and the response. The approach is very clever but straightforward and is often done in two stages. First, the treatment is projected onto the instrument. The resulting vector is exactly aligned with the instrument and therefore shares the instrument's orthogonality to the covariates. Second, replace the response by the fitted values of `treatment ~ instrument`. In doing this, it doesn't matter whether the covariates are included or not, since they are orthogonal to the projected treatment variable.

If you have an appropriate instrument, the construction of a meaningful model to investigate causation can be straightforward. The challenge is to find an appropriate instrument. For experimenters dealing with imperfections of compliance or drop-out, the experimental intent makes a valid instrument. For others, the issues are more subtle. Often, one looks for an instrument that pre-dates the treatment variable with the idea that the treatment therefore could not have caused the instrument. It's not the technique of instrumental variables that is difficult, but the work behind it, "the gritty work of finding or creating plausible experiments" [43], painstaking "shoe-leather" research[44]. Finding a good instrumental variable requires detailed understanding of the system under study, not just the data but the mechanisms shaping the explanatory variables.

Imagine, for instance, a study to relate how the duration of schooling relates to earnings after leaving school. There are many potential covariates here. For example, students who do better in school might be inclined to stay longer in school and might also be better earners. Students from low-income families might face financial pressures to drop out of school in order to work, and they might also lack the family connections that could help them get a higher-earning job.

An instrumental variable needs to be something that will be unrelated to the covariates — skill in school, family income, etc. — but will still be related to the duration a student stays in school. Drawing on detailed knowledge of how schools work, researchers Angrist and Krueger [45] identified one such variable: date of birth. School laws generally require children to start school in the calendar year in which they turn six and require them to stay in school until their 16th birthday. As a result, school dropouts whose birthday is before the December 31 school-entry cut-off tend to spend more months in school than those whose birthday comes on January 1 or soon after. So date of birth is correlated with duration of schooling. But there's no reason to think that date of birth is correlated with any covariate such as skill in school or family income. (Angrist and Krueger found that men born in the first quarter of the calendar year had about one-tenth of a year less schooling than men born in the last quarter of the year. The first-quarter men made about 0.1 percent less than the last-quarter men. Comparing the two differences indicates that a year of schooling leads to an increase in earnings of about 10%.)

Matched Sampling

In matched sampling, you use only a subset of your data set. The subset is selected carefully so that the treatment is roughly orthogonal to covariates. This does not eliminate the actual causal connection between the treatment and the covariates, but when fitting a model to the subset of the data, the coefficient on treatment is rendered less sensitive to whether the covariates are included in the model.

To illustrate, imagine doing an observational study on the link between aspirin and stroke. Perhaps you pick as a sampling frame all the patients at a clinic ten years previously, looking through their medical records to see if their physician has asked them to take aspirin in order to prevent stroke, and recording the patients age, sex, and systolic blood pressure. The response variable is whether or not the patient has had a stroke since then. The data might look like this:

Case #	Aspirin Recommended	Age	Sex	Systolic Blood Pressure	Had a Stroke
1	Yes	65	M	135	Yes
2	Yes	71	M	130	Yes
3	Yes	68	F	125	No
4	Yes	73	M	140	Yes
5	Yes	64	F	120	No
... and so on ...					
101	No	61	F	110	No
102	No	65	F	115	No
103	No	72	M	130	No
104	No	63	M	125	No
105	No	64	F	120	No
106	No	60	F	110	Yes
... and so on ...					

Looking at these data, you can see there is a relationship between aspirin and stroke — the patients for whom aspirin was recommended were more likely to have a stroke. On the other hand, there are covariates of age, sex, and blood pressure. You might also notice that the patients who were recommended to take aspirin typically had higher blood pressures. That might have been what guided the physician to make the recommendation. In other words, the covariate blood pressure is aligned with the treatment aspirin. The two groups — aspirin or not — are different in other ways as well: the no-aspirin group is more heavily female and younger.

To construct a matched sample, select out those cases from each group that have a closely matching counterpart in the other group. For instance, out of the small data set given in the table, you might pick these matched samples:

Case #	Aspirin Recommended	Age	Sex	Systolic Blood Pressure	Had a Stroke
5	Yes	64	F	120	No
105	No	64	F	120	No
2	Yes	71	M	130	Yes
103	No	72	M	130	No

The corresponding pairs (cases #5 and #105, and cases #2 and #103) match closely according to the covariates, but each pair is divided between the values of the treatment variable, aspirin. By constructing a subsample in this way, the covariates are made roughly orthogonal to the treatment. For example, in the matched sample, it's not true that the patients who were recommended to take aspirin have a higher typical blood pressure.

In a real study, of course, the matched sample would be constructed to be much longer — ideally enough data in the matched sample so that the power of the study will be large.

There is a rich variety of methods for constructing a matched sample. The process can be computationally intensive, but is very feasible on modern computers. Limits to practicality come mainly from the number of covariates. When there is a large number of covariates, it can be hard to find closely matching cases between the two treatment groups.

A powerful technique involves fitting a **propensity score**, which is the probability that a case will be included in the treatment group (in this example, aspirin recommended) as a function of the covariates. (This probability can be estimated by logistic regression.) Then matching can be done simply using the propensity score itself. This does not necessarily pick matches where all the covariates are close, but is considered to be an effective way to produce approximate orthogonality between the set of covariates and the treatment.

Example 18.3: Returning to Campaign Spending ...

Analysis of campaign spending in the political science literature is much more sophisticated than the simple model vote ~ spending. Among other things, it involves consideration of several covariates to try to capture the competitiveness of the race. An influential series of papers by Gary Jacobson (e.g., [33, 46]) considered, in addition to campaign spending by the incumbent and vote outcome, measures of the strength of the challenger's party nationally, the challenger's expenditures, whether the challenger held public office, the number of years that the incumbent has been in office, etc. Even including these covariates, Jacobson's least-square models showed a much smaller impact of incumbent spending than challenger spending. Based on the model coefficients, a challenger who spends $100,000 will increase his or her vote total by about 5 percent, but an incumbent spending $100,000 will typically increase the incumbent's share of the vote by less than one percent.

In order to deal with the possible connections between the covariates and spending, political scientists have used instrumental variables. (The term found in the literature is sometimes **two-stage least squares** as opposed to instrumental variables.) Green and Krasno [47], in studying elections to the US House of Representatives in 1978, used as an instrument incumbent campaign expenditures during the 1976 election. The idea is that the 1976 expenditures reflects the incument's propensity to spend, but expenditures in 1976 could not have been caused by the situation in 1978. When using this instrument, Green and Krasno found that $100,000 in incumbent expenditures increased his or her vote total by about 3.7 percent — much higher than the least squares model constructed without the instrument. (Jacobson's reports also included use of instrumental variables, but his instruments were too collinear and insufficiently correlated with `spending` to produce stable results.)

Steven Levitt (whose later book *Freakonomics* [48] became a best-seller) took a different perspective on the problem of covariates: matched sampling. (Or, to use the term in the paper, **panel data**.) He looked at the elections to the US House between 1972 and 1990 in which the same two candidates — incumbent and challenger — faced one another two or more times. This was only about 15% of the total number of House elections during the period, but it is a subset where the covariates of candidate quality or personality are held constant for each pair. Levitt found that the effect of spending on vote outcome was small for both challengers and incumbents: an additional \$100,000 of spending is associated with a 0.3 percent vote increase for the challenger and 0.1 percent for the incumbent — neither spending effect was statistically significant in an F test.

So which is it? The different modeling approaches give different results. Jacobson's original work indicates that challenger spending is effective but not incumbent spending; Green and Krasno's instrumental variable approach suggests that spending is effective for both candidates; Levitt's matched sampling methodology signals that spending is ineffective for both challenger and incumbent. The dispute focuses attention on the validity of the instruments or the ability of the matching to compensate for changing covariates. Is 1976 spending a good instrument for 1978 elections? Is the identity of the candidates really a good matching indicator for all the covariates or lurking variables? Such questions can be challenging to answer reliably. If only it were possible to do an experiment!

18.3   Conclusion

It's understandable that people are tempted to use correlation as a substitute for causation. It's easy to calculate a correlation: Plug in the data and go! Unfortunately, correlations can easily mislead. As in Simpson's paradox, the results you get depend on what explanatory variables you choose to include in your models.

To draw meaningful conclusions about causation requires work. At a minimum, you have to be explicit about your beliefs about the network of connections and examine which potential explanatory variables lie on correlating pathways and which on non-correlating pathways. If you do this properly, your modeling results can be correctly interpreted in the context of your beliefs. But if your beliefs are wrong, or if they are not shared by the people who are reading your work, then the results may not be useful. There's room for disagreement when it comes to causation because reasonable people can disagree about the validity of assumptions.

Other analysis techniques — for instance matched sampling or instrumental variables — can ease the dependence of your results on your assumptions and beliefs. But still there is room for interpretation. Is the instrument really uncorrelated with the covariates? How complete is the set of covariates included in your matched sampling?

Ultimately, for a claim about causation to be accepted by skeptics, you need to be able to demonstrate that your assumptions are true. This can be particularly challenging when the skeptics have to take statistical methodology on faith. You'll find that many decision makers have little or no understanding of methodology, and some critics are willfully ignorant of statistics. On the other hand, it's appropriate for the modeler to show some humility and to work honestly to identify those assumptions that are not themselves adequately justified by the data, problems with the sampling process, and the potential mis-interpretation of p-values. A good experiment can be invaluable, since the experimenter herself determines the structure of the system and since the statistical analysis can be straightforward.

It's sometimes said that science is a process of investigation, not a result. The same is true for statistical models. Each insight that is demonstrably supported by data becomes the basis for refinement in the way you collect new data, the variables and covariates you measure in future work, the incisive experimental interventions that require labor, resources, and expertise. However well your data have been collected and your models have been structured and built, the conclusions drawn from statistical models are still inductive, not deductive. As such, they are not certain. Even so, they can be useful.

Reading Questions

1. Is the point of a controlled experiment to create variability or to avoid variability?

2. What is an experimental variable? In what ways is it the same and in what ways different from an explanatory variable?

3. What is the purpose of randomization in conducting an experiment? What gets randomized?

4. Why might blocking be preferred to randomization?

5. What is the point of matched sampling and instrumental variables?

Further Readings & Bibliography

The reader interested in learning more about statistics will do well to start with some history. David Salsburg's *The Lady Tasting Tea* [49] gives an entertaining and readable survey of 20th century statistics and statisticians. Stephen Stigler's *Statistics on the Table* [50] reaches back a century further in history and has a more conceptual focus. Ian Hacking's *The Emergence of Probability* goes back, as the title says, to the emergence of the concept of probability in the seventeenth century.

Chapter 1. Overview. For essays about the application of statistics in context and in practice, the various editions of *Statistics: A Guide to the Unknown* are hard to beat.[51, 52] Each *Guides* essays is oriented around a particular social, political, medical, or scientific issue. In contrast, most statistics textbooks ([39, 53, 54, 55] are among the good choices) are arranged around topics in statistical methodology. The cited books cover a complete gamut of statistical topics — sampling, descriptive statistics, statistical tests — but emphasize the statistics of single variables or the relationship between pairs of variables. They build on high-school algebra and do not require college-level calculus. At a somewhat more advanced mathematical level, the well-titled *Statistical Sleuth* introduces multivariate regression. At a still higher level, for those who are comfortable with college-level linear algebra, an excellent multivariate modeling text is [56]. For classroom learning activities in introductory statistics, [57, 58] provide many ideas.

An excellent, non-statistical introduction to constructing models, with a strong emphasis on models as "purposeful representations," is [59].

Many materials about the R package [5] are available at the project web site: `www.r-project.org`. Good references for R (and the language it is based on, S) are [60, 61, 62]. Some introductions to statistics using R are [63, 64, 65].

Chapters 2 & 3. Data and Description. Introductory statistics books (e.g. ([39, 53, 54, 55]) provide a good introduction to methods and issues in collecting data and describing variables numerically and graphically. For advanced modeling methods with units of analysis at different levels, see [66].

The series of books by Tufte [67, 68] has been rightfully influential in showing how to present data graphically (and beautifully). For technical displays of statistical data, see Cleveland's *Visualizing Data.*[69]

Important criticisms of the emphasis on conventional descriptions of center and spread are provided by the best-selling books by Gould [70] and Taleb [71].

The elementary but classic *How to Lie with Statistics* [72] has many examples of the use of quantitative information in a way that misleads; it's not so much about statistics as it is about lying.[73]

The somewhat obscure statistic "unalikeability" is described in [74] and [75].

Chapters 4 & 5. Group-wise Models and Confidence Intervals Bradley Efron introduced randomization methods such as bootstrapping to many social and natural scientists and statistical workers. [76, 77, 78] An early attempt to introduce randomization into teaching statistics at an introductory level is [79]. Hardly any introductory statistics textbook even mentions resampling or bootstrapping, though thankfully there are signs this is starting to change.

Chapters 6 - 9. Modeling and Correlation. The modeling notation is described in an influential advanced book by Chambers and Hastie.[62] Box, Hunter, & Hunter give good reasons to take fitted models with a grain of salt. [2, pp. 397-407]

Stigler provides an account of the invention of correlation.[80] For a variety of different ways to interpret correlation, see [81]. Gawande writes for a general reader about why simple model formulas can be more useful for prediction and diagnosis than human judgment.[82]

The idea of using geometry to inform statistical reasoning started perhaps with Ronald Fisher at the start of the 20th century.[83] It was unfortunately seen as obscure and statistics pedagogy was rooted in algebra. Starting in the 1980s, David Saville and Graham Wood have been writing about the uses of geometry in teaching statistics. [84, 85, 86]. Other articles appear from time to time, e.g., [87, 88]. The classic book *Statistics for Experimenters* [2] contains a thread using geometry to complement algebraic explanations. See also [89]. Farebrother describes mechanical analogies for fitting [90] and gives an early history [91] .

Chapter 11. Modeling Randomness. Statistical pedagogy has tended to focus on the derivations of probability distributions. This may be because, in the years before computers were widely available, the algebraic techniques used in those derivations were important also in the analysis of probability. Instead of derivations, the chapter emphasizes operations on probability distributions and introduces a few distributions that are important in statistics or in modeling generally.

The random walk, mentioned in several later chapters, is a very important random phenomenon with many links throughout science. Robert Brown's observation of the movement of pollen grains in 1827 is reported in [92]. One of the famous trio of papers from Albert Einstein's 1905 *annus mirabilis* is about Brownian motion, [93]; Perrin [94] won a Nobel prize for his work confirming Einstein's theory experimentally. The accessible book by Berg [95] reveals many aspects of random walks in biology. There are also best-selling accounts, e.g., [96, 97, 98].

Chapters 12 - 15. Statistical Inference. Descriptions of the classic tests — t-tests and so on — are the bread and butter of statistics textbooks. A discussion of the search for significance and how this can render p-values uninterpretable is the subject of an editorial by Freedman.[19] Other papers on multiple comparisons and inconsistency are [24, 99]; important critiques of statistical inference are [100, 101]. Good and Hardin's book, *Common Errors in Statistics (and How to Avoid Them)*, is a useful reference.[102] Ziliak and McCloskey [103] criticize ways in which statistical "significance" has become a cult that interferes with effective reasoning rather than supporting it.

Chapters 17 & 18. Causation and Experiment. The work of Judea Pearl on causation is the inspiration for the material on hypothetical causal networks. A book-length treatment is [34]; the last chapter should perhaps be read first as an introduction. Many of Pearl's papers are available on the web. The "gentle introduction" in [104] is a good place to start.

Box, Hunter, and Hunter [2] is a well regarded survey of experimental design, artfully combining theory and practice. Cobb [105] provides a carefully graded path through experimental design and analysis accessible; it's sophisticated but accessible to a non-mathematical reader.

For background on instrumental variables, see [43, 106]. For matched sampling: [107, 108, 109, 110]. The propensity-score method has been tested in situations where there were parallel studies — one experimental and one observational: informed skepticism is called for. [111, 112, 113, 114] The best-selling book *Freakonomics* [48] entertainingly reports many clever attempts to extract information about causation from observational data.

References

[1] George Cobb. The introductory statistics course: A ptolemaic curriculum? *Technology Innovations in Statistics Education*, 1(1), 2007.

[2] George E.B. Box, J. Stuart Hunter, and William G. Hunter. *Statistics for Experimenters: Design, Innovation, and Discovery*. Wiley, 2nd edition, 2005.

[3] Robert Hughes. *The Fatal Shore: The Epic of Australia's Founding*. Vintage, 1988.

[4] John M Chambers. *Software for data analysis: Programming with R*. Springer, 2008.

[5] R Development Core Team. *R: A language and environment for statistical computing*. R Foundation for Statistical Computing, Vienna, Austria, 2005. ISBN 3-900051-07-0.

[6] Daniel T Kaplan. Computing and introductory statistics. *Technology Innovations in Statistics Education*, 1(1):Article 5, 2007. http://www.escholarship.org/uc/item/3088k195.

[7] David Bellhouse. Ann landers survey on parenthood. web pamphlet: www.stats.uwo.ca/faculty/bellhouse/stat353annlanders.pdf, 2008. accessed Jan. 2008.

[8] James A. Hanley. "transmuting" women into men: Galton's family data on human stature. *American Statistician*, 58(3):237–243, 2004.

[9] A.F. Blakeslee. Corn and men. *Journal of Heredity*, 5:511–518, 1914.

[10] Mark F. Schilling, Ann E. Watkins, and William Watking. Is human height bimodal. *The American Statistician*, 56(3):223–229, 2002.

[11] DR Appleton, JM French, and Vanderpump MPJ. An example of simpson's paradox. *American Statistician*, 1996.

[12] John M Chambers and Trevor J Hastie. *Statistical Models*. Wadsworth, 1992.

[13] Deborah Lynn Guber. Getting what you pay for: the debate over equity in public school expenditures. *Journal of Statistics Education*, 7(2), 1999.

[14] Francis Galton. Co-relations and their measurement, chiefly from anthropometric data. *Proceedings of the Royal Society of London*, pages 135–145, 1888.

[15] College Board. Research report no. 2008-5: Validity of the sat for predicting first-tyear college grade point average. Technical report, College Board, 2008.

[16] A.A. Bailey and P.L. Hurd. Finger length ratio (2d:4d) correlates with physical aggression in men but not in women. *Biol. Psychol.*, 68(3):215–222, 2005.

[17] Rachel Carson. *Silent Spring*. Houghton, 1962.

[18] John Tierney. Fateful voice of a generation still drowns out real science. New York Times, June 5 2007.

[19] David A Freedman. Editorial: Oasis or mirage? *Chance*, 21(1):59–61, 2008.

[20] E W Montroll and M F Schlesinger. Maximum entropy formalism, fractals, scaling phenomena, and $1/f$ noise: a tale of tails. *Journal of Statistical Physics*, 32(209), 1983.

[21] Roger A. Pielke Jr. Who decides? forecasts and responsibilities in the 1997 red river flood. *Applied Behavioral Science Review*, 7(2):83–101, 1999.

[22] Ronald A. Fisher. On a distribution yielding the error functions of several well known statistics. *Prod. Int. Cong. Math., Toronto*, 2:805–813, 1924.

[23] New oxford american dictionary.

[24] David J. Saville. Multiple comparison procedures: the practical solution. *The American Statistician*, 44(2):174–180, 1990.

[25] Office of Federal Contract Compliance Programs. *Federal Contract Compliance Manual*, chapter Chapter III: Onsite Review Procedures. US Department of Labor, 1993, revised 2002.

[26] Richard Shavelson Stephen Klein, Roger Benjamin. The collegiate learning assessment: Facts and fantasies. Technical report, Council for Aid to Education, http://www.cae.org/content/pro_collegiate_reports_publications.htm, 2007.

[27] Paul Basken. Test touted as 2 studies question its value. *The Chronical of Higher Education*, 54(39):A1, June 6 2008.

[28] S. Koutros et al. Meat and meat mutagens and risk of prostate cancer in the agricultural health study. *Cancer epidemiology biomarkers and prevention*, 17:80–87, 2008.

[29] Rod Minchin. personal communication. 2008.

[30] http://www.prostateline.com/prostatelinehcp. Web site, 2008.

[31] Charles Dana Wilber. *The Great Valleys and Prairies of Nebraska and the Northwest*. Daily Republican Print, Omaha, Neb., 3rd edition, 1881.

[32] Leonard J. Schmidt, Brooke Warner, and Peter A. Levine. *Panic: Origins, Insight, and Treatment*. North Atlantic Books, 2002.

[33] Gary C. Jacobson. The effects of campaign spending in congressional elections. *The American Political Science Review*, 72(2):469–491, 1978.

[34] Judea Pearl. *Causation: Models, Reasoning, and Inference*. Princeton Univ. Press, 2000.

[35] Daniel J. Boorstin. *Cleopatra's Nose: Essays on the Unexpected*. Vintage, 1995.

[36] A Hrobjartsson and PC Gotzcsche. Is the placebo powerless? update of a systematic review with 52 new randomized trials comparing placebo with no treatment. *Journal of Internal Medicine*, 256(2):91–100, 2004.

[37] BE Wampold, T Minami, SC Tierney, TW Baskin, and KS Bhati. The placebo is powerful: estimating placebo effects in medicine and psychotherapy from randomized clinical trials. *Journal of Clinical Psychology*, 61(7):835–854, 2005.

[38] A Hrobjartsson and M Norup. The use of placebo interventions in medical practice — a national questionnaire survey of danish clinicians. *Evaluation and the Health Professions*, 26(2):153–165, 2003.

[39] David Freedman, Roger Purves, and Robert Pisani. *Statistics*. WW Norton, 4th edition, 2007.

[40] J Bruce Moseley et al. A controlled trial of arthroscopic surgery for osteoarthritis of the knee. *New England Journal of Medicine*, 347:81–88, 2002.

[41] TB Freeman. Use of placebo surgery in controlled trials of a cellular-based therapy for parkinson's disease. *New England Journal of Medicine*, 341(13):988–992, 1999.

[42] CL Campbell, S Smyth, G Montalescot, and S R Steinhubl. Aspirin dose for the preventage of cardiovascular disease: a systematic review. *Journal of the American Medical Association*, 18:2018–2024, 2007.

[43] Joshua D. Angrist and Alan B. Krueger. Instrumental variables and the search for identification: from supply and demand to natural experiments. *Journal of Economic Perspectives*, 15(4):69–85, 2001.

[44] David A. Freedman. Statistical models and shoe leather. In Peter Marsden, editor, *Sociological Methodology 1991*. American Sociological Association, 1991.

[45] Joshua D. Angrist and Alan B. Krueger. Does compulsory school attendance affect schooling and earnings? *Quarterly Journal of Econometrics*, 106(4):979–1014, 1991.

[46] Gary C. Jacobson. The effects of campaign spending in house elections: new evidence for old arguments. *American Journal of Political Science*, 34(2):334–362, 1990.

[47] Donald P Green and Jonathan S Krasno. Salvation for the spendthrift incumbent: Reestimating the effects of campaign spending in house elections. *American Journal of Political Science*, 32(4):884–907, 1988.

[48] Steven D Levitt and Stephen J Dubner. *Freakonomics*. William Morrow, 2005.

[49] David Salsburg. *The Lady Tasting Tea: How statistics revolutionized science in the twentieth century*. W.H. Freeman, New York, 2001.

[50] Stephen M Stigler. *Statistics on the Table: The History of Statistical Concepts and Methods*. Harvard Univ. Press, 1999.

[51] Roxy Peck, George Casella, George Cobb, Roger Hoerl, Deborah Nolan, Robert Starbuck, and Hal Stern. *Statistics: A Guide to the Unknown*. Duxbury Press, 4th edition, 2005.

[52] Judith M. Tanur, Frederick Mosteller, William H. Kruskal, Erich L. Lehmann, Richard F. Link, Richard S. Pieters, and Gerald R. Rising. *Statistics: A Guide to the Unknown*. Duxbury Press, 3rd edition, 1989.

[53] David S Moore, George P McCabe, and Bruce Craig. *Introduction to the Practice of Statistics*. W.H. Freeman, 6th edition, 2007.

[54] Anne E Watkins, Richard L Scheaffer, and George W Cobb. *Statistics in Action: Understanding a World of Data*. Key College Publishing, 2004.

[55] David E Bock, Paul F Velleman, and Richard D De Veaux. *Stats: Modeling the World*. Addison Wesley, 2nd edition, 2006.

[56] David A. Feedman. *Statistical Models: Theory and Practice*. Cambridge University Press, 2005.

[57] Allan J Rossman and Beth Chance. *Workshop Statistics: Discovery with Data*. Wiley, 2nd edition, 2008.

[58] Andrew Gelman and Deborah Nolan. *Teaching Statistics: A Bag of Tricks*. Oxford Univ. Press, 2002.

[59] Anthony M. Starfield, Karl A. Smith, and Andrew L. Blelock. *How to model it*. McGraw-Hill, 1990.

[60] William N Venables and Brian D Ripley. *Modern Applied Statistics with S*. Springer, 4th edition, 2002.

[61] Phil Spector. *Data Manipulation with R*. Springer, 2008.

[62] John M Chambers and Trevor J Hastie. *Statistical Models in S*. Chapman & Hall, 1992.

[63] Peter Dalgaard. *Introductory Statistics with R*. Springer, 2nd edition, 2008.

[64] John Verzani. *Using R for Introductory Statistics*. Chapman & Hall, 2005.

[65] Michael J Crawley. *Statistics: An Introduction using R*. Wiley, 2005.

[66] Andrew Gelman and Jennifer Hill. *Data analysis using regression and multi-level/hierarchical models*. Cambridge Univ. Press, 2007.

[67] Edward R Tufte. *The Visual Display of Quantitative Information*. Graphics Press, 2nd edition, 2001.

[68] Edward R Tufte. *Beautiful Evidence*. Graphics Press, 2006.

[69] William S Cleveland. *Visualizing Data*. Hobart Press, 1993.

[70] Stephen J. Gould. *The Mismeasure of Man*. W.W. Norton, 1996.

[71] Nassim Taleb. *The Black Swan*. Random House, 2007.

[72] Darell Huff. *How to Lie with Statistics*. Norton, 1954. illustrated by Irving Geis.

[73] J. Michael Steele. Darell huff and fifty years of how to lie with statistics. *Statistical Science*, 20(5):205–209, 2005.

[74] Gary D. Kader and Mike Perry.   Variability for categorical variables. *Journal of Statistics Education*, 15(2), 2007. http://www.amstat.org/publications/jse/v15n2/kader.html.

[75] Alan Agresti. *Categorical Data Analysis*. John Wiley and Sons, 1990.

[76] Bradley Efron. Bootstrap methods: Another look at the jackknife. *The Annals of Statistics*, 7:1–26, 1979.

[77] Bradley Efron. Computers and the theory of statistics: Thinking the unthinkable. *SIAM Review*, 21:460–480, 1979.

[78] Bradley Efron and Robert J. Tibshirani. *An Introduction to the Bootstrap*. Chapman and Hall, 1993.

[79] Julian L Simon. *Resampling: The New Statistics*. Resampling Stats, 1974-1992.

[80] Stephen M Stigler. Francis galton's account of the invention of correlation. *Statistical Science*, 4(2):73–79, 1989.

[81] Joseph L Rodger and W Alan Nicewander. Thirteen ways to look at the correlation coefficient. *The American Statistician*, 42(1):59–66, 1988.

[82] Atul Gawande. *Complications: A Surgeon's Notes on an Imperfect Science*. Metropolitan/Henry Holt, 2002.

[83] David G. Herr. On the history of the use of geometry in the general linear model. *The American Statistician*, 34(1):43–47, 1980. see 2682995.pdf.

[84] David J. Saville and Graham R. Wood. A method for teaching statistics using n-dimensional geometry. *The American Statistician*, 40(3):205–214, 1986.

[85] David J. Saville and Graham R. Wood. *Statistical Methods: The Geometric Approach*. Springer, 1997.

[86] David J. Saville and Graham R. Wood. *Statistical Methods: A Geometric Primer*. Springer, 1996.

[87] Johan Bring. A geometric approach to compare variables in a regression model. *The American Statistician*, 50(1):57–62, 1996. see 2685045.pdf.

[88] David Bock and Paul F. Velleman. Why variances add — and why it matters. In Gail F. Burrill and Portia C. Elliot, editors, *Thinking and reasoning with data and chance*. National Council of Teachers of Mathematics, 2006.

[89] Michael J. Wichura. *The Coordinate-free Approach to Linear Models*. Cambridge University Press, 2006.

[90] Richard W. Farebrother. *Visualizing Statistical Models and Concepts*. Marcel Dekker, 2002.

[91] Richard W. Farebrother. *Fitting Linear Relationship: A History of the Calculus of Observations 1750-1900*. Springer, 1999.

[92] Robert Brown. *Miscellaneous Botanical Works*, volume 1. London, Royal Society, 1866. quoted in MP Crosland (1971) *The Science of Matter.*

[93] Albert Einstein. Investigations on the theory of the brownian movement. In A.D. Cowper, editor, *Collected Papers*, volume 2. Dover Publications, 1956.

[94] M. Jean Perrin. *Brownian Movement and Molecular Reality.* Taylor and Francis, London, 1910.

[95] Howard C Berg. *Random Walks in Biology.* Princeton Univ. Press, 1993.

[96] Burton G Malkiel. *A Random Walk Down Wall Street: The Time-Tested Strategy for Successful Investment.* W.W. Norton, 2007.

[97] Leonard Mlodinow. *The Drunkard's Walks: How Randomness Rules Our Lives.* Pantheon, 2008.

[98] Nassim Nicholas Taleb. *Fooled by Randomness: The Hidden Role of Chance in Life and in the Markets.* Random House, 2008.

[99] David J. Saville. Basic statistics and the inconsistency of multiple comparison procedures. *Canadian Journal of Experimental Psychology*, 57(3):167–175, 2003.

[100] Charmont Wang. *Sense and Nonsense of Statistical Inference.* CRC, 1992.

[101] Richard A. Berk. *Regression analysis: A constructive critique.* Sage publications, 2004.

[102] Phillip I. Good and James W. Hardin. *Common Errors in Statistics (and How to Avoid Them).* Wiley Interscience, 2003.

[103] Stephen T Ziliak and Deirdre N McCloskey. *The Cult of Statistical Significance: How the Standard Error Costs Us Jobs, Justice, and Lives.* Univ. of Michigan Press, 2008.

[104] Judea Pearl. Causal inference in statistics: A gentle introduction. In *Computing Science and Statistics, Proceedings of Interface '01*, volume 33, 2001.

[105] George W Cobb. *Introduction to Design and Analysis of Experiments.* Springer, 1998.

[106] Sander Greenland. An introduction to instrumental variables for epidemiologists. *International Journal of Epidemiology*, 29:722–729, 2000.

[107] D.B. Rubin. Using multivariate matched sampling and regression adjustment to control bias in observational studies. *Journal of the American Statistical Association*, 74:318–328, 1979.

[108] P.R Rosenbaum and D.B. Rubin. Constructing a control group using multivariate matched sampling methods that incorporate the propensity score. *The American Statistician*, 39:33–38, 1985.

[109] P.R. Rosenbaum. *Observational Studies.* Springer-Verlag, 2nd ed. edition, 2002.

[110] B.B. Hansen. Full matching in an observational study of coaching for the sat. *Journal of the American Statistical Association*, 99(467):609:618, 2004.

[111] K Arceneaux, A S Gerber, and D P Green. Comparing experimental and matching methods using a large-scale voter mobilization experiment. *Political Analysis*, 14:37–62, 2006.

[112] D A Lawlor, G DaveySmith, D Kundu, and et al. Those confounded vitamins: what can we learn from the differences between observational vs randomised trial evidence. *The Lancet*, 363:1724–1727, 2004.

[113] R Kunz and A D Oxman. The unpredictability paradox: review of empirical comparisons of randomised and non-randomized clinical trials. *British Medical Journal*, 317:1185–1190, 1998.

[114] William R Shadish, M H Clark, and Peter M Steiner. Can nonrandomized experiments yield accurate answers? a randomized experiment comparing random and nonrandom assignments. *J. American Statistical Association*, 103(484):1334–1356, 2008.

Additional Resources

The Internet provides a large number of resources for statistical modeling. Some important ones for this book are:

- Exercises and Projects written for this book.
  www.mosaic-web.org/StatisticalModeling/Exercises

- Datasets used in this book (and their documentation):
  www.mosaic-web.org/StatisticalModeling/Data

- Software:

    - The R environment: www.r-project.org
    - The RStudio interface to R: www.rstudio.org
    - The mosaic package available through www.r-project.org.
    - Extensions to the mosaic package:
      www.mosaic-web.org/StatisticalModeling/Software.

Traditional Tests

As you work with data and the statistical techniques described in this book, you will face many occasions when you need to communicate with others who have studied statistics in a very different way.

This book presents a view of statistics centered on modeling: response and explanatory variables, model terms, vectors, fitting, and so on. The major emphasis is on explaining case-to-case variation in the response variable. An important theme is the role of covariates: variables that might not be of direct interest, but which plan an important role in shaping the response. The basic technique involved is "fitting a model."

The large majority of people who have studied statistics, however, have taken a different approach, an approach founded on simpler concepts: counts, means, proportions, etc. Those simpler concepts are adequate for many important purposes, particularly the analysis of straightforward laboratory experiments. But they do not extend to cover situations covariates are involved. That's why I wrote this book: to provide broader access to statistical techniques that are suited for dealing with problems of realistic complexity.

This section offers a "translation guide" to map the traditional concepts and methods into the modeling techniques featured in this book.

The Structure of Data

In this book, a systematic, widely used, and powerful format for data has been emphasized: the data table. As you know, tables are organized into rows (one for each case) and columns (one for each variable).

Many people are not aware of the general-purpose data table format. Instead, you will be presented with data in a variety of formats. For example, here is some of Galton's height data in a non-general format:

Sex	Heights (inches)				
Female	69.2	69.0	65.5	67.0	62.5
Male	73.2	71.0	68.5	72.0	68.0

Your first task in communicating with others may be to put their data into the format of data tables.

The Response Variable

Although the term **response variable** is commonly used in statistics, in fields such as economics people will use equivalent terms like **dependent variable**. And many people won't recognize "response variable" at all; to them it's just the quantity they are measuring.

This book has considered two kinds of response variables: quantitative and yes/no variables.

In the traditional approach, quantitative variables are usually approached in terms of mean values, while yes/no variables are treated in terms of proportions or counts. It's common for people to think of a mean as fundamentally different from a proportion. But means and proportions are closely related; for a yes/no variable, treating "yes" as 1 and "no" as 0, the proportion of yeses is exactly the same thing as the mean of that variable.

An Isolated Explanatory Variable

Many of the methods featured in the traditional approach to introducing statistics relate to situation where (to use modeling language) only one explanatory variable is of interest and either there are no covariates or, commonly, they are simply ignored. Call this situation that of an **isolated explanatory variable**.

Group Means

When the isolated explanatory variable is categorical, the question often has to do with whether the groups defined by the explanatory variable are different from one another.

The modeling approach involves fitting a model of the form A ~ G. You can then perform ANOVA to see if the explanatory variable G has a connection to the response, or look at individual coefficients in the regression report to compare the model value of A each group within G to that of a reference group. Of course, the model values of A for the simple model A $\sim$ G will be the group means within each group. The null hypothesis is that variable G is not linked with A.

In the traditional approach, there are several different sorts of "tests" that are performed. The choice of the test depends on how many different groups there are within G.

Two Groups in G

When there are two levels of the categorical variable G, the traditional question for quantitative A is, "Are the means of the two groups equal?" (When A is yes/no, the traditional question refers to proportions rather than means.)

Several "tests" are considered by the traditional approach:

The equal variance two-sample t-test compares the means of the two groups. The null hypothesis can be stated as this: In the population, the two groups have equal means.

    The equal variance t-test is exactly the same thing as ANOVA on the model A $\sim$ G.

The unequal variance two-sample t-test also compares the means of the two groups, but takes into account the possibility that the two groups have different variances. There is hardly any advantage to this test unless the two groups are very different in variance. If the groups have similar variances, the unequal-variance t-test will generally give a very similar answer to the equal-variance t-test. If the two groups have very different variances, you can use a non-parametric test as described in Section 15.6.

The p-test is a test of proportions. This is essentially equivalent to ANOVA on the model A $\sim$ G, when A is a yes/no variable. (The distinction between linear regression and logistic regression doesn't matter when there is an isolated explanatory variable that's categorical.)

The rank-sum test is a non-parametric approach to comparing typical values of two groups. The modeling equivalent is rank(A) $\sim$ G, as described in Section 15.6.

The paired t-test compares a set of subjects who have each been measured in two situations, for instance before and after an intervention. An example of a paired test in a modeling framework is given in Section 15.2.

    A paired t-test actually involves two explanatory variables: the before-and-after variable G and a variable that identifies each pair, call it P. The paired t-test is equivalent to ANOVA on the model A $\sim$ G + P.

The signed-rank test is a non-parametric equivalent to the paired t-test. It corresponds approximately to ANOVA on the model rank(A) $\sim$ G + P

More than Two Groups in G

When G has more than two levels, the standard test is called **one-way anova**. This is exactly the same thing as the general ANOVA method applied to the simple model $A \sim G$.

The non-parametric version of one-way anova is called the **Kruskal-Wallis test**. It is equivalent to $\text{rank}(A) \sim G$.

You may have noticed that all of the traditional tests for an isolated explanatory variable have the form of ANOVA on $A \sim G$ or, for non-parametric tests, $\text{rank}(A) \sim G$. Modeling provides a simple, unifying framework for the traditional tests.

The Slope

When the isolated explanatory variable is quantitative — call it B — the question is traditionally phrased in either of two ways: Is the slope non-zero? or Is the correlation coefficient non-zero?

In modeling terms, the traditional approach corresponds to examining the model $A \sim B$ using either ANOVA or the regression report.

Two Explanatory Variables

With two or more explanatory variables, the modeling techniques become indispensable. The traditional approach assigns different names to tests that are closely related. Here are common tests for a quantitative response variable:

two-way anova is equivalent to ANOVA on the model $A \sim G+H$, where G and H are both categorical variables.

analysis of covariance is equivalent to $A \sim B+G$, where B might be either categorical or quantitative.

When the response variable has a yes/no form, a traditional question is whether the joint influence of G and H is different from their separate influences. The test prescribed is called the **chi-squared test**. This is equivalent to logistic regression on the model $A \sim B + G + B{:}G$ and examining the interaction term.

No Explanatory Variables

Sometimes the apparatus of statistics is used to make statements about grand means and grand proportions. For instance, you might want to quantify the precision of a measurement. Traditional tests such as the **one-sample t-test** or the **test of one proportion** are equivalent to models of the form $A \sim 1$.

R Operator Index

Items in `typewriter font` are R functions or arguments.

A * identifies functions defined in the mosaic package, which can be loaded into R with the statement

```
> require(mosaic)
```

=, 27
$, 45

anova, 299
    in logistic regression, 317
arithmetic, 30
as.character, 33
as.factor, 150
auto.key=, 122

bwplot, 62
bwplot, 70, 121

coef, 148
columns
    in data frame, 45
Confidence Intervals, 233
    confint, 234
    interval=
        in prediction, 236
confint, 98, 99
confint, 234
counts, 71
cross*, 149
CSV files
    reading, 43
cumulative probability
    p-functions, 216
cut, 83

Data
    access variables with $, 45
    as.factor, 150
    cross*, 149
    data= in lm, 121
    importing to R, 43
    ISMdata*, 43

read.csv, 43
data= in lm, 121
data, 44
date, 27
deal*, 48
densityplot, 69, 122
Descriptive Statistics
    mean, 65
    median, 65
    pdata, 65
    props, 71
    qdata, 65
    sd, 65
    var, 175
do, 99

exp, 31

fetchData, 44, 83
fitted, 84
fitted, 125, 161
    in logistic regression, 316

glm, 315

histogram, 59, 67
Hypothesis Testing
    anova, 299
    pf, 274
    rank, 300
    resample*, 272
    shuffle*, 272
    summary
        for linear models, 273
        for logistic regression, 315

I for transformation terms, 127
Importing data to R, 43
Inf, 32
interval=
    in prediction, 236
IQR, 66
ISMdata, 43

key in graphics, auto.key=, 122

min, 46
lm, 124, 147, 161
log, 31

makeFun, 236, 316
max, 46, 66
mean, 99
mean, 46, 65
median, 65
min, 66
mm, 83
Modeling
    : and *, 126
    coef, 148
    data= in lm, 121
    fitted, 125, 161
        in logistic regression, 316
    glm, 315
    I for transformation terms, 127
    lm, 124, 147, 161
    predict, 235
        in logistic regression, 316

`resid`, 161
`summary`
  for logistic regression, 315
regression report with `summary`, 148

`NaN`, 32

`pdata*`, 65
`pf`, 274
Plotting & Graphics
  axis limits, 122
  `bwplot`, 70, 121
  `densityplot`, 69, 122
  `histogram`, 67
  `rug`, 58
  `xlab=` & `ylab=`, 121
  `xyplot`, 120
`predict`, 235
  in logistic regression, 316
Probability
  p operators, 216
  q operators, 215, 216
  random generators, 213
probability
  p-functions, 216
`props`, 71

`qdata*`, 65
`quantile`, 65
quantiles
  q-functions, 215

R Syntax
  arithmetic, 30
  assignment =, 27
  Inf & NaN, 32
`range`, 66
`rank`, 300
`rbinom`, 213
`rchisq`, 213
`read.csv`, 43
reading CSV files, 43
Regression report with `summary`, 148
`resample*`, 48, 211, 272

Resampling
  `resample*`, 48, 211, 272
  `shuffle*`, 272
`resid`, 161
`rexp`, 213
`rf`, 213
`rlnorm`, 213
`rnorm`, 213
`rpois`, 213
`rt`, 213
`rug`, 58
`runif`, 213

scatter plots, making, 120
`sd`, 65
`seq`, 27
`shuffle*`, 272
Simulations
  coin flip, 211
`sqrt`, 31
`summary`
  for `lm`, 148
  for linear models, 273
  for logistic regression, 315

`tally`, 197
`transform`, 83
trigonometry, 31

`var`, 65, 175
variables
  in data frame, 45

`with`, 66

`xlab=` for axis label, 121
`xlim=` for axis limits, 122
`xyplot`, 120

`ylab=` for axis label, 121
`ylim=` for axis limits, 122

Concept Index

accuracy, 220, 232
    computer arith, 31
achieved significance level, *see* p value
adjustment, 134, 185, 188, 191
    computation, 194
    faulty, 193
aggression, 173, 270
algebraic notation
    vs computer, 29
    vs model notation, 119
algorithm, 26
all-cases-the-same, 75
alternative hypothesis, 249, 296
    definition, 251
analysis
    unit of, 38
analysis of covariance, 280, 377
analysis of variance, *see* ANOVA
Anderson, Michael, 15
angle
    and correlation, 171
ANOVA
    and collinearity, 284, 292
    and sample size, 296
    and sum of squares, 281
    order dependence, 282
    report, 263
    table, 263, 276
    term-by-term, 277
    vs regression report, 292
antibiotics, 347
aprotinin (drug), 178
arithmetic
    accuracy, 31
    R notation, 30
    with vectors, 153
aspirin, 351, 353
assignment
    computer value, 27
astrology, 261, 265
athletic ability, 331

Avogadro constant, 31
axis (in graphics)
    limits in graphics, 122
    labels, 121

backdoor pathway, 334
balanced assignment, 353
Bayesian, 200
bell shaped distribution, *see* normal
bias
    coefficients, 232
    non-response, 41
    sampling, 41
    self-selection, 41
bin, 59
binomial model, 202
Blake, William, 342
blind experiment, 346, 347
block pathways, 334
blocking in experimental design, 353
blood, 54
Bonferroni correction, 268, 271, 292
bootstrapping, 89, 92, 97, 310
box and whisker plots, *see* box plots
box plot, 62
    drawing, 70, 121
    outliers, 70
Box, George, 13
Braque, Georges, 101

campaign spending, 325, 329, 334, 361
cancer, 312
car prices, 158
cases, 35
categorical variable, 63
    crossing, 149
    from quantitative, 150
    in model formula, 133
    levels, 63
    reference level, 133

unalikeability, 64
causal loops, 333
causation, 109, 320
    and covariates, 334
    and observational studies, 354
    and regression, 293
cause and effect, 17
census, 40, 50, 94
    precision, 19
    statistical inference on, 94
    versus sample, 94
    vs sample, 50
ceteris paribus, 179
Chambers, John, 23
character string
    object type, 32
chi-squared distribution, 312
chi-squared test, 377
classification
    using models for, 17
Cobb, George, ix
code book, 37
coef. of determination, 165
    R^2, 165
    and F, 259
    computing, 175
coefficients, 129–147
    as slopes, 138
    comparing with different units, 141
    computing best fitting, 147
    fitting, 152
    interpreted in context, 141
    NA (redundancy), 163
    sign, 134
    Simpson's paradox, 144
    t-test, 291
    units, 140
coin flip, 198
    simulation, 211
Collegiate Learning Assess-

ment (test), 294
collinearity, 194, 230
   and ANOVA, 284
   and correlation, 168
   and p-value, 292
   and standard errors, 229
   measuring, 285
columns
   in data frames, 45
comma-separated values, 44
command, 23
comparing model designs, 155
complex numbers, 32
compliance
   experimental, 351
computation, 25
   connecting, 29
   foundations, 22
conditional probability, 249, 312
conditioning
   on explanatory vars., 103, 104
confidence, 93
confidence interval, 79, 87, 93, 97, 220, 223
   computation, 234
   conf. level, 228
   for prediction, 235
   for small samples, 226
   on model value, 226
   on prediction, 226
confidence intervals, 98
confidence level, 79, 93, 98, 228
confounding, 180
   latent variables, 358
console panel, 25
contrapositive, 243
control, 343
   experiment, 19, 343
   negative, 348
convenience sample, 41
conventional wisdom, 247
correlating pathway, 332, 334
correlation
   accidental, 346

and nonlinear relation-ships, 168
coefficient, 165–174
   collinearity, 168
   destroying, 357
   experimental variables, 345
   sign of, 168
   vs causation, 322
counterfactual, 19, 321, 324
counts
   categorical variable, 63
   computing, 71
covariate, 180, 189–191, 275
   adjustment for, 185
   causation, 334
   in hypothesis tests, 276
   leaving out, 193
   propensity score, 361
coverage interval, 51, 52
   computing, 214
   level, 214
   quantiles, 66
cross-sectional, 43, 294
   sampling, 42, 109
crossing categorical variables, 149
cumulative probability
   computing, 216
Current Pop. Survey, 280, 290, 293
curvature
   and transformation terms, 117

Darwin, Charles, 264
Darwin, Erasmus, 264
data, 19
   and causation, 109
   character, 32
   collection, 110
data frame, 35, 38, 44
   adding a new variable, 47
   object type, 32
   variables of, 45
Data set

Cherry Blossom Ten-Miler 2008, 42, 81, 85, 95
Cherry Blossom Ten-Miler Longitudinal, 43
College grades, 92
Galton's height data, 58, 65, 130, 136, 166, 173, 226, 257, 272, 276
Kids' foot measurements, 47, 235
Marriage licenses, 261, 278
SATs by state, 142, 190, 225
Swimming world records, 44, 113, 125, 148, 162, 175, 233
Ten-mile race, 220
Trucking Jobs, 186, 224
Used car prices, Ford Taurus, 158
Used car prices, Honda Accord, 182
Utility bills, 101, 120, 150, 168
Wages from CPS, 105, 120, 136, 138, 160, 195, 230, 280, 299
Whickham smoking data, 79, 82, 304, 315
deductive reasoning, 242
degrees of freedom
   in denominator, 261
   in numerator, 261
denominator
   deg. freedom, 261
density, 69
   units, 61
density plot, 59, 69
   drawing, 69
dependent variable, 104, 375
   see response var., 104
derivative, 134

partial, 134, 144, 195
description
    using models for, 17
descriptive statistics
    computing, 65–66
design of models, 110
deviance, 56, 311, 317
deviation, 55
diagnosis, 17
disaggregating, 81
discrimination, 338
    sex, 15
    wage, 15
    wages, 105
distribution
    bell-shaped, 61
    box plot, 62
    normal, 61
    shape of , 61
dividing into groups, 192
dose-response, 348
double blind, 346
Dow Jones Ind. Avg., 251
dummy variable, *see* indicator
    variable

earthquakes, 208
Ecclesiastes, 198
effect size, 134
    partial derivative, 195
    units, 141
efficiency, 192
Einstein, Albert, 275, 342
electron mass, 19
endogenous, 327
equal variance two-sample t-
    test, 376
equiprobability, 211
error
    obsolete term., 55
ethics, 344
Excel, 24, 43
exogenous, 327
experiment, 178, 193
    vs observation, 178
    and blocking, 352, 353
    and comparison, 342

and orthogonality, 351
balanced assignment, 353
blind, 347
design, 288, 349
homogeneity, 345
intent, 351, 356
intervention, 351
randomization, 352
subject, 343
unit, 343, 345
units, 343
variable, 343
vs adjustment, 193
experimentation, 328
explanatory variables, 49, 103,
    110, 111
    conditioning on, 104
exponential prob., 208
external validity, 40
extrapolation, 138
extremes
    disadvantages of, 50

F
    and R^2, 259, 264
    deg. freedom, 261
    formula, 261
    shape of distr., 265
    significance, 270
    statistic, 259
fail to reject the null, 251
Fiji, 35
finger length, 173, 270
Fisher, Ronald, 258, 259
fitted model values, 83
    computing, 125, 161
fitting, 130, 152
    criteria, 156
    lm operator, 124
    software, 161
Fitzgerald, F. Scott, 238
flooding, 227
Freedman
    David, 268
frequentist, 199
function, 103

Galileo Galilei, 178
Galton, Francis, 49, 264
gaussian distribution, *see* nor-
    mal
genetics of height, 263
geometry
    of partitioning, 77
global warming, 321
Google Spreadsheets, 43
Google spreadsheets, 24
Gould, Stephen J., 49
GPA, 92
grade-point average, 92
Grand Forks, ND, 227
grand mean, 74, 75, 135
graphics
    axis labels, 121
    axis limits, 122
    limits of, 129
    multiple variables, 123
    statistical, 67–71
    two-variable, 120
gravity, 31
greenhouse gases, 321
group-wise mean, 74
group-wise means, 136
group-wise slopes, 139

Hamming, Richard, ix
heart surgery, 178
height
    Galton's data, 49
    genetics, 263
hiring discrimination, 269
histogram, 58, 59
    drawing, 67
    living, 59
holding constant, 134, 189
Holding other factors constant,
    80
Holmes, Oliver Wendell, 129
Horace, 230
Hughes, Robert, 18
Hume, David, 245, 255
hypernatremia, 54
hypothesis testing, 238

alternative hypothesis, 249
  covariates, 276
  glossary, 251
  group means, 376
  in regression report, 273
  logic, 238–251
  multiple comparisons, 267
  non-parametric, 295
  null hypothesis, 246
  outcomes, 251
  p value, 247
  power, 250
  sample size, 251
  significance level, 249
  test statistic, 246
  Type I error, 248
  Type II error, 250
hypothetical causal network, 325, 327

imaginary numbers, 32
in-sample, 268
incomes, 207
independent, 200
independent variable
  see explanatory var., 104
indicator variable, 133
inductive
  vs deductive, 363
inductive reasoning, 245
infinity
  INF on computer, 32
instrumental variable, 357–359
intent to treat, 355, 356
interaction
  multi-collinearity, 117
  symmetry between variables, 116
interaction term, 112, 115, 131
  computing model values, 149
  interpreting, 132
  partial derivatives, 144, 195
  slopes, 139
intercept, 112

grand mean, 135
groupwise, 138
importance of including, 118
suppressing, 118
term, 113
vector, 153
interpreter, 26
intervention
  and causation, 320
  using models for, 17
inverse percentiles, 205
IQ, 207, 331
isolated explanatory variable, 375

Karlin, Samuel, 152
Kruskal-Wallis test, 377

Landers, Ann, 41
Lao-Tsu, 218
latent variable, 326, 358
  proxy, 350
least absolute value residual, 156
least squares, 153, 155, 156
least worst-case residual, 156
levels, 37
  categorical variable, 63
Levitt, Steven, 362
likelihood, 311
linear dependence, 160
linear models, 131
  as approximation, 144
  vs logistic, 307
linear, least-squares models, 76
link value, 308
  in logistic regression, 316
Lippman, Walter, 35
living histogram, 59
log-odds ratio, 314
logistic models, 76
logistic regression, 111, 308
  fitting, 315
  propensity score, 361
logistic transformation, 308

lognormal probability model, 207
longitudinal, 43, 294
  sampling, 42, 109
Lumiere Brothers, 322

Macalester College, x
main terms, 112, 114
margin of error, 79, 232
marriage, 261
  license, 278
Mars Climate Orbiter, 31
matched sampling, 357, 358
maximum likelihood estimation, 311
mean, 53, 206
  grand, 74
  group-wise, 74, 136
  intercept coef., 135
mean square, 57, 264
median, 53
  box plot, 62
misinterpreting confidence intervals, 93
model
  causation, 320
  definition, 16
  group-wise, 74
  uses, 17
model coefficient, 130
  slope, 108, 130
  standard error, 222
model design, 110
  comparing, 155
  multi-collinearity, 161
  notation, 118
  process, 152
  strategy for, 146
model fitting, 152
  lm operator, 124
model formula, 130
  categorical variable, 133
  coefficients, 129–147
model function, 104
model notation
  vs algebra, 119
model probabilities, 312

model subspace, 175
model terms, 111–118
    "shape", 112
    interaction, 131
model value, 104
    calculating, 149
    mean, 135
monotonicity, 117
multi-collinearity, 117, 160, 225
    and ANOVA, 284
    approximate redundancy, 160
    correcting, 161
multicollinearity, 152
multiple tests
    Bonferroni correction, 292
mutatis mutandis, 181

NAN, 32
National Weather Service, 227
natural gas, 102
negative control, 348
nested models, 173
    and R^2, 172
neutrinos, 19
nitrogen fixing plants, 15
non-causal links, 327
non-correlating pathway, 332, 334
non-parametric statistics, 295, 296, 300
non-response, 41
nonlinear relationships
    and correlation, 168
normal
    distribution, 61
    obsolete term., 55
    probability model, 206
notation for model design, 118
null deviance, 311
null hypothesis, 246, 247
    and population, 255
    definition, 251
    fail to reject, 251
numbers
    complex, 32

INF and NaN, 32
numerator
    deg. freedom, 261

object
    basic types in R, 32
objectivity, 14
objects, in R, 28
odds, 314
odds ratio, 314
OFCCP, 269
on average, 134
one-sample t-test, 378
one-way anova, 377
order dependence in ANOVA, 282
ordinal, 38
orthogonal, 158
orthogonality, 172
    creating, 351
    in experiment, 352
    randomization, 352
    through instrumental variables, 358
    through matched sampling, 358, 361
out-of-sample, 268
outcome set, 199
outlier
    and non-parametrics, 300
    and rank transform, 296
    in box plots, 70
outliers, 63

p value, 247, 248
    adjusting, 268
    definition, 252
    from F statistic, 264, 274
    multiple tests, 267
paired t-test, 279
panel data, 362
parameters, 202
    binomial model, 202
    exponential probability model, 208
    F distribution, 265

lognormal probability model, 207
    normal probability model, 206
    poisson model, 203
    uniform distribution, 206
parsec, 31
partial derivative, 134, 144, 195
    interaction, 195
partial derivatives, 185
partial relationship, 178, 181, 184–185
partitioning, 77, 156
    geometry of, 77
    Pythagorean theorem, 157
    sum of squares, 157
    sums of squares, 162
    variation, 49, 105, 156
        correlation coefficient, 165
partitioning variability, 76
partitions the variation, 75
pathway, 332
    backdoor, 334
    blocking, 336, 339, 350
    experimental intervention, 351
    rules for blocking, 334
    sampling variable, 336
Pearl, Judea, 333
percentile, 51, 204
    and coverage interval, 51
    box plot, 62
    computing, 52
    quantile operator, 65
permutation test, 257
    computing, 272
    history, 258
perpendicular, 158
Picasso, Pablo, 13
Pisa, Leaning Tower, 178
placebo, 345–347
placebo effect, 346, 347
Plotting & Graphics

adding a key, 122
Poincaré, Henri, 101
point estimate, 79
Poisson, 203
poisson model, 203
polio vaccine, 346
population, 39
    and null hypothesis, 255
positive control, 348
power, 250, 296, 298, 349
    and sample size, 251
    computing, 250
    definition, 252
    experimental design, 349
    F statistic, 299
    sample size, 296
precision, 13, 19, 93, 220, 232
prediction
    confidence interval, 227, 235
    from models, 108
    interval, 226
    using models for, 17
prediction confidence interval, 227
prevalence, 314
probability, 199
    computing, 216
    subjective, 200
    with linear models, 307
probability calculus, 200
probability model, 199
    binomial, 202
    exponential, 208
    lognormal, 207
    normal, 206
    parameters, 202
    poisson, 203
    sampling from, 212
    uniform, 205
probability values
    in logistic regression, 316
propensity score, 361
proportions
    computing, 71
prospective studies, 269

prostate cancer, 312, 314
Proxima, 31
proxy, 350

quantiles, 205, 214
    and coverage intervals, 66
    computing, 215
quantitative variable
    dividing into groups, 189
    to categorical, 150
quartile, 53
quintiles, 53

R software
    arithmetic notation, 30
    mathematical functions, 31
    names of objects, 28
    operator, 26
R^2, 165
    and F, 264
    nested models, 172
    unitless, 167
race
    and wages, 280, 293
random assignment, 352, 354
random number generation, 41
random sample, 41
random variable, 201
random variation, 343
random walk
    model walk, 259
    and F, 259
randomization, 352
range of extremes, 50
rank transform, 295
rank-sum test, 376
rate, poisson model, 203
rates and partial relationships, 189
re-sampling, 89
recurrent networks, 333
redundancy, 152, 160
    and NA, 163
    fitted model values, 163
    in categorical variables, 164

reference group, 136
reference level, 133, 136
regression
    and causation, 293
regression report, 175, 223
    computing, 148, 161
    hypothesis testing, 273
relational data base, 99
relationship
    as function, 103
    partial vs total, 178
relevance, 345
repeated measures, 280
replication, 349
representative sample, 40
resampling, 211
    distribution, 223
    with replacement, 48
residual, 56, 83, 104, 135
    and standard error, 229
    computing, 161
    least squares, 155
    standard deviation, 171
    sum of squares, 156
    too small, 155
    vector, 154
residual variability, 76
residual variation, 75
residual vector, 158
response variable, 49, 103, 104, 110, 375
    choice of, 110
retrospective studies, 269
right skew, 61
roulette, 210
rounding, 31
rug plot, 58
Rutherford, Ernest, 13

Sagan, Carl, 238
Salk vaccine, 346
sample, 39, 50, 94
    representative, 40
    versus census, 94
sample size, 39
    and standard error, 229
    hypothesis testing, 251